STREAMS
LAKES
PONDS

STREAMS
LAKES
PONDS

By ROBERT E. COKER

CHAPEL HILL
THE UNIVERSITY OF NORTH CAROLINA PRESS

Illustrations on the following pages are used with permission:

Kathleen E. Carpenter, *Life in Inland Waters,* Macmillan and Company, Ltd., London, 1928, p. 214.

John Henry Comstock, *Introduction to Entomology* (9th ed.), Comstock Publishing Associates, a division of Cornell University Press, 1947, p. 250.

David R. Cook and Rodger D. Mitchell, *Turtox News,* 30 (8), 1952, p. 131.

E. O. Essig, *Insects of Western North America,* The Macmillan Company, 1926, p. 250.

Norman C. Fassett, *A Manual of Aquatic Plants,* McGraw-Hill Book Company, Inc., 1940, pp. 202, 203.

A. D. Imms, *A General Textbook of Entomology,* E. P. Dutton and Co., Inc., 1948, pp. 107, 250.

Vernon L. Kellogg, *American Insects,* Henry Holt and Co., 1906, p. 106.

John T. Lloyd, *Biology of Caddisfly Larvae,* The Lloyd Library and Museum, Cincinnati, 1921, pp. 110, 245.

Walter Meunscher, *Aquatic Plants of the United States,* Comstock Publishing Associates, a division of Cornell University Press, 1944, p. 203.

L. C. Miall, *Natural History of Aquatic Insects,* Macmillan and Company, Ltd., London, 1934, pp. 110, 250, 252.

James G. Needham and Hortense Butler Heywood, *A Handbook of the Dragonflies of North America,* Charles C. Thomas, Baltimore, 1929, p. 243.

Robert W. Pennak, *Fresh-water Invertebrates of the United States,* Roland Press, 1953, p. 163.

Gilbert M. Smith, *The Freshwater Algae of the United States,* McGraw-Hill Book Company, 1950, pp. 198, 211.

Henry Baldwin Ward and George Chandler Whipple, *Freshwater Biology,* John Wiley and Sons, Inc., 1918, pp. 113, 198, 211, 214, 224, 225, 228, 243.

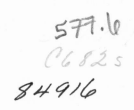

Acknowledgment

Adequate acknowledgment cannot be made to all who helped by their writings, their conversations, or their loans of illustrations. I should, however, mention the special kindness of some who have consented to read certain chapters, to suggest corrections, and to offer critical comments. Particularly to be named are Dr. Ruth Patrick, Dr. Victor A. Greulach, Dr. E. C. Markham, Dr. A. Victor Masket, Dr. H. C. Yeatman, and C. M. Coker. At an earlier stage, drafts of some chapters were read by Dr. C. S. Jones and Dr. D. G. Frey. For any errors or deficiences that remain, none of the helpers has any share of the responsibility which rests entirely upon the author.

Contents

Illustrations

FIGURES

PLATES

Introduction

VALUES OF INLAND SURFACE WATERS

Although about three-fourths of the surface of the earth is water, the fourth that is land seems to us of more importance. It is where we live. Could we re-acquire gills, fins, and other adaptations to life in water, doubtless land would seem of minor concern. In such case, and even as intelligent fish, we would be wrong, of course; for what would a fish do without land? Many times in the following pages we shall note how the neighboring lands affect the fish of stream or lake. The inherent nature of in-draining areas, the treatment they receive from man, and all that meteorological conditions do to them, largely determine the potentialities for fish in water. The bottom of stream or lake is mainly overflowed land; in later pages we shall have to emphasize repeatedly the critical significance of bottoms in relation to productivity. The bottoms of the pond, so often ignored by the fish farmer, the bordering meadows and cultivated lands, the forests and highways are equally important with climate and weather as controlling factors in pond life.

This is not to say that just plain water is needed only to keep the fish wet and to obviate thirst—important considerations, to be sure. Fish cannot live on water alone, but they need it in great quantity. Why? Not just to provide room for lots of fish; chiefly because only a large volume of water can carry adequate amounts of essential respiratory gases, along with other nutrients. The gases, carbon dioxide and oxygen, must be gotten from the water, and water carries little of them per unit of volume. In any body of water it is the gas situation that primarily counts.[1] With turbulence and more opportunity for the whole water to keep in balance with atmosphere as to gases, the fish can do with less water—as in a shallow stream. Furthermore, water in bulk is required to carry the basic nutrients which, let it be remembered, come from land.

If the fish, assuming it had the thought or feeling to do so, should not depreciate the land, upon which it has such dependence, perhaps we of the land might have great appreciation of the water upon which we are equally dependent. Had we now the time and the desire we could consider the raw fact that human beings are not so terrestrial as we ordinarily think. A physiologist could tell us that actually land animals and man have never gotten entirely out of the water. We simply carry our water with us. We have it in our pockets, so to speak. Nothing gets into the flesh of our bodies for its maintenance or growth—neither oxygen nor food—until it has been dissolved in water. Indeed, the living protoplasm of plant or animal is itself an aqueous substance.

Now, however, we consider only outside waters—water outside of the body—upon which the fish depends but which it has the good fortune to have always at hand. We humans are just as dependent as is the fish upon outside water, even though our connection with it is usually indirect. Unlike the fish we have to expend energy and material to find our water and then to keep it with us. Most of the outside water is in the seas, which are abitrarily excluded from present consideration.[2] Most of us live well-removed from the seashore. The waters we see from day to day are rain and snow and some of their resultants—springs, streams, ponds, lakes, swamps, marshes, and bogs. We

1. Even when we speak of food as the controlling factor, we know that other foods are available only where respiration is possible. A highly polluted stream may be extremely rich in potential nutriment, but no place for a fish if the free oxygen is too greatly depleted.

2. The oceans have been considered by the present writer in another volume: *This Great and Wide Sea,* University of North Carolina Press, Chapel Hill, 1947 and 1949.

see little of soil water, but we know of its great importance to all of us. The situation with regard to it and the problems are fully presented in a recent book on *The Conservation of Ground Water,* by Dr. Harold E. Thomas (1951). We deal with it here only in certain of its relations to the more evident surface waters.

To be sure, the surface waters of the earth, exclusive of the oceans and their extensions in gulfs, bays, and estuaries, are insignificant in total area. But surface expanse is no safe criterion of values. Let us put a few leading questions.

Ought we to drain all marshes and swamps, or to drain any without due thought for remote effects? Should we let streams and lakes take care of themselves as best they can under the impacts of an expanding agricultural and industrial civilization? Should we think of soil water as something "the Lord will provide," regardless of what we do to surface water and to soils? These are not just rhetorical questions. Not many years ago they would have seemed just that. Really, they are significant questions which from day to day receive practical answers. Such answers as were given in the past do not at this time seem to have been altogether sound. Sometimes now they receive better answers, but only sometimes. If we are to judge from what actually happens all around us to streams, lakes, and marshes, we must conclude, I am sure, that the effective answers to those simple questions are still quite diverse, so far as they are given by actions of particular individuals, of various industries, or of the several communities. It seems to be a fact that at least some watery areas are drained that were better as they were, that lands are sometimes "reclaimed" that were better left wet, that soil water tables in particular regions, not generally perhaps, are lowered with disadvantages outweighing the advantages, and that streams are too generally discolored, de-oxygenated, or otherwise rendered less fit for primary uses.

What are the primary uses of interior waters? Certainly the first need of water for primitive man was for drinking. Gideon's small army of victory was selected through the test of quick lapping of water from the open pool. For good reason, that method of scooping wild water on the run from pool or stream may not in this day be approved military practice. Even now, however, a first question with prospective purchase of a farm is whether or not there is water good for man and ample for domestic animals. A second historical use could be thought to be for bathing, if it be assumed that primitive man bathed, or for clothes washing, if he can be imagined to have had anything to launder. I suspect that the second original value of interior waters was found in its yield of food—fish, ducks, crayfish, and other aquatic animals as well as plants. Just now the requirement of food from fresh-waters is less general. Yet, deprivation from it would be a serious loss to many people. Consider only carp from the Illinois River, white fish from Lake Erie, shad and rock fish from eastern and western rivers, catfish from the Mississippi, and salmon from the Columbia and other river systems. Consider also Canada with something like half the surface area of fresh water of the world and the world's largest commercial freshwater fishery, amounting in value in 1921 to 21 million dollars.[3]

Certainly an early use of streams and lakes was for travel and transportation—a use that has persisted but with notable changes. Waters originally offered the best highways. In the settlement of this country the first communities were at the mouths of rivers or inward along their banks. What great cities now are not found on rivers—though the streams may presently serve purposes other than ingress and egress? Much of the change in navigability of streams is due to uses or abuses of the lands that drain into the streams. Really, we should leave out "uses" and say only "abuses" for it is justifiably maintained that no proper use of lands could impair the navigability of the water into which they drain. Everyone knows of streams up which a couple of generations ago steamboats wended their majestic way, but where the whistles and the splashing wheels have long been unheard. Nor can the disappearance of the river boats be attributed principally to the development of improved transportation by land. Waterways still serve where great expense is incurred in keeping channels open. Man may have first traveled afoot along a woodland trail; but the raft of logs, the hollowed tree trunk, or the

3. Canadian Fisheries Annual, 1953.

bundle of reeds came early to give the waterways enduring rank. Such is the prestige of priority that to this day a land highway, even a "superhighway" or a railway, may not block a channel of navigation. Except where the bridge is made extremely high, the millionaire or the statesman in his car on the bridge must wait patiently while the crude fishing craft or the cabin cruiser sputters its leisurely way through the open draw.

Still keeping to the more obviously practical or economic values of streams and lakes, it may be remarked that one reason why industrial centers, and even isolated industrial plants, adhere so generally to the banks of rivers is that so many manufacturing establishments use quantities of water for their operations or else require water in volume for removal and dilution of their wastes. The water used is returned to the stream but usually not in the condition in which it was received. If the users do not kill the goose that lays the golden egg for themselves, they at least so cripple her that she will not soon lay quality eggs for the next fellow along the line. Communities, too, large or small, and even country homes, need water for domestic purposes. What they use from any source or for any purpose—home water, laundry water, street water, fire water (meaning, in this case, water used by the fire company) goes back into the stream and, commonly, in sadly altered condition. The old goose-killing act comes into play again. No modern community would use water from streams or lakes without incurring expense for its purification. So many of the streams near cities are out of bounds for bathing, and often not even pleasant for boating or fishing. Recreational and health values may be completely lost except for the few who do not know—or do not care.

Finally, even in this brief survey it is not being impractical to consider esthetic values. Providing that a body of water is fairly clean or, at least not repugnant to the sense of sight or of smell, its proximity has a concrete money value derived from esthetics. Are not the "riverside" homes and the "lakeview" apartments frequently held at premium prices? Often, to be sure, and regrettably, they are at a discount. Diversity in land forms, with hills, valleys, and plains, helps to make scenery; but so also do streams, lakes, ponds, marshes, savannahs, and everglades. Considering only economic values deriving from esthetics, it is not necessary to ask Washington about the Columbia River Drive, New York about the Hudson River highways, or the thoroughfares bordering the Finger Lakes. Neither is there need to inquire about the budgetary meaning—to Colorado of its brooks, rivers, and lakes; to Wisconsin of its thousands of lakes; to Florida of its boiling springs, its innumerable sinkhole pools, or its expansive Everglades. North Carolina cannot question the income-producing features of its streams and rivers, its many manmade reservoirs or its inland "bays," so-called, and its savannas. The case for the worth of waters is easily made without even reference to their value for recreation, health, and uplift of spirit.

It is not suggested that all these values are everywhere threatened with destruction. Such havoc is far beyond the possibilities for human activity at its blundering best. What can be brought to mind, however, is that, far too frequently and too widely, the desirable and inevitable development of a thriving agricultural and industrial society has resulted in substantial and certainly undesirable impairment of primary values of interior waters. I have seen a beautiful sparkling river of the mountains bordered by lofty, green and flowered hills, changed suddenly at a particular place to continue for many, many, miles between similar scenic mountain sides, but only as a dark, murky, and repugnant stream. I know a small natural lake, almost crystal clear, ideal for bathing and boating, surrounded more and more by summer homes, and, incongruously, good for fishing; but, the scientists report, it is in process of change, not from industry but from domestic pollution, to a different type of lake.[4] Any reader can multiply such instances of loss of values.

The question now is not how to check the growth of communities or of industries, but rather how to have a populous and prosperous society without taking the losses we may justly call deplorable. The question is more easily stated than it is answered. A couple of laws will not bring the solution, although intelligent legislation is necessary procedure.

4. In technical language, it is undergoing "eutrophication" (p. 49, below).

The desideratum is wider understanding both of the need for betterment and of the complexity of the problems presented. General understanding may give more effective support to the broadly cooperative effort that is requisite to the fullest possible alleviation of present difficulties. From one side, and in quite recent years, soil conservationists and farmers are registering real gains. From another, sanitarians, health officers, parasitologists, and pathologists advance with greater or less success. Isaac Walton leagues, fish conservationists, sportsmen, and fish farmers work vigorously for protection of the waters and their renewable resources and for greater productivity of ponds, lakes, and streams. Hydrologists and engineers involved in power development or maintenance of navigability find their own good reasons for concern with the whole problem of water conservation, flood control, and regulation of stream flow. Owners of stream-bordered lands, and, indeed, just everyday folks, typified by the familiar John Q. Public, have good cause for wanting better surface waters and a proper maintenance of soil water.

After this brief presentation of some simple matters of fact that should be of common interest, it may be well to add that the present volume is in no way designed as propaganda. It has developed solely from a belief that there are those who would like a better understanding of what goes on in the generally unseen realms beneath the glimmering film topping the still water, the rippling surface of the brook, or the silent winding face of the broad river. One easily sees and handles the grass upon which the easy-breathing cattle feed. The living world within the waters is not only invisible to the casual observer; it offers far more complexity. If the wanted "cattle" here are fish, even breathing may become a real difficulty, and not infrequently an unconquerable one with death the result. The essential "grass," in great part, may be of microscopic dimensions and unavailable except as it is consumed by water fleas, larvae, or small worms, which in turn are consumed by small predators; only after several steps of conversion is the basic "pasturage" made into fish. These are only suggestions of the many differences between the living worlds of land and water, respectively.

There are many good books on life in fresh water. The present volume intends no competition with standard works. Rather, it may, by its numerous references, lead the possibly interested reader to refer to more technical volumes or articles that he might not otherwise consult. The effort of the author, it may be said, has been the difficult one of holding a median course between the good reference works and an over-popular and perhaps misleadingly simple presentation of a story that has so many facets. Omission of some facts and references is unavoidable. Occasional recurrence of ideas or facts is believed justifiable, because one cannot deal adequately with the several fields without some thought in each case of basic principles governing life in all waters.

I

WATER AND ITS CONTENTS

CHAPTER I

A Little About Water

WATER IS A PECULIAR SUBSTANCE, EVEN THOUGH ONE SO FAMIL-
iar that we take it for granted. Among ordinary liquids
it stands quite apart. Water must be drunk, or in some way taken
into living bodies, because there is no life without it. Not only
aquatic animals, but we and all animals and plants that have
gotten away from water as a home are inevitably dependent on
water. No necessity of life gets into our tissues from the intestines or from the lungs except after prior solution in water. Crop
plants utilize mineral salts only as they become dissolved in water.
The real difference in the lives of aquatic and terrestrial organisms
is this: the former have outside water always at hand—to be
imbibed and to be held with minimum of effort; the latter have
to find the indispensable water and be equipped to keep it with
them—they lap, dip, or pump, they may have to travel for it,
some get it only from their food; they may need to develop root
systems, protective coverings, or other special activities or structures. Thirst or other manifestations of water deficiency are not
the common experience of animals and plants in fresh water.

When aquatic animals move, they push their way through a
relatively dense and thickish medium; they need a more or less
streamlined form. Animals that move through the light and
tenuous atmosphere require little streamlining unless they are
swift movers; they expend less energy in displacement of the
surrounding medium. On the other hand, terrestrial animals
lack the advantage of being constantly buoyed up by the medium

in which they live; consequently, they need supporting structures, such as the legs of animals, the trunks and stems of plants, not characteristic of organisms that are primarily adapted to life in water.[1]

Density, as an impediment to movement, requiring appreciable expenditure of energy for displacement of the surrounding medium, and viscosity, offering substantial resistance to free movement, are common qualities of liquids. They are not peculiar to water. What we are immediately concerned about, if we are properly to interpret the conditions of life in water, are some of the singular properties of this particular fluid—properties that one does not always have in mind. Let us note some of these as briefly as is possible.[1a]

The heat relations of water are most noteworthy. Any solid or liquid generally contracts as it cools. So does water over a wide range of temperature, but not without a peculiar break. The peculiarity of water is that it does not contract with cooling through the lower range of temperature above freezing; *reversal occurs when water is cooled below* 4° C. (39.1° F.).[2] With further cooling it expands, becoming less dense. Expansion is gradual until the freezing point is reached; then suddenly, as it congeals, water undergoes *drastic expansion,* adding about 1/11 to its liquid volume.[3] Remarkably few substances behave in this way; bis-

1. It may be remarked, of course, that some plants with supporting stem and some animals with walking legs, originally developed for life on land, have become secondarily adapted in other ways to life in water, and also that crabs and lobsters, at least, find legs useful for walking on the bottom of the sea. Yet legs for support, rather than for clinging or for capture of food, are not general features of the structure of aquatic animals, as they are for most terrestrial animals.

1a. Since this chapter was written, the lively and instructive book entitled *Water,* by Thomson King (Macmillan, 1953), has appeared. He says aptly: "Water is a fascinating paradox in that it is the most common and the most uncommon of substances. It is common because it is plentiful and familiar. It is uncommon because its qualities, properties, and characteristics are strange, rare, and, in some cases, unique."

2. This is approximate. Actually, the temperature of maximum density is at about 3.98° C. at one atmosphere of pressure. Where higher pressure prevails, as in deep lakes, the temperature of maximum density may be lowered by as much as half a degree. (See Hodgman, 1941, Rawson, 1950.)

3. We are concerned, of course, only with the formation of ice under natural conditions on the surface of the earth. But this is not the whole story of the peculiar behavior of liquid water in the change to the solid forms we call ice. Physicists tell us that if ordinary ice formed at what we call "freezing temperatures" is placed under sufficient pressure without increase of external temperature, it turns back to water with

muth does. The significance to life of this almost unique quality of water can be grasped in part when we recognize that, before freezing, cooling water will always rise to the surface of the container where ice will form as a top layer and remain as such. A lake of any depth, except in an Arctic climate, will never freeze solid. Regardless of weather conditions, fresh water below the ice will not ordinarily be much below 4° C. Sometimes land animals may have to endure temperatures far below zero; a fish, in fresh water, except where it is in very shallow, is insured against an environmental temperature lower than several degrees above the freezing point.

Water has also remarkable *heat capacity*. The heat that, applied to an empty iron pot, would make it red hot may raise the temperature of a corresponding volume of water only a few degrees. Distinction must be made between heat and temperature. Water absorbs an exceptional amount of heat with relatively small rise in temperature; it holds much more heat than is indicated by its tangible "hotness." So, again, while the land animal may have to suffer a temperature above 100° F. (about 38° C.), a fish rarely has to endure a temperature above 80° F. (about 27° C.). Furthermore, the daily range of temperature in a lake is small as compared with that on land. Conversely, however, where exceptional conditions cause a rapid fall of temperature in shallow water, the fish, because it is unaccustomed and ill-adapted to quick changes, may suffer injury: "fish numbs" are well-known.

Water has a uniquely high *latent heat of evaporation*. It vaporizes most rapidly at the boiling point, beyond which it is not heated in liquid form, (except at abnormal pressures). But, fortunately, some evaporation occurs at all temperatures; even ice evaporates slightly without melting. It takes as much heat to vaporize one unit of volume of water as to raise 539 units by one degree in temperature.

The adage that "the watched pot never boils" certainly derives

loss of volume. But there are half a dozen different kinds of ice to be formed by proper manipulation of pressure and temperature, and *loss of volume,* rather than gain, may go with the ice formation. As has been said, "water is abnormal" and becomes increasingly abnormal with subjection to high pressure (Bridgman, 1952).

in part from the patience-taxing delay resulting from the high heat capacity of water and the great amount of heat taken up by the more rapid vaporization at the high temperature prevailing just before the boiling point is reached; seemingly, the pot just will not boil when it ought to! Water vapor represents great storage of heat, and surface water through its capacity to evaporate can relieve the atmosphere of a great amount of heat. Later condensations may release the heat at other places. We know about hot muggy days; but ordinarily the gain in heat from condensation is more than counterbalanced by the cooling effect of the evaporation that quickly follows the rainfall.

Because of its remarkable heat capacity, heat of evaporation, and heat of fusion, water, as liquid, solid or vapor, is unrivalled for storage and release of heat. It can take in or give off a lot of heat with small change in its own temperature. The climatic tempering effects of lakes or the ocean in summer or winter are well known. It is well known, too, that the freezing of a lake, or of a tub of water in a greenhouse, protects the environment to some extent from the extreme changes of temperature that might occur without the freezing water. Consequently, for animals and plants that live in water, changes in temperature from hour to hour, from day to day, or from season to season can take place only slowly and within a relatively narrow range.

As a *chemical solvent* water stands among fluids almost, if not quite, alone. About half the known chemical elements have been found in solution in natural waters, even if in some instances only as traces. It is suspected that no element is entirely lacking in fresh or salt water somewhere. We can at least be sure that any substance needed to make the body of any particular kind of plant or animal is soluble or in some way is held in water. If it were not water-soluble, how could the organism get it into its system? It takes a lot of carbon, hydrogen, oxygen, and nitrogen to make living matter, but it also takes lesser amounts of other substances. If we consider more broadly the elements that some plant or animal needs to have in "trace" quantity, the list of biologically useful elements grows greatly. Even the farmer without scientific training has now some concept of the need for boron, zinc, copper, and cobalt which the crop plants may utilize only *after* their solution in the water of the soils.

Furthermore, it is a peculiar property of water that it is an *inert solvent,* exercising practically no chemical action on most of the substances it dissolves. This is important biologically, because the materials required by living matter and found in solution in the water can be delivered to the organisms in relatively unmodified form; the water itself is unchanged and can be used as a solvent over and over again.[4]

An important corollary to the solvent qualities of water is that no natural water is chemically pure—fortunately for the plants and animals that live in water. Practical "purity" is, of course, a relative term; water that is wholesomely "pure" and favorable for a bacterium or a protozoa may for us be impure or even offensive and unhealthful. Almost everywhere in nature water is more or less heavily loaded with dissolved matter, some of which is useful to one organism or another, and all of which, perhaps, is availed of by some type of organism, sometime or somewhere.

Notwithstanding its general chemical inertness, water does have a physico-chemical effect on acids, bases, and salts that go into solution. Hardly any other substance rivals water in capacity to split or to *ionize* dissolved material. Molecules of most dissolved substances are broken into component particles called *ions* that bear electrical charges, charges that give basis for nearly all electrical phenomena of solutions, whether in batteries, in plants, or in the nerves of animals. Ions are not at rest but engage in a continual play of recombining and dissociating. Any natural body of water has at least several substances in solution and to a great extent ionized. With even a few substances in solution, there will be more kinds of ions and many possibilities of their recombinations. A consequence of much biological significance is that there are available to organisms in water something of the order of twice as many kinds of ions as there are of dissolved ionizable substances and that the number of available recom-

4. To certain readers it will be apparent that for some of the thoughts expressed in this chapter the writer owes acknowledgment to Dr. Lawrence J. Henderson, *The Fitness of the Environment* (New York: Macmillan, 1924), an acknowledgment he is glad to make.

binations is comparable to the square of the number of dissolved salts. In short, the chemical environment of plants and animals in water is greatly enriched through the high ionizing capacity of the special liquid in which they live.

Another peculiarity of water is that, of all the ordinary liquids except mercury, it has the highest *surface tension*. Probably most of us had first intimation of the surface tension of water when we observed fine dust or pollen remaining afloat on a pool. We soon learned that with delicate manipulation we could float a needle on water in a glass. The surface membrane is strong enough to support the heavy needle, dust, or pollen; but, once that membrane is broken in any way, the heavy needle sinks rapidly to the bottom, the dust more slowly. We may have marvelled that an insect or a spider could run back and forth across a pool without breaking through the uppermost film. Again we have noted that water dropped on an object that is not easily wetted, as on a cabbage leaf or a dog's back, tends not to spread, but rather to form spherical droplets, which are masses with minimum surface. We learn to make an emulsion of water and oil, when, with violent shaking, the two liquids of different surface tension are caused to be interspersed one within the other, innumerable isolated droplets of one substance within the continuous medium of the other. We have all seen water actually climb up the lining of a capillary tube. All these seemingly incongruous phenomena are just the crudest manifestations of the quality of surface tension. They give faint intimation of the great biological significance of surface tension in the physiology of plants and animals of land or water. Only the physiologist or the biophysicist can deal properly with the part played by surface tension in all physiological processes.

Reference may be made to certain other significant but not peculiar characteristics of water. Water is transparent, but not perfectly so. The radiations of shorter or longer wave lengths than those of the visible spectrum are mostly absorbed (changed to heat) in the uppermost layers of the water into which they penetrate. Not only that, but the wave lengths within the range of the visible spectrum are *differentially absorbed*. This means that, as light penetrates to some depth in water, it is changed not only in quantity but also in quality. If one could read his newspaper while sitting on the bottom of a clear lake at considerable depth, his light would, of course, be dimmer than at the surface, but it could also be different in its nature, lacking most of the red and orange rays and a great part of the violet. If the depth was sufficiently great and the water entirely pure, one might have to read with only a blue light. If then we were comparing the light environment of plants on land with that of those in the lake or in the sea, it would have to be recognized that water plants suffer not only *reduced intensity* of light, but also the greater or less *loss of certain components* of the white light of the world above.

The viscosity of water demands some attention. Although relatively low, it is none the less a feature that has noteworthy effects on aquatic organisms. It is in apparent adaptation to the viscosity and the density of the medium that free living aquatic organisms so generally display the streamline form. In respect to the rate of sinking and the energy that must be expended to maintain position at a desirable level, viscosity is the more important of those two variables. Both vary inversely with temperature, but the density of the organism varies with temperature in the same way as does that of the water, so that weight displacement is not significantly changed. Viscosity varies greatly with temperature, being approximately doubled by a fall of 25° C.[5] The energy required by an animal for movement through the water increases with increase in viscosity, or with lowering temperature. Under the same conditions, sinking of animals or plants as a result of the downward pull of gravitation is retarded: less energy need be expended for maintenance of swimming or drifting level. In a later chapter we shall see that varying viscosity has also much to do with patterns of circulation in the lake. Since warm water is less viscous (or more fluid) than cold water, the animal may have to spend more energy to keep at a desired level in summer than in winter. It is a fact that some drifting organisms show seasonal changes of form, apparently in adaptation to the seasonal changes in viscosity.

5. Change in viscosity is of the order of 3½% per degree of temperature, although it is not uniform over the temperature scale, the increase in viscosity with fall of temperature being greater at lower temperatures.

CHAPTER 2

Light and Heat in Water

The Problem in Water

WHY NEED WE BE CONCERNED ABOUT SOLAR RADIATION IN LAKES and streams? Commonly we think of radiation from the sun in terms of light and heat but that, of course, is not all of it. Life in great part is energy, and the real source of energy is the sun. For life on land we take light for granted. It is all around us and over our crops and generally in plenty during the daytime. That is not so in water, and for several reasons. In the first place, water reflects more light than land. What is even more significant is that, while light reflected from land can be used by the leaves of trees, light reflected from the water surface is lost to submerged plants. In the second place, except in heavily shaded areas, light is plentiful for land plants at any level above ground to which they can reach; in water on the other hand, light and its energy diminish with distance from the surface until, deep down, there may be virtually none. Again, on land the quality, or composition, of light is the same for grass on open ground and for leaves at the tree-top. In water, because of differential absorption of wave leagths, the quality of light undergoes change with every inch of depth; plants close to the surface enjoy more nearly the same quality of light as bathes the grass on land than do plants that live deeper; both the intensity and the *range of wave lengths* of light are more and more restricted with depth. In fact, as has been mentioned in another place, at great enough depths in relatively pure water there would be little more than blue light. In some natural waters, because of special conditions, the deeper light is nearly all red. Lest the contrast made between conditions of light for terrestrial and aquatic plants, respectively, seems too sweeping, it may be remarked that grass on the floor of a forest, dependent largely on light filtered through the leaves of trees above, would suffer deficiencies in some wave lengths, particularly in the red and blue regions of the spectrum.

In partial compensation for dimness of light a large part of the productive life in water consists of plants with minute bodies, which have high ratios of surface to volume and so give maximum exposure to whatever light is available. It seems also to be true of most microscopic aquatic plants and of many aquatic animals that they work best in light of only moderate intensity.[1] Usually the top water of a pond is not as densely populated at midday as in early morning or late afternoon; consider in this connection the reported vertical distribution of life in the notably translucent Crater Lake. (p. 14)

The basis of life is a process called *photosynthesis,* a word that may be roughly translated as "putting together with the use of sunlight." Photosynthesis involves the linking of molecules of water and carbon dioxide to form sugar; the link is the energy of sunlight at certain wave lengths; chlorophyll in plants is the agent that can apply the link. The crucial fact is that the formation of sugar is the basis of all organic production and the solar energy so stored is all that plants and animals have for growth or work. If for fields and forests, as previously mentioned, we take the energy of light for granted, we cannot do so for large parts of most bodies of water. Lakes and streams differ widely among themselves in depth of the brightly illuminated zone, and in the consequent activity of the productive green plants within that zone. It is partly because of such differences that different waters are so unlike in respect to internal productivity.

Having in mind that both productivity and oxygen liberation

1. Dr. Gordon A. Riley (1941) refers to "numerous experiments that show the optimum point for photosynthesis in the summer to *be a few meters below the surface.*" (Italics mine).

depend on photosynthesis, it is plainly desirable to know something about the *general* conditions of illumination below the
surface. Because of differential absorption of light components
by water, plants in the deeper part of the illuminated zone do
not receive the same character of light as do those in the upper
part. Now the different wave lengths have different values biologically; hence for the study of life in water it is important to
investigate, not only depth of penetration and decrease in intensity
of light with depth, but also the changes in *constitution* of the
light at various depths. If, for example, we are concerned with
the potential productivity of plants at 10 meters in a particular
lake, we need to know, not only if light is there, and how much,
but also *what kind of light* is there.

Water absorbs readily the shortest wave lengths of solar energy, those beyond the range of the visible spectrum. Within
the range of visible light it absorbs the longer wave lengths more
effectively than it does the shorter. Consequently, the light that
penetrates to the deeper parts of lakes is relatively poor in red
and orange rays and relatively rich in green and blue rays as
compared with light at the surface of the lake. Of course, the
intensity at all wave lengths is lower in the water than at the
surface, but in clear water the reduction in intensity is greatest
in the red-orange portion of the spectrum. It is of interest that,
although the most effective wave lengths for photosynthesis are
in the red region of the spectrum, plants can use in photosynthesis even green light, to the extent to which it is absorbed by the
plant. Blue light is next most effective to red, but all portions
of the visible spectrum can be utilized to some extent. Aquatic
plants seem to be able to carry on an adequate rate of photosynthesis at lower light intensities than can terrestrial plants, except
perhaps those that thrive in the dim light of a dense forest.

Answers to the questions posed in preceding paragraphs are
not easily found, but at least we need to learn at approximately
what depths either rooted plants or the generally more important
drifting microscopic plants (the phytoplankton) can live and
actually contribute to the stock of organic matter and the supply
of free oxygen. With animals we are further concerned because

light affects vertical migrations. Certain small animals with limited powers of locomotion, and many larger and more active ones, move upward in mass by night and downward by day. We should know to what extent these movements are responses to light and what particular wave lengths affect the different migrating animals.

Light has particular significance to animals that possess light-receptive organs of any nature. Even in water vision must play some part in the discovery and capture of food and certainly in the avoidance of enemies. At substantial depths the period of daylight is much shorter than it is at the surface. We want to know at what depths and for how long each day there is sufficient illumination for the vision of fish and other animals with eyes or for the stimulation of the many small organisms that are not provided with true eyes but yet are equipped with light-sensitive structures. Again, keeping in mind that the spectral composition of light is different under water, we may be interested in the adaptation of visual organs to the narrower range of wave lengths available at considerable depths.

We have spoken of light or other forms of solar radiation as being "absorbed," which means transformed into heat. In another place reference has been made to the remarkable capacity of water to absorb, to store, and to release much heat with only moderate change in temperature. It has been mentioned, too, that the range of temperature in water is less than on land and that the daily and the seasonal fluctuations are much less and more gradual than are those of the atmosphere or land. Since the metabolic activities are in great degree functions of temperature, it can be said that life in water proceeds in general at a more uniform rate. Temperature comes frequently into our discussion of lakes and streams and no more need be said at this place.

It is not appropriate to go here into details of penetration, absorption, and scatter of solar radiation coming to bodies of water. Naturally the proportion that is reflected will depend upon altitude of the sun above the horizon and the corresponding angle of incidence of direct radiation; and solar altitude continually changes with time of day and with season. Most of the infra-red, at one end of the spectrum, is quickly absorbed, as is ultraviolet at the other end. Absorption means warming the water, which is biologically significant. We are interested, both in the penetration of destructive rays and of rays within the visible spectrum that are useful in photosynthesis and in vision—and of rays useful in formation of vitamins. Seemingly, the ultraviolet that is not absorbed in the upper few meters has little intensity. There is "confusion regarding the degree to which the lethal ultraviolet rays penetrate the water" (Henrici, 1939). It is certain, however, that bacteria and other organisms derive substantial protection from the absorptive capacity of water above them.

In very clear ocean water, such as that of the central North Atlantic, light penetrates almost as well as in distilled water (Clarke, 1939), the blue going deepest with appreciable intensity below 100 meters. The penetration in richer coastal water is less, and in most inland lakes still less; but lakes and ponds vary greatly in transparency. For those not equipped to use more elaborate equipment for measurement of light penetration as a whole, or by particular wave lengths, which is desirable, transparency is roughly measured by use of a white, or white and black plate (a supper plate is not too bad in an emergency), which is lowered on a line until it can no longer be seen by the operator in a boat or on a dock; depth of disappearance is recorded. Designed for this purpose is the *Secchi disk,* a circular plate of metal about 20 cm. (eight inches) in diameter, painted white and black in alternating quadrants. Measurement of transparency taken in this way is not, of course, a true measure of light penetration, but is useful for comparisons. The disk may disappear within a few inches if the water is turbid. In the notably clear Crystal Lake, Wisconsin, it is visible to about 15 meters. Crater Lake in Oregon can have few, if any rivals for transparency: the disk can be seen at the remarkable depth of 40 meters, or about 131 feet. In that lake green plants grow at a depth of 120 meters. It is interesting that, in association with the great clarity of water, life in the body of Crater Lake seems to be concentrated at 50 to 200 meters, with a maximum at 75 meters (246 feet). Both upper water and lower water were reported to be "desert." (See Utterback et al.,

1942, and Hasler, 1938.) Perhaps waters of deep springs of Florida are even clearer.

Difference between waters with respect to transparency is due to what is in them—dissolved substance, inorganic matter in suspension and plants and animals adrift in the water. Blue may be expected to go deepest, as in distilled water, but this is not always the case; something in the water of Trout Lake of Wisconsin, for example, absorbs the blue in the upper three meters; red extends deepest (Birge and Juday, 1930). Actual water color affects penetration of particular wave lengths, depending on the nature of the coloring substance. Turbidity from silt interferes with penetration, and therefore, with productiveness of lake, pond, or stream. Living plants and animals of the plankton (the drifting life) make "clouds" in the water as effective in intercepting light rays as are the clouds of water particles in the sky above the land.

Except at places within the tropics, and at certain times, light direct from the sun approaches a smooth surface of water by an oblique, not a vertical, path. The surface of water is, however, not always smooth; rays may fall on a wave slope at almost any angle. Furthermore, much of the light of significance in a natural body of water is not in direct path from the sun; it is reflected from clouds or other components, even molecules, of the atmosphere; it is *scattered light.* Scatter occurs also in water, where light is reflected from solid particles, alive or dead, or from molecules. We see the surface of the lake or the bottom in shallow water by reflected light. When we look into water too deep for the bottom to be seen it is really scattered light that gives us our impression of the water, as blue, green or of other color, just as it is scattered light of the atmosphere that gives us the blue sky.

It is important to remember that, because so much of the light entering water travels obliquely, the rays that one may say traverse water for a distance of 50 meters do not necessarily reach a *depth* of 50 meters. Here, however, *refraction,* or bending toward the vertical, helps to take light to a deeper level. Furthermore, the greater the angle of incidence of penetrating light, the greater is the refraction: the result is that rays which penetrate at all, even when the sun is near the horizon, are so refracted as not to deviate from the vertical by more than about 48° (Sverdrup et al., 1942—referring to sea water).

It is to be remembered that "day" under water must be shorter than above water, and night longer. Effective length of the period of daylight diminishes with depth; there must be depths at which the early morning rays of sunlight appear only just before the sun is nearest the zenith and the last rays vanish soon after the hour of noon, sun time; at a particular depth in a deep lake, duration of effective daylight may be only a matter of minutes.

Animals depend on plants for free oxygen liberated through photosynthesis, for which plants require a certain intensity of sunlight; but plants, also, in respiration, use free oxygen. It is the positive difference between production and consumption of free oxygen by plants that supports the respiration of animals. That balance varies, of course, with time of day, with season, with meteorological conditions, *and with depth;* if there is too little light because of hour or depth, the plant becomes a net consumer and a competitor of animals for what free oxygen is about. The depth at which consumption of free oxygen by plants and its liberation through photosynthesis are in exact balance is called the *compensation* depth or level. This varies, not only with time of day and season and with character of the water and its content, but also with the kind of plant and the intensity and wave lengths of light that it requires. At a particular place we are interested in averages, or means (for all hours and for several days), of balances between production and consumption of oxygen by the existing plant community as a whole.

Finally, radiation that is absorbed gives warmth to the lake. Shallow waters may be warmed in considerable part by conduction and radiation from the directly heated bottom (by radiation the bottom absorbs). Where the water is too deep for the bottom to be directly warmed, absorption of radiation (and warming) by water and by living or dead particles in it can take place only in *upper waters.* If deeper waters are warmed at all, it must be chiefly through *some form of circulation;* this requires special consideration in the next chapter.

If, then, one is concerned with the gross productivity of lakes, there would seem to be one very practical inference from what has just been said. Because original production is in the zone of photosynthesis, it follows that increment of depth beyond the effective photosynthetic zone may not add substantially to total productivity. Productivity, as far as it depends upon solar radiation, is a function of surface *area* rather than of volume of water. Of course, the dark bottom of a deep lake may harbor animals that would not thrive in a shallow lake. Other things than light are needed for production. Nevertheless, "Other things being equal, the production of food in the open water is a function of surface, not one of depth" (Birge, 1922).

Swingle and Smith (1941), in their experiments with fertilized fish ponds, found it better to express measures of production in terms of area rather than of volume. They said (p. 219):

Apparently the depth of water, within the limits used in this experiment, had little effect on the amount of fish that a given pond area could support. Hence production expressed as weight of fish per acre of water would appear to be a more accurate measure than weight of fish per unit volume of water.

Other things equal, a lake of greater area but of less volume than another should be the more productive. But in nature things are never just equal. Hence, however valid the rule in theory, its general applicability has limitations.

A quotation from Clarke (1939) may conclude this chapter:

It thus appears that most of the light incident on the surface of lakes or oceanic areas is absorbed by the water itself or by detritus and that only a very small part can be utilized by plants or animals. We conclude that aquatic organisms are existing under very unfavorable circumstances in regard to the utilization of solar energy. It is for this reason that the intensity, amount, and composition of the light are so frequently found to be limiting or highly significant factors in the aquatic environment.

CHAPTER 3

Gases and Heat: Distribution, Circulation, Stratification

Why Joint Consideration

IN NOTICES REGARDING HUMAN HABITATIONS THE JOINT MENTION of "gas and heat" seems natural enough. In treatment of the homes of fish the combination, at first glance, may seem incongruous. It is not so, however, although the term "gas" has here a somewhat different significance. Gases we now have in mind are those involved in the respiration and metabolism of plants and animals. Incidentally, their assimilation and liberation by organisms are accomplished by liberation or by absorption[1] of heat and are controlled to great extent by temperature. The amount of heat liberated by the activities of life in a body of water may not be very significant; but the quantity of essential respiratory gases available in water is markedly affected by the temperature prevailing, while respiratory *need* is also affected—with a ratio of inverse order. What makes it particularly necessary to discuss gases and heat together is that the distribution of gases and heat between upper and lower waters of a lake is in no little degree effected by the same mechanism, the movement of water driven by the wind. Where there is "wind distributed heat" there is wind distributed oxygen and carbon dioxide. In streams both are distributed by

1. Net *energy-absorbing* reactions, not common in processes of life, are postulated for some bacteria operating under anaerobic conditions (Phelps, 1944).

stream flow and the resulting turbulence. Of course, heat is also dispersed by radiation, by conduction, and by convection currents (which must also convey dissolved gases). Gases are independently distributed in small degree by diffusion and by rising bubbles. Obviously the circulation of gases and heat can best be considered together.

Gases Essential for Life

All life is work, meaning transformation of energy. Therefore, among the necessities for maintenance and increase of life, the sources of energy and the means of getting at it are of equal rank with the supplies of building materials. Energy is from the sun. Its absorption and storage is effected by plants in photosynthesis, requiring *carbon dioxide*. The release of energy in the processes of life is generally dependent upon oxidation. Hence, a continuing source of *oxygen* is a first requirement.

For oxygen, special emphasis must be placed on the word "continuing," because organisms have almost no capacity for internal storage of oxygen for oxidative purposes. Proteins, carbohydrates, and water are as necessary for animals as is oxygen, but all these can be stored in the body; occasional replenishment is consistent with an active and prosperous life. Cold-blooded animals, with no requirement of fuel for maintenance of body temperature, may go for weeks or even months without liquid or solid food. Warm-blooded animals, including man, are known to survive for weeks without food and for days without water. On the other hand, oxygen deprivation for only a short time, a matter of just a few minutes with man, is injurious or fatal. Starvation is slow; suffocation is rapid. Furthermore, for the great majority of animals oxygen for oxidative uses can be availed of only in the free state, as the gas occurs in solution in the surrounding water or in the liquid bathing the cells. Conceivably, for a few animals, as for some bacteria and yeast cells, other sources of oxygen are practicable; but, if so, these are exceptions in the animal world.

It is the solubility of gases that poses some of the distinctive problems of aquatic life. Terrestrial animals are surrounded by a medium, the atmosphere, so richly provided with oxygen and so mobile in itself that oxygen-shortage may occur only under unusual and generally man-made conditions, as in a tightly closed room. The student of terrestrial life, although concerned with the special respiratory equipment of particular animals, pays no heed to the outside sources of oxygen. On the other hand, aquatic animals often face a serious oxygen problem, sometimes a critical one. This is because the oxygen dissolved in water is small in amount as compared with oxygen in an equal volume of air and also because the water itself is so lacking in mobility, when compared with the atmosphere. Consequently, in considering life in water, it is of the first order of importance to inquire into the sources and the means of distribution of free oxygen.

It is well-known that plants, through photosynthesis, must transform the radiant energy of the sun into the latent energy of an organic compound before the oxidative processes of animals can utilize it for transformation again into the kinetic forms of heat and work that accompany all manifestations of life. Granting sunlight in proper wave-lengths, the raw materials for fuel formation are water and carbon dioxide. As we are concerned now only with life in water, we take water for granted. Carbon dioxide is, then, the crux of the synthetic problem in respect to the storage of energy and is of equal importance with oxygen.

As oxygen is a waste product of photosynthesis of green plants, so carbon dioxide is a waste product of the metabolism of both plants and animals and of many kinds of bacteria. The stocks of both of these gases in water are governed, partly by the conditions of organic metabolism within the water, partly by those of physical interchange between water and atmosphere at their point of contact, and partly also, as we shall see, by the conditions of circulation of the water; furthermore, certain chemicals in the water affect the reserves of carbon dioxide, as is discussed in another place.

We will keep in mind that the requirements of animals in respect to free oxygen are quite diverse. Fish are generally assumed to need a concentration of about five parts per million, although some are less tolerant than others. Brook-trout may require very much more, although even they can endure an ex-

tremely low concentration for brief periods. The ordinary fluctuations in carbon dioxide content have little untoward effects on
fishes, which readily make appropriate physiological adjustments,
although quick changes may be disturbing to them.[2]

The ultimate source of most free oxygen is the photosynthetic
activity of plants,[3] in which plants, using the energy of sunlight, break down molecules of carbon dioxide (CO_2) and water
(H_2O), and, through a series of steps, recombine the parts to
form sugar ($C_6H_{12}O_6$) and liberate the excess oxygen as a gas.
Oxygen is utilized in the respiration of both animals and plants
and also in the decomposition of organic matter (involving respiration of the agents of decomposition). The oxidation of the
sugar, or of things made from it, gives back the energy (originally derived from the sun) in the forms of work and heat, while
setting free water and carbon dioxide. It is, happily, an endless
circle. The processes of respiration and decomposition primarily
maintain the supply of carbon dioxide, as the photosynthetic
plants maintain the supply of oxygen.

Other Gases

Our concern just now is with the gases necessary for life, the
vital gases they are appropriately called; but a number of other
gases occur in solution in natural waters, derived, partly by absorption from the atmosphere, partly as products of decomposition
in the absence, or virtual absence, of oxygen. Nitrogen, an atmospheric gas seemingly used in water (in elemental form) in only
a small way, is mentioned on another page. Chief among gases
liberated by organisms when free oxygen is deficient are: the
inflammable *methane* (CH_4) which in some cases greatly exceeds
carbon dioxide in amount and which often escapes as bubbles
rising to the surface, especially when a mucky bottom is disturbed,
and *hydrogen sulphide.* There may also be some *hydrogen,* at

2. "Fishes have been found to tolerate a wide range of CO_2 tension in water by
increasing the alkaline reserve of their blood in waters of high CO_2 tension and decreasing their alkaline reserve in water of low CO_2 tension. However, if fishes alternate
quickly between waters above a certain minimum difference in CO_2 tension, they
become deranged and die regardless of the O_2 content of the water." (Abstract of
Power's et al., 1939, in Biol. Abst., 1939.)

3. It is supposed to be true of the atmosphere that there was no oxygen-richness
until plants liberated the oxygen gas.

least briefly, *ammonia* and *carbon monoxide*. See the chapter on "Stream Pollution."

Solubility and Pressure

Because we shall have to speak of "partial pressures" of gases, it may be well to recall certain elementary principles of solubility of gases. The solubility of gases in water depends upon pressure and temperature. By Henry's law the concentration of gases in saturated solution in water is proportional to the pressure at which the gas is supplied. By Dalton's supplementary law of "partial pressures," each of the several gases in a mixture, such as the atmosphere, has a pressure proportional to its concentration in the mixture. Those proportions in the atmosphere are, roughly, by volume: nitrogen 78%, oxygen 21%, carbon dioxide 0.03%. This is disregarding water vapor and the gases of minor biological interest, such as argon and helium, which are small in amount, although there is much more argon than carbon dioxide. Given an atmosphere of pure oxygen or pure carbon dioxide or pure nitrogen, the solubilities would be very much greater for each gas, especially for carbon dioxide and oxygen, each of which has relatively small partial pressures in the atmosphere of the earth. Under ordinary conditions in nature, however, and in connection with interchange between water and atmosphere, we are concerned only with the solubilities under the conditions of the partial pressures of the several gases in the atmosphere. When in limnology one speaks of water "saturated" with oxygen or carbon dioxide, one means saturated with respect to prevailing atmospheric pressures and the partial atmospheric pressure of the particular gas: *the water will hold no more with the partial pressure of the gas as it is.* It would be better to say, under such conditions, that the water is "in equilibrium" with the atmosphere with reference to the particular gas. Because solubility of gases is a function of pressure, it follows that water below the surface may hold in solution a greater volume of any gas than it could hold at the surface.

When we speak of "equilibrium with the atmosphere," it is not to be understood that the several gases dissolved in water are in the same proportions as in air. As a matter of fact, each gas has its own coefficient of absorption in water, that of carbon dioxide being some 30 times greater than that of oxygen and that of nitrogen about half that of oxygen. At the pressure of one atmosphere (760 mm.) and the partial pressure of oxygen in the atmosphere (about 21%) oxygen constitutes more than a third (about 35%) of the gases in "saturated" solution. Even at that the amount is small. At the best, a liter of pure water, under pressure of one atmosphere and at a temperature of 15° C., will hold around seven cubic centimeters of gaseous oxygen; a liter of air has about 210 cubic centimeters of the same gas. Obviously, it takes nearly 30 liters of oxygen-saturated surface water to supply to a fish the same quantity of oxygen that one liter of air offers to a rabbit—and the water is not everywhere saturated. This points unmistakably to the oxygen problem for aquatic animals.

With an atmosphere of pure carbon dioxide (which does not exist in nature), a liter of gas would dissolve in about a liter of water at a pressure of 760 mm. and a temperature of 15° C. In nature, however, we deal with the very low partial pressure of carbon dioxide in the atmosphere, of which it constitutes only some three one-hundredths of one per cent; under these conditions a liter of pure fresh water at 15° C. may have about the same volume of dissolved free carbon dioxide (0.3 cc.) as does a liter of air. These comparisons are very rough but perhaps they are illuminating. Especially when the reserves of carbon dioxide are taken into consideration, this becomes apparent. When water is compared with land as a place to live, aquatic plants are in a far better position with respect to their need for carbon dioxide than are aquatic animals and plants with regard to requirements in free oxygen. As regards dissolved gases, the oxygen problem is the one for concern.

Obviously, it is nitrogen, the predominant atmospheric gas, that occurs in solution in water in substantially less proportion than in the atmosphere. From the point of view of most living organisms this is perhaps fortunate, for the other two gases are vital necessities, while dissolved nitrogen can be utilized, so far as is now known, only by nitrogen-fixing bacteria, some fungi and blue-green algae. To excess nitrogen in solution is attributed, in some cases, the "gas disease" of fishes, which sometimes may occur in hatcheries, at least.

Temperature and Solubility of Gas

There is a definite relation between temperature and the solubility of gases. The lower the temperature, between 0° C., and 100° C. the greater the amount of oxygen that may be dissolved in water. Table 1 is illustrative of the effect of temperature on solubility of the vital gases. The figures used are computed from data of solubilities in a standard reference work (Hodgman, 1941). Although carried to but one or two decimal points, the figures have an appearance of greater accuracy than is dependable in any situation. There are variables other than temperature: atmospheric pressure may change from hour to hour, affecting solubility of gases; pressure within the water increases with depth, enabling the water to hold more gas in solution if it can get it; in natural water what is called the "salt effect" modifies solubility of gases. For carbon dioxide particularly, the alkalinity of the water changes in marked degree the amount of the gas that may be held in one form or another. For any particular situation, therefore, the figures of solubility of carbon dioxide in pure water are of less interest than are those for oxygen.

It is evident from the table that natural waters at 5° will hold about half again as much oxygen (and nearly twice as much car-

Solubility of Oxygen and Carbon Dioxide in Pure Fresh Water at Different Temperatures, When Exposed to Air Containing 20.99 Per Cent Oxygen and 0.03 Per Cent CO_2 and Under a Pressure of 760 MM. (Volume of Gas When Reduced to 0° C.)

Temperature Centigrade	O_2 p. p. m.	O_2 cc. per liter	CO_2 p. p. m.	CO_2 cc. per liter
0°	14.6	10.3	1.00	0.51
5°	12.7	9.0	0.83	0.43
10°	11.3	8.0	0.70	0.36
15°	10.1	7.2	0.59	0.31
20°	9.1	6.5	0.51	0.26
25°	8.3	5.9	0.43	0.23
30°	7.5	5.5	0.38	0.20

bon dioxide) as at 25°. As will be seen later, it is when the water of a deep lake is at a temperature of about 4° C. that the great mass of deep water receives its primary charge of oxygen. Were there no depletion by the processes of life and no replenishments, the deep cold waters, which are also under heavy pressure, would have in sumner a much higher oxygen content than the upper water, which could not, when warmed in summer, hold what it had gained in winter.

It should be remembered that the figures in the table are for an assumed mean atmospheric pressure (760 mm.) at sea level. D. S. Rawson has prepared a nomogram, convenient for "obtaining oxygen-saturation values at different temperatures and at different altitudes, also for transforming oxygen values from one kind of unit to another. This is found in Special Publication No. 15 of the Limnological Society of America, 1944, and in Welch, 1948, p. 366.

Interchange Between Water and Atmosphere

Atmosphere and waters are interchanging reservoirs of both oxygen and carbon dioxide. The two media tend to keep in equilibrium with respect to gas tension, but the contact between them is only at the surface of the water. The much higher rate of diffusion of gases in air and the relatively great mobility of that medium justify us in giving no further thought to the distribution of gases in the atmosphere. With the water it is different. Because of the low diffusion rate of gases in water the direct effects of interchange can extend only a little way below the surface. Wave action helps only in the topmost layers. Distribution to the depths depends upon more deep-reaching turbulence or upon circulation of masses of water. It has been estimated for Lake Constance in Switzerland, assuming that the lake was deprived of all dissolved oxygen and then left dependent upon diffusion alone and kept at 10° C., that it would require a million years for the bottom water to be brought into equilibrium with the atmosphere; the inadequacy of diffusion is made all the more impressive when we note that this calculation is based on the assumption that no processes of depletion took place during the million years. Obviously, then, if the effects of interchange with the atmosphere are to be generally felt in the lake below the very top stratum, reliance must be upon internal movements of water; we must soon inquire into this.

When the surface of the lake is cooler than the deeper layers and the temperature is above 4° C., convection currents will answer well and a uniform distribution of gases and of heat from surface to bottom is readily brought about; but, from what we have already learned about the expansion of water above and below 4° C. and from knowledge that warming by the sun occurs chiefly at and near the surface, it is obvious that effective convection currents can prevail only for short periods in fall and spring, when, in temperate and cooler climates, the surface temperature becomes lower than bottom temperature, if it is not yet down to 4° C. When surface and bottom temperature have reached 4° C., the temperature of maximum density, change of temperature of the surface water *in either direction* can result only in keeping upper water at the top.

Gases of Metabolism in Water

Interchange of gases between water and atmosphere is only a part of the story of dissolved gases in water. Before considering the problem of distribution within the water, let us first recall certain basic facts of liberation of gases in the metabolism of organisms living in the water. (1) Photosynthesis with use of carbon dioxide and liberation of excess oxygen by plants can occur only in lighted areas of the lake; if the lake has much depth, these are only the shallow marginal waters and the upper illuminated layer of offshore water. (2) On the other hand, use of oxygen and liberation of carbon dioxide by animals occur at any depth. (3) Aerobic decomposition, with oxygen depletion and carbon dioxide liberation, takes place, not only in the shallows, but also in the dark depths where no direct renewal of the dissolved oxygen supply can occur; in deep lakes of substantial size, decomposition may occur predominantly in the deeper parts. (4) Green plants in the dark, as well as animals, are consumers of oxygen without simultaneous compensatory replenishment through photosynthesis. (5) Where light is dim or duration of the daily period of illumination is very short, as in the deeper layers of illuminated water, photosynthetic activities may be so weak that plants actually produce no more, or even less, oxygen than they require themselves; the depth at which consumption and production of oxygen by green plants are in balance is known as the "compensation level." (6) In very clear water with luxuriant growth of floating algae, there may be so much photosynthetic activity at a depth of some meters (where total pressure of air and water is much more than one atmosphere) that the water holds in solution a much greater proportion of oxygen than could be retained at the surface; relative to surface conditions, the water is decidedly "supercharged" with oxygen; the gas is in normal state of solution for the temperature and for the pressure at that depth; yet, if some of the water is taken in a bottle, and is brought to the surface, it may actually effervesce under the reduced pressure, or appear milky with tiny bubbles of gas.

The Problem of Distribution

The interchanges at the surface between water and atmosphere, the imperfect penetration of light, and the distribution of plants, animals, and bacteria of decomposition, such as have been mentioned, must inevitably tend to bring about some sort of *stratification* with respect to gas content. Upper waters rich in dissolved oxygen may overlie waters poor in oxygen and perhaps overly rich in carbon dioxide. The several strata will differ also with respect to tolerability for organic life of the several types. Such stratification may be prevented or modified by circulation of the water resulting from outside causes. The conditions of circulation and their effects on distribution of the vital gases becomes, then, a matter of special concern to the student of life in water.

As regards streams, the natural action of gravity provides for regular movements and a mixing that is effective in proportion to gradient, volume of flow, and nature of the stream bed. In a mountain brook, falls and riffles provide the most effective aerating mechanism that could be devised. Even in slow streams, the fact that friction with sides and bottom retards flow, while upper water moves more rapidly, results in a certain degree of rolling and mixing. The content of dissolved oxygen in sluggish streams, and even in swift ones, may be partially dependent, however, upon the amount of decomposing organic matter borne, so that heavily polluted streams sometimes carry very inadequate supplies of free oxygen.

With small ponds or very shallow lakes, where light penetrates to all depths and photosynthetic plants may exist everywhere, the distribution of oxygen may present no special problem. Here again, however, conditions alter cases; prolonged periods of calmness, excessive decomposition of organic debris, or the blanketing of the surface with a dense mat of floating algae that shades too effectively the lower water, may cause oxygen deprivation and suffocation of the more sensitive animals. The dead and decomposing bodies of these first casualties only increase the draft upon the limited stock of dissolved oxygen; the condition sometimes becomes catastrophic for animal life of the pond as a whole. Pond owners may be made painfully aware of this.

In the cases of lakes that have sufficient depth or that carry enough suspended water or color to have regions of darkness by day, the circulation and the distribution of dissolved gases requires a regular mechanism and a source of energy behind the mechanism. The power that propels the circulation is chiefly the wind. Of course, the energy of the wind, like the energy of organic activity, derives originally from the sun, which brings about the occurrence of areas of low and high pressures and consequent shifting of masses of air over the face of the earth.

Thermal Stratification

There are times when temperature change alone will cause effective vertical mixings. For the effective vertical distribution of gases and temperature, it is necessary only for superficial waters to become heavier than waters below. This, as we know, must occur whenever surface becomes cooler than deeper water, unless the temperature is below $4°$ C.; cooling below that temperature causes water to become lighter, so that colder water no longer sinks but floats. It is evident that in lakes of temperate regions the sinking of surface waters must occur sometime in the fall, either at or before the lowering surface temperature has reached 4° C. The complete mixing that occurs at this time is what is known as the *fall overturn;* it is said to be sometimes observable to the eye, when the rising bottom waters may come to the surface with a load of discoloring silt; presumably this would occur under conditions of turbidity stratification which is discussed elsewhere. The story with reference to tropical lakes will be different, but we disregard these at this time.

Since, for reasons previously given, the bottom waters of a deep lake, barring exceptional cases, will not have a temperature much below 4° C. the fall overturn is not to be escaped if freezing or near freezing temperatures occur at any period of the year.

In the cold of winter, and particularly in the heat of summer, conditions are quite otherwise. Surface water, warmer and lighter in summer, and cooler or even frozen in deep winter (and much lighter as ice), tends to remain on top. A density stratification may then occur at any time when the temperature of the whole lake is not at approximately 4° C.

The water of melting ice in the spring is lighter than deeper water which is usually around the maximum density at 4° C. As the surface water warms, it becomes heavier until at about 4° C. there is no difference in density from top to bottom. Winter winds could have no effect on the water as long as it was sheltered under a roof of ice; now, however, wind causes surface water to drift before it and to be at a higher level on the leeward side. Gravity requires a return circulation, which to some extent may be along more protected shores but must chiefly be downward, backward, and upward on the other side. The whole body of water is in a "sort of rotation." Surface and bottom waters become completely mixed; temperature is approximately the same throughout. This is the *spring overturn,* perhaps better called the *spring circulation.*

As surface water accumulates heat, to become distinctly warmer and lighter, the movement downward requires displacement of heavier and more viscous (less fluid) cold water of the depths; thus there is a "thermal resistance" to mixing. In short, with density and, more strongly, viscosity serving as brakes, the water below offers significant resistance to displacement by lighter and more fluid waters above. The warmer waters of the return current, moving against the direction of flow of wind and surface water may, then, not go far down, but may flow back at a level not far beneath. Only a very strong wind can effect thorough mixing. With ordinary breezes the warmer and lighter water tends to stay at upper levels, to glide back at no great depth and to keep above the great mass of colder water. The whole lake becomes layered. There is an upper stratum of warm water which becomes warmer day by day as it circulates from surface to a moderate depth with repeated exposure to sun and air; this overlies a body of colder water which has little or no opportunity to gain heat from the sun or oxygen from the atmosphere. There is now a definite *summer thermal stratification* with an upper warm water mass, known as the *epilimnion* (upper lake mass), and a lower non-circulating cold mass called the *hypolimnion* (lower lake mass). Where the two masses are in contact there is a transition zone in which temperature falls rapidly with depth. This intermediate zone the Germans appropriately call the *metalimnion* (transition lake mass), or *Sprungschicht* (jump-layer) (cf. French *"couche de saut thermique,"* layer of thermal jump). In America it is more commonly designated with equal appropriateness as the *thermocline*[4] (temperature slope) (Fig. 1).

In lakes the thermocline varies in position and in thickness with the lake or with seasonal and other conditions; speaking in terms of approximation, it may have its upper limit at 5 to 10 meters (15 to 30 ft.). It is generally understood to be the stratum in which the fall of temperature with depth is as much as one degree centigrade per meter of depth (or, roughly, .5 F. per foot). In epilimnion and hypolimnion the fall of temperature is less, and likely to be very much less, than a degree per meter. In fact, these are regions of approximate homogeneity in temperature.

4. "The Thermocline and Its Biological Significance" was the subject of a presidential address to the American Microscopical Society given in 1903 by Dr. E. A. Birge, who mentioned that he first employed the term in 1897. (Birge, 1904.) The terms *epilimnion* and *hypolimnion* were used by the same investigator in 1910. Roughly corresponding terms for the ocean are *epithalassa, hypothallassa,* and *thermocline.*

In general, larger lakes with greater windsweep have deeper thermoclines. Small shallow lakes may lack thermal stratification; but I have seen two definitely stratified artificial lakes not over 20 and 9 feet in depth, respectively. Welch (1952, p. 57) mentions waters not over half a meter in depth and showing diminutive thermal stratification. Particularly in ponds or small lakes, the inflow of cold spring waters or cool tributary streams may tend to maintain low temperature in bottom waters, with resulting stratification.

Returning now to consideration of the hypolimnion, we have in the depths of a lake a body of water, indeed a very substantial part of large lakes, which is largely isolated from surface influences, except as there may be some light in the upper part.[5] Yet it receives regular organic enrichment through the falling bodies and wastes of animals and plants of the epilimnion. This enrichment with decomposable matter serves to cause a drain upon the oxygen supply acquired at the time of overturn, additional to that resulting from the metabolism of the animal and non-green plant inhabitants. A condition of progressive oxygen depletion follows in what is known as the *summer stagnation* period. As Birge (1904) describes it:

> During the summer, then, our typical northern lakes really consist of two lakes, one superimposed on the other: first, the lake above the thermocline, whose temperature is high and whose water is kept in active movement by the wind; and, below this, the stagnant mass of water below the thermocline, having a low temperature, denser and more viscous than the upper water, in which the gaseous and other products of decomposition are accumulating and from which they are only slowly and partially discharged (p. 18).

It is not unusual in deep lakes for the bottom water, by the end of summer or early autumn, to show virtually complete want of dissolved oxygen and, accordingly, to be uninhabitable for most animals. Strange enough, however, there is a limited but

5. In very transparent water, or where the epilimnion is not very thick; a good deal of photosynthesis may occur in the upper part of the hypolimnion. At this depth there could under these circumstances be a dissolved oxygen content notably higher than what the water could hold if through circulation it were brought to the surface (Birge, 1906).

characteristic fauna of such stagnant depths. (See Table 19 in Welch, 1952, p. 184). Most prominent among the animals of the "oxygen-free" depths are the red worms, Tubifex and Limnodrilus, red-blooded midge larvae of the genus Tendipes (Chironomus), the transparent "phantom larvae" of the midge called Chaoborus, or Corethra (which, however, migrates to upper oxygen-rich levels at night), and several species of the finger-nail clams, Musculium and Pisidium, some ostracods, copepods, and rotifers.[6]

Once the summer stratification has occurred, and barring its drastic disturbance, as by storms, the waters of the hypolimnion remain cold. Beyond mixture with upper warm waters, the only sources of heat are: (1) warmer waters entering from streams[7] or deep springs; (2) mechanical transfer of heat by bodies moving down from the warmer waters above; (3) oxidation of organic matter, living or dead; and (4) direct penetration of solar radiation (which may not be insignificant in very clear and infertile lakes) (Ricker, 1937).

It is obvious that in north-temperate or colder regions, or wherever the covering of ice persists through the winter, a *winter stagnation* must prevail; for photosynthetic activity beneath the ice is markedly reduced and circulation is slight if any. The depletion of oxygen in ice-covered waters seems in many cases to be a very practical condition and sometimes a fatal one to fish and other animals in shallow lakes or ponds, where the volume of unfrozen water, and consequently the initial amount of oxygen, is small relative to the abundance of animal life.[8]

6. Deevey (1941), with substantial grounds, questions the continued existence of any bottom-living animals (excluding Protozoa apparently) in "the complete absence of oxygen."

7. As will be seen below, turbid tributary waters may underflow the clearer upper waters of a lake (Chapter 5).

8. "A very thin layer of water just below the ice is near freezing temperature, and, for a relatively short distance below, the rise in temperature is rapid, up to about 3° C. From that point on to the bottom, the rise in temperature may be very slight. This vertical temperature distribution, when plotted in the usual way, gives a graph which in mere form has a certain resemblance to the curve of thermal distribution during the summer stagnation period, except that the curve is reversed and lacks the epilimnion portion. This condition is sometimes spoken of as an *inverse stratification,* but it falls far short of the stratification of the summer period, and it is an open question whether it should be referred to as a true stratification" (Welch, 1952).

Birge (1907) has made an illuminating analogy of the lake to a higher animal, such as man. The taking of gases from the atmosphere at the surface, the return of gases to it, and the conveyance of absorbed atmospheric gas away from the surface, he aptly terms the "external respiration" of the lake. The gaseous interchange between the various organisms in the lake and the water around them he calls the "internal respiration."

As a feature of "external respiration," the hypolimnion of northern lakes "takes a breath" of air only in fall and spring. During the remainder of the year its oxygen supply undergoes steady depletion without replenishment, its carbon dioxide supply enrichment without adequate elimination. In thinking of the changes in gas supply in the hypolimnion, it must be remembered that the "deep breath" is taken at the very best time, when the temperature is lowest and the capacity of the water to absorb oxygen is at its highest, and also that the deep region, even in summer, is one of low temperature and correspondingly slow metabolic activity. With regard to cold-blooded animals (and we have little to do with warm-blooded animals in lakes), it is a general rule, but not an accurate or entirely dependable one, that metabolic activity is practically doubled with a rise of 10° C. Insofar as this rule applies, the organic activity of a fish or an insect in the depth of a deep lake may be only about one-fourth the activity of a corresponding animal in the upper layer in summer. The emphases in this paragraph are on the facts that, when the hypolimnion is first isolated at the beginning of the warm season, it has a particularly full charge of oxygen, and that, during the period of isolation, the processes causing depletion are relatively slow. These conditions may be expected to retard the onset of seriously deleterious stagnation.

The date of the beginning of effective stratification is not the same with different lakes; generally it comes much earlier in small than in large lakes. The thickness of the epilimnion and the depth of upper and lower limits of the thermocline vary also within wide limits according to location, size and form of the lake, and topography of bottom; they vary, too, with weather conditions from year to year, and, in any given year, with season.

In general, as the epilimnion cools down in late summer and early fall, it must appropriate the upper water of the thermocline, while the latter begins to take in the upper part of the hypolimnion; so that there is progressive thickening of epilimnion and lowering of the position of the thermocline, until there is virtually no stratification preceding the time of the fall overturn.

To illustrate the biological effects of summer stratification, we cannot do better than to quote an early paper of Dr. E. A. Birge (1906):

If you study the lake in the early spring, when the temperature conditions are uniform you will find these animals [microscopic life, including crustacea and rotifers] through the lake at all depths, and in very considerable numbers. . . . [In the summer, on the other hand, after the lake has undergone thermal stratification]: It almost startles the student to see how sharp is the division between the inhabited and uninhabited portions of the lake. If you lower a hose into the lake and pump the water from various depths into a fine net you will catch a great abundance of animals in the water from the lower part of the circulating layer. This stratum indeed is often more densely populated than any other portion and may contain thousands of crustacea and rotifers per gallon. But if the hose is lowered another meter, or even a half meter, an entire change appears. The water is perfectly clear and appears to the eye as fit for life as that above it, but you may pump many gallons of the water without securing more than a very few animals and these mainly sickly or injured forms which have evidently been caught as they were slowly sinking to the bottom (p. 152).

In summary, then, a lake in temperate regions undergoes a prolonged period of thermal stratification with separation of the whole water into more or less clearly distinguishable masses, one lying upon another. There is an epilimnion, high in temperature, rich, even to "saturation," perhaps, with the gases requisite for organic life. Next below is a thermocline, varying in thickness and in distance below the surface, but tending to descend with the passage of summer. Between the thermocline and the bottom is a deeper hypolimnion, largely isolated for the time and comprising often the greater part of the mass of the lake; it is a region without significant circulation and with greater or lesser trend toward stagnation and uninhabitability for most animals; it may endure a definite period of real summer stagnation. Whenever, during a period of declining temperature, the surface temperature becomes the same as that of the bottom, or lower (if not below 4° C.), the winds may cause a complete circulation of the lake water. If the surface temperature becomes lower than that of the bottom, and is still above 4° C., an overturn must occur and result in a condition of uniformity at all depths for temperature and dissolved gases.

The resulting condition of physical homogeneity may prevail during a further period of declining temperature until the lake water reaches the point of maximum density at 4° C. (39.1° F.). As the surface temperature falls below this level, another stratification occurs, with colder water on top. With the fluctuations of temperature characteristic of autumn weather, overturn and this sort of faint stratification may alternate for a time. The formation of a persistent ice sheet introduces a period of winter stagnation, with virtually the whole lake below the ice constituting the hypolimnion and undergoing progressive depletion of oxygen and accumulation of the waste gases of organic metabolism. With the melting of the ice in spring and the warming of the surface to 4° C., a condition of uniformity of temperature from surface to bottom again permits a complete circulation of the water of the lake under the influence of the winds.

Degree of depletion of oxygen during the winter depends upon many factors. While the unfrozen water is cut off from direct contact with the atmosphere, the free oxygen is being continually used in respiration of animals, plants, and bacteria of aerobic decomposition. Under such conditions depth of lake and total volume of water have some significance. Replenishment of oxygen by green plants in the water is conditioned upon penetration of sunlight, but the amount of light available beneath the ice cover varies with weather conditions, with thickness of ice, and with the amount of snow, a few inches of which act as an effective light screen. To some extent oxygen may be replenished from without, if there is a flow through the lake from tributaries to outlet, offering a substantial check against stagnation. Changes of water level that cause upheavals or subsidences of the ice sufficient to break through the surface may permit exposure of water to atmosphere or the indrainage of oxygen-rich water of rain or melting snow. The length of time the ice cover persists makes a great difference.

At any rate, "winter-kills" of fish and other animals are well-known for northern ponds; yet one cannot always be sure if the fish die from mere suffocation or from over-exposure to toxic substances released in decomposition. More extensive winter-kills may be expected in more fertile water (having greater demand on the oxygen supply both in respiration and in decomposition). This is one of the dangers faced in artificial fertilization of northern ponds that develop heavy and long-lasting covers of ice and snow. The interested reader may consult Welch (1952) and Greenbank (1945). A popular article by Charles Cadieux in *The Fisherman* of February, 1953, and entitled "Death Under the Ice" is of interest in this connection.

It is not only the scientists who know about this. I knew an uneducated "john-boater" with a cabin on an island in the Mississippi River having a "slue," or bayou, subject to winter kill of fish. In the fall he cut large trees so that their bushy tops fell into the water. He said that the natural rises and falls of the ice level during the winter caused crunching and cracks among the branches of the tree, admitting air into the water to save the fish for his spring seining.

It may be remarked that the stability of the hypolimnion during the period of summer thermal stratification may not be so fixed as was formerly supposed. There can be circulation attributable to invasion of tributary waters with density greater than that of the upper waters of the lake. Density may be higher because of either low temperature or of turbidity. The denser inflow, instead of mixing with the light top water of the lake, may creep down toward the depths to find its proper level, as will be discussed later in connection with "underflow." Besides producing mechanical disturbance in the deeper waters, the stream water may bring in new supplies of oxygen. (Bryson and Suomi, 1951.)

Yet another sort of movement in lakes may cause shifts in the deeper waters. If a pan of water is sharply tilted and brought

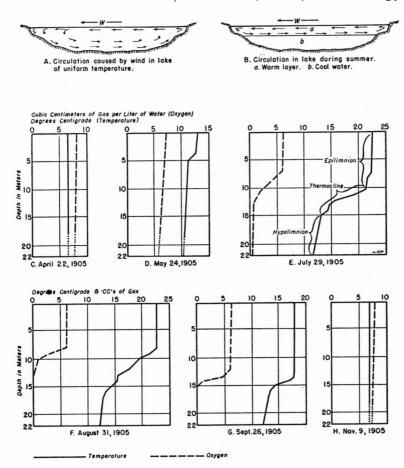

FIGURE 1. Thermal stratification in lakes.

To illustrate graphically the phenomena of stratification, we can hardly do better than adapt some of Birge's earliest figures. At the top of Figure 1 are diagrams showing: (*a*) the circulation caused by wind, when, as in late fall or in spring, the water of a lake in temperate regions has a uniform temperature from top to bottom, that temperature being about 4° C.; and (*b*) the circulation in summer, when only the upper stratum of warm water (A, the epilimnion) is moved by the winds while the deeper and colder water (B, the hypolimnion) is relatively at rest. The thermocline, or stratum of transition from warm to cold water, would be in the region a little above and below the line between A and B.

In the next six graphs the changing conditions of temperature and oxygen supply are shown in chronological sequence. These are all for Lake Mendota in 1905. In *c* it is obvious that the temperature, indicated by vertical line T, was uniform from surface to bottom on April 22. Dissolved oxygen, indicated by vertical line O, is hardly less at the bottom than at the top. Conditions a month later, May 24, are shown in *d,* where there is indication of the formation of a thermocline at a depth of four to five meters. The oxygen line shows a distinct decline in dissolved oxygen with depth; the depletion of oxygen in deeper water follows with the relative isolation of bottom water from the upper layers where oxygen used is readily replaced by absorption from the atmosphere and by photosynthesis in the illuminated zone. The bottom water has become warmer, but not so much so as has the upper water. Summer conditions are shown in *e* and *f,* where the thermocline extends from seven or eight meters to about fifteen meters. In *e* (for July 29) the oxygen curve follows roughly the temperature curve, with very little free oxygen anywhere in the hypolimnion. By August 31 (*f*) the hypolimnion is completely depleted of oxygen, with a definite condition of "summer stagnation."

By September 26, as shown in *g,* both air and surface water temperatures have been lowered—for water, from about 22° to about 18°. Consequently, the vertical line for temperature has shifted in the epilimnion to the left; this, alone, would automatically make the top of the thermocline lower; as yet there had been no notable change as to temperature or dissolved oxygen in the deeper water. With continual cooling during the autumn, the surface temperature fell below the summer bottom temperature of around 12° C. (and, accordingly, became denser than the water below it); convection currents caused it to sink and be replaced by the warmer and lighter deep water; with passing hours, the new surface water loses heat (and gains oxygen) to sink and be replaced; the whole lake has an approximately uniform temperature from top to bottom—and is well oxygenated throughout. In short, the "fall overturn" has occurred; the cycle is completed: the graph *h,* representing conditions on November 9, is virtually identical with the graph *a* for April 22.

It must be emphasized that the graphs used here for illustration apply to a certain lake, Mendota, in a particular year. In some lakes the bottom temperature might not rise appreciably above 4° C.; in some, with little plankton, full stagnation at the bottom would not occur at all; there can be an almost infinite number of variations in the details of the picture for different lakes and some differences from year to year.

---

back to level there will follow repeated swings of the water up and down in reciprocal alternation on the two sides of a middle "node." This free oscillation, as a "standing wave," continues for some time with a "period" depending on the diameter, the depth, and the form of the pan. No one tilts a lake, of course, but the waters of a lake or of a bay, at least the upper waters, may have somewhat similar periodic swings or oscillations that are called *seiches.* A seiche may result from differences of pressure over different areas. Causes of differences in pressure may be sharp wind changes, large scale differences in barometric pressure or heavy run-off at one end of a lake. Earth tremors, too, like the shaking of a pan of water, may start seiches that will not immediately subside. A seiche of any sort cannot well prevail without some disturbance of the deeper water. (See Bryson and Kuhn, 1952.) If there is rise and fall of masses of water on either side of the node where level is stationary, there must be *horizontal flow* of water from one side to the other as can easily be demonstrated in a laboratory model. (See Ruttner, pp. 42 and 44 and reference to Mortimer.)

This, at best, is only a cursory account of a whole series of complexly interrelated phenomena involving, not only such geographic and geologic conditions as the location, size, and form of a body of water, the surrounding topography, and the nature of tributary water, from springs, soils, and streams, but also a diversity of chemical, physical, meteorological, and biological phenomena. The interested reader should not be satisfied with this generalized story, but should read fuller and more detailed accounts, such as are given in some of the original papers of Birge and Juday, in the books of Welch and Ruttner, or in the more technical papers of Hutchinson.[9]

The Great Lakes present special and complex patterns of thermal stratification that we cannot consider here. We pass over, too, the *meromictic* lakes or parts of lakes in which there is permanent stratification. Let us keep in mind, also, that the more or less regular seasonal cycles applicable to lakes of some depth need not be expected to hold for ponds or other shallow still waters. In

9. It must not be overlooked that overturns, such as have been discussed, arise from changes in density (with viscosity playing its part). Unlike conditions in the sea, where density reflects either temperature or salinity or both, it is a general rule for lakes that density is governed chiefly by temperature. Nevertheless, that rule is not invariable; there are lakes, or parts of lakes, in which, because, of chemical content, deeper water is always denser than upper water. Colder water can and does remain above somewhat warmer water of sufficiently higher salt content. In such case, the deepest water cannot participate in the general overturn; at least a part of the density stratification is persistent. A body of water in which deepest water does not get into the circulation at any season—that is to say—one in which some stratification is enduring—is called *meromictic* (part mixing), in contrast to those called *holomictic* (complete mixing), in which overturn is complete in response to changes in temperature and to winds. Most lakes in temperate regions are holomictic. Consideration is not given here to tropical lakes or to arctic lakes; both offer special conditions.

these the night cooling of surface waters may effect complete circulation from top to bottom, moderate winds may cause general mixing, springs and rainfall have more pronounced effects. Diurnal and irregular overturns, if they may be so called, make quite another picture. Nevertheless, small ponds do often show distinct stratification, both thermal and chemical, as may also the sluggish parts of deep rivers.

It is obvious now, that, in contrast to a stream or a small pond, a lake of any size shows homogeneity in respect to temperature and dissolved gases from surface to bottom for only relatively brief periods during the year. It should also be clear that without winds the deeper waters in lakes of temperate and colder regions would never be much warmer than 4° C. The elevation of the temperature of the lake above 4° C. is effected largely through "wind-distributed heat." Hence the winds they never feel are of great importance to animals that live in the depths.

Transfer of Heat from Land to Water

We have seen something of the complex interrelations of physical and biological conditions in respect to the distribution of gases, where the winds, the warming or cooling of surface waters, convection currents, and other conditions play such significant parts. A few more comments are essential to the completion of even the main lines of the picture.

The interchanges of heat between the lake and the outside world occur so largely at the surface that we may, for present purposes, disregard any other place of interchange. The high heat coefficient of water has been mentioned in connection with the consideration of the properties of water. The sun's rays that penetrate ordinary waters warm them directly to some extent. The waters also derive heat by conduction from the air and, *indirectly,* by radiation and conduction from suspended particles that absorb radiation more readily than does the water. Among these are detritus, inorganic materials, and plankton organism. In marginal areas, the water is warmed by heat that was absorbed by the bottom and conducted or radiated back into the water; shallow waters warm more readily than deeper waters. Con-

sequently, the extent of shallow water and the amount of suspended matter have much to do with the temperature of the
upper layers of water.

A part of the heat absorbed by the water of a lake is derived
by conduction from the warm air overlying it. Air itself is only
slightly warmed in a direct way by the rays of the sun; chiefly
it is warmed by contact with the heat-absorbing land which has
a low heat coefficient. Therefore, in a most important way winds
promote the absorption of heat by the surface water through
transfer of heat from land through air to water. On the other
hand, the high heat coefficient of evaporation comes into play, so
that the greater part of the heat taken from the air, but derived
from the land, is used, not for raising the temperature, but for
changing the water from liquid to vapor. It requires a relatively
great amount of heat to bring about a rather small rise in temperature of the water.

The reciprocal cooling influences of bodies of water on the air
and on the climate of surrounding regions and the contribution
of lakes and ponds to water vapor in the atmosphere do not concern us here.

CHAPTER 4

Gases and Heat: Some Chemical and Biological Relations

Chemical Relations

I N THE PRECEDING CHAPTER THE SUPPLY OF ESSENTIAL GASES IN THE waters was considered largely on the basis of the purely physical operations of absorption and circulation. That is hardly half the story. Without trying to make at all complete the account of dissolved gases and their relations to biological productivity, we do need to mention briefly some important chemical and biological phases of the general problem, particularly with reference to carbon dioxide.

Not all the carbon dioxide available for plant metabolism in water is in gaseous form. By reaction with water carbon dioxide forms carbonic acid (H_2CO_3), which occurs as such and, in dissociation, as the radical HCO_3. In the forms of gas and acid, the absorption of carbon dioxide is readily measurable in pure water p. 24. But in natural waters the acid reacts with available bases to form carbonates, which are only slightly soluble. Common examples are the carbonates of calcium and magnesium ($CaCO_3$ and $MgCO_3$). In such form the carbon dioxide is said to be *fixed* or *bound*. With an excess of the acid more enters into combination to make bicarbonates, such as calcium bicarbonate ($Ca(HCO_3)_2$). The bicarbonates are readily soluble and give hardness to the water.[1] The extra carbon dioxide in the bicarbonate is said to be *half-bound*. The linkage is weak; boiling, or even the activities of green plants, effects the removal of one acid radical to leave the insoluble carbonate as "precipitating chalk," as scale on the boiler, or as a marly deposit on the bottom of a lake. Marl may be temporary, going into solution with renewed excess of carbonic acid; or it may be permanent, when the marl is quickly overlaid by other sediments to make it inaccessible to the agents of solution, or when the addition of calcium to the water is such as to result in precipitation of marl in excess of the draft made upon it by dissolved carbon dioxide.

Thus we have carbon dioxide in water in five forms: the free gas, the acid, both undissociated and dissociated, the bound and the half-bound. In water of any degree of alkalinity the bicarbonates constitute significant reserves of carbon dioxide; with real appropriateness they are sometimes called "chemical carriers" of carbon dioxide. It is to be remembered that carbon dioxide and water build the bulk of all organic matter and that they are the chief wastes from living plants and animals. The inevitable combination of the two substances in lakes, ponds, and streams is, with sunlight, the foundation of productivity. A reasonable degree of alkalinity, assuring reserves of carbon dioxide, should offer reinforcement of productive capacity.

The relative proportions of the different forms of carbon dioxide in water vary with the chemical content of the water and with the conditions of supply and demand for free carbon dioxide. Accordingly, the amounts and proportions vary, among lakes, with the nature of the drainage basin and with degree of organic activity. More, or more lively, animals give out into the water more carbon dioxide; more, or more actively photosynthetic, plants mean a greater net intake of the gas. The numbers and the activity of both plants and animals are conditioned upon the

1. Bicarbonates give "temporary hardness" to water, because, with rising temperature and lowering of solubility of carbon dioxide (particularly in boiling), or with demand from photosynthetic plants, the dissolved bicarbonate is changed back to the less soluble carbonate which precipitates out. Calcium sulfate, on the other hand, gives "permanent hardness," since it is not so easily removed. Permanent hardness can of course be relieved by chemical means: addition of washing soda, sodium carbonate, results in formation of sodium sulfate and calcium carbonate, which is precipitated.

fertility of the water in a broad sense; they are regulated also by temperature and light, both of which undergo constant change with season, with weather, and with time of day; at any time and place, too, temperature and light are different at different depths. Consequently, the stock of carbon dioxide in water is, in merchandising terms, a lively one.

Liberated abundantly in natural waters, and having a high absorption coefficient, carbon dioxide is also relatively free to move back and forth between water and atmosphere. It forms a weak acid in water, but its capacity readily to combine with bases, when present, to form carbonates and bicarbonates and to be easily released from bicarbonates serves to moderate deviations from neutrality and, with bases present, to preserve an acid-base equilibrium that is favorable to life. Nevertheless, since supply of carbon dioxide and demand for it fluctuate freely with changes in conditions of light, the reaction of the water changes with hour of the day and with weather. The water of a pond, especially one of soft water, is likely to give a more acid reaction in the early morning than in the afternoon of a day during which green plants, in photosynthesis, have made heavy withdrawals of carbon dioxide. The fluctuations in reaction expressed by the pH, often minor but sometimes quite notable, seem not to be detrimental to life, except under special conditions.

As a practical matter, a certain degree of hardness is to be rated a favorable condition for the growth and multiplication of plankton algae and rooted aquatics and, therefore, for the animals which breathe the free oxygen liberated by plants and feed directly or indirectly upon plants. Nevertheless, the conditions of productively are too diverse and too complexly interrelated for the application of any rule of thumb in a particular situation.

The importance of carbon dioxide in water can hardly be over estimated. In summarizing studies of the chemistry of natural fresh waters of the United States, Clarke (1924) remarked that, since water carrying carbonic acid is the primary agent of rock decomposition, it is an almost necessary inference that carbonates should be the principal salts in nearly all fresh waters. . They form about half of all the solid compounds held in solution; see p. 77.

This brief discussion of chemical relations may be concluded with a hint of substantial omissions. Because the bodies of plants and animals and much of the wastes from them are, on the whole, heavier than water, it follows obviously that in still water there must be a general drift downward of the materials that go to make up organic bodies. So far as this occurs there is improverishment of upper waters, enrichment of bottom waters, depletion of any supply of free oxygen in deep waters, and accumulation of organic sediment on the bottom. Hence the great importance of any mechanisms that effect general circulation or overturn, regular or occasional. Without them, the top waters must eventually become unproductive for lack of the requirements of life other than respiratory gases and light; the deep waters would be unproductive, whatever their chemical fertility, for want of both light and oxygen. Important as these mechanisms of circulation are, they do not, however, give the whole story—by any means.

So far as productivity of the whole body of water is concerned, much depends upon what goes on biochemically at and immediately below and above the surface of contact between bottom sediments and free water. Here is a place where free water, with whatever load it may have of dissolved gases and salts, the bottom sediments and the organisms of the bottom have many interesting and quite complex interrelations, which vary between lakes and in the same lake at different times. It is not practicable in this place to go into the exciting biochemistry based on the diverse and continually changing interrelations at and about the bottom. The interested reader may consult Ruttner (1953, pp. 156ff.), Mortimer (1941, 1942) and other writers. It is sufficient to say here that what happens from time to time in the uppermost few millimeters of bottom sediment and in the water just above the bottom has much to do with future living conditions at and near the very top of the lake.

Biological Relations

The functions of green plants in photosynthesis, the liberation of carbon dioxide in respiration of animals, plants, and aerobic bacteria, the liberation of other gases by anaerobes, and the use of free nitrogen by nitrogen-fixers have necessarily come into the picture at various places in preceding pages. It has been seen, also, that the numbers and activities of plants and animals are affected by such physical and chemical conditions as light, temperature, fertility, and alkalinity. The size of the lake, its form, whether shallow or deep, whether with steep or gently sloping sides, and the extent of shore line relative to area are features that determine volume relative to area and the proportions between shallow and deep water; they notably affect the proportionate volume of the hypolimnion when stratification occurs. Such "morphometric" features have much to do, perhaps not so much with total production, as with the kinds of plants and animals the lake may support and how they are distributed within the lake. The topography of the lake bottom has both direct and indirect effects on populations: direct as to plants or animals that like shallow or deep water; indirect in several respects, a chief one of which must now be considered.

If a lake rich in organic life is compared with one having a scant or "dilute" population of drifting microorganisms, one may expect to find notable differences in the quantities of wastes and dead bodies that sink to the bottom, and in the resulting amount of decomposition with demand on the limited supply of oxygen in a region where the supply is not regularly renewable. Significant quantitative questions arise: How much decomposable matter falls to the bottom? How active are the processes of decomposition? How rapidly is the original stock of oxygen depleted? The amount of decomposable matter raining down depends upon density of populations above and that depends primarily upon the fertility of the upper water. The activity of agents of decomposition is controlled in considerable degree by temperature. Rate of depletion of free oxygen depends, not only upon the activity of animals and the bacteria of decomposition, but also upon how great was the original stock of dissolved oxygen. The bottom waters of most deep lakes, as we have seen, are well charged with oxygen at the times of the "spring overturn" (and the "fall overturn" as well). Obviously, the greater the volume of hypolim-

Pl. 1. *Nevada Falls, Yosemite National Park, California,
594 feet, Merced River.*

Courtesy of North Carolina News Bureau,
Department of Conservation and Development

Pl. 2. *Pearson's Falls, Saluda, North Carolina.*

nion, which tends to become isolated and remain cold during the summer, the greater is the available stock of oxygen and the less likely is extreme stagnation to follow. It is obvious that for most kinds of animals at the bottom, the worst possible conditions are fertility above and a hypolimnion of small volume.

Most animals of non-migratory habit will, of course, be permanently excluded from a region that is uninhabitable for them during only a brief period of the year. There seem, however, to be some that, by becoming inactive and in some way "estivating," can survive through a period of virtually complete oxygen depletion. (See Welch, 1952, and Deevey, 1941). Animals that are capable of movement from place to place and that are tolerant of changes in pressure and temperature may engage in periodic migrations into the bottom waters when these are oxygen-rich and out of them when they are oxygen-poor. Other yet more tolerant animals may make irregular and brief excursions in search of food in the oxygen-poor waters of the depths. The food will be animals of extreme tolerance which find means of survival even where dissolved oxygen is minimal in amount. Yellow perch in search of food may remain in oxygen-free water for a couple of hours, using oxygen in the swim bladders (Pearse and Achtenberg, 1921, p. 339).

Temperature Tolerance

It is necessary now to consider briefly a rough grouping of animals as to tolerance of a wide or only a narrow range of temperature. In temperate climates all cold-blooded aquatic animals, unless they burrow deeply, must at some time endure temperatures as low as 0° C. (32° F.), or thereabouts—they are not generally subjected to a lower temperature. Most of them endure also without harm the higher temperatures of summer; they are tolerant of heat within a relatively wide range. They are called *eurythermal,* the word being derived from Greek words meaning "broad" and "related to heat." One thinks of large-mouth black bass, bream, and many other "warm-water" fishes. On the other hand, there are aquatic animals, such as the brook trout and other vertebrates, as well as invertebrates, that cannot endure the ordinary summer temperatures of low altitudes in temperate regions. Such animals are called *stenothermal,* narrowly heat-tolerant. We are not concerned here with high-temperature steno-therms, such as animals of hot springs. Cold stenotherms, except in high latitudes, are necessarily restricted to the cool springs, the upper reaches of mountain brooks, or to the lower regions of deep lakes in which thermal stratification occurs to isolate a permanently cold hypolimnion. The lake trout (*Cristivomer*), the blackfin (*Leucichthys*), and, presumably, the burbot (*Lota*), are stenothermal species of lakes. In spring or fall, when all the waters are cool, a stenothermal fish may freely roam the whole lake; in summer it must confine itself to the deeper and colder waters. Obviously such a fish can live through the year only in a deep lake with an adequate hypolimnion. To meet the respiratory needs of the fish, the hypolimnion must also be one that holds oxygen in requisite quantity all the summer, not one in which stagnation occurs.

The most favorable conditions for lake trout are, then, to be expected, *not* in a lake that is rich in food in marginal and upper zones, but, rather, in plankton-poor waters. Such are lakes to which relatively little fertility is contributed by the surrounding lands, in which production is not high and decomposition not excessive, and in which, consequently, oxygen in deep water persists.

Types of Lakes

It is appropriate now to distinguish three types of lakes, according to the completeness of the organic cycle within them. Lakes that are rich in nutritive materials, and, therefore, in plankton organisms and in shore vegetation and the associated animal life, are called *eutrophic;* the word may be roughly translated as "well-fed." In such lakes there must occur excessive sedimentation, and consequent loss to the organic cycle. Reduction of organic matter, or decomposition, does not keep pace with production, and the lake tends to become filled; through the centuries, the hypolimnion grows progressively smaller in proportion to the productive epilimnion. The richness of the lake, while it endures, is maintained only because there is regular inflow of nutritive substances from the drainage basin. The deep water stagnates in summer. Red chironomid midge larvae, good indicators of oxygen depletion, may be found in the bottom sediment. The phantom midge larvae (Corethra, or Chaoborus), which can feed at night in the rich upper water and, carrying oxygen in thin air sacs, retire by day to the stagnant depths, are more or less typical of eutrophic lakes. The upper and marginal waters may support in summer good populations of warm-water fishes. Fish that require cold waters are not in place here, since the only cold water available in summer is deficient in oxygen.

Other lakes are relatively poor in nutritive materials and organic life and are more nearly self-contained; that is to say, there is more nearly a balance between production and reduction. These are called *oligotrophic,* from Greek words meaning "little" and "nourishment." Oligotrophic lakes have, generally speaking, a longer life ahead; they are "younger" in life-expectancy, if not in years, as contrasted with the "mature," or "aging" eutrophic lake. The smaller amount of decomposable material falling to the bottom promotes the retention of oxygen in a relatively large hypolimnion and makes it a favorable home for stenothermal animals. The midge larvae to be expected are the colorless kinds, notably Tanytarsus. In general the historical trend for lakes is from oligotrophy to eutrophy, but there are exceptions and reversals, so that the rule is not invariable. The organic cycle in extremely oligotrophic lakes may be said to be approximately a "closed" cycle; the lake is nearly self-contained.

Finally, there are lakes in which, from one cause or another, there is such an excessive accumulation of humic materials that the processes of decomposition are checked, the waters become discolored (brownish), acid, and habitable for only a relatively small number of species, which may, however, in the absence of competition, find rich nutriment and be very prolific. Northern bog lakes are good examples. Such lakes are substantially dependent for basic nutritive material upon their surroundings; for within them production and reduction are far out of balance. They are sometimes called *dystrophic* (ill fed); they are rapidly on the way to disappearance through the building up of the bottoms and encroachment of shores by the accumulation of undecomposed material. They might be described as "senescent"; the areas they occupy become, successively, moors or marshes and dry land.

It need not be supposed that any lake can surely be assigned to one or another of the types just described. Obviously, there must be all shades of gradation between infertile, highly fertile, and strongly unbalanced lakes. There must also be continuity in the transition between clearly unbalanced and senescent dystrophic waters and more or less choked natural ponds, mere bogs, marshes, and dry land. There have been attempts to draw fixed lines, marked by specific criteria for the class on each side of a line; but general acceptance of any proposed criteria seems yet unobtainable. Some have introduced the type *mesotrophic,* with subdivisions, lying between oligotrophic and eutrophic, or, along another line, between oligotrophic and dystrophic.[2]

In dealing with the products of nature, which often seems "footloose and fancy-free," one must be resigned to the difficulty or impossibility of finding sharp natural boundaries for the classes that our habit of mind, or our operative convenience, requires us to make. The fact that one cannot with assurance assort all people into the three groups of "young," "middle-aged," and "aged," or of "short," "medium-sized," and "tall," does not detract from the frequent usefulness of such categories. In the first example just mentioned—not too close an analogy, be it understood—the uncertainties would be even greater if middle-aged people would sometimes become younger or the young become

2. See, particularly, Lundbeck (1936) and Deevey (1941).

Lundbeck makes two subdivisions of oligotrophic, two of mesotrophic, and three of eutrophic lakes. So far as these seven types (above dystrophic) may be recognized by the particular kinds of midge larvae that predominate in the bottom, they are characterized as follows: *Orthocladius* marks extremely poor oligotrophic lakes (a), *Tanytarsus* the less poor oligotrophic (b); mesotrophic lakes are distinguished, respectively, (a) by *Stichochironomus* and (b) by *Sergentia;* in the three subdivisions of eutrophic lakes there is, at one extreme (a) having *Chironomus bathophilus* alone, at the other (c) having the red-blooded *Chironomus plumosus* alone, with an intermediate type (b) harboring both of those species. Of course, these "indicator" midge larvae are associated with a good many other animals, some having further index value.

Deevey did not find the distinctions so clear-cut in Connecticut lakes. Without attempt at a close examination of his observations and analyses, it may be mentioned that he classifies Connecticut lakes in five groups as (reversing his order): unstratified lakes (diverse in character and fauna), *Trisocladius* lakes (typologically uncertain), *Tanytarsus* (mesotrophic), "Mesotrophic *Chironomus*" lakes, and *Chironomus* lakes (essentially eutrophic?, with *C. bathophilus*). Apparently he found no strictly oligotrophic or dystrophic lakes.

senescent without a period of middle age—and perhaps they do in rare cases. With lakes the problem of classification on the basis of nutritive conditions and the associated populations of living things is even more difficult, because so many complicating factors affect the relationships between fertility of water and the life it supports. Such are, primarily, the form of the bowl of the lake, with diverse proportions of deep and shoal water, and temperature, as between low-land and alpine lakes.

As illustrative of the significance of the form of the bowl of a lake, it may be pointed out that, where the upper stratum of 10 meters (about 33 feet) includes the greater part of the water, the lake is likely to be eutrophic and rich in the drifting life called plankton. Such a lake has a generally saucer-shaped bowl, the sides sloping in gradually from the margins. Where that upper stratum has less volume than the remainder, the lake may be expected to be oligotrophic and comparatively poor in drifting life. In this form of lake the bottom slopes in more steeply and the bowl in cross section tends toward the U-form (Rawson, 1942).

In general the productivity of a lake is affected by: (1) edaphic conditions (relating to the chemistry and physics of soils of bottom and of drainage basin); (2) climate (referring to amount of sunshine, giving light and heat, and to rainfall and indrainage); (3) geographic location as to both latitude and altitude; (4) morphometry, as evidenced by depth, form of bowl, and proportions of deep and shallow water; (5) size, a small lake, other things equal, being more productive in proportion to volume than a large one; and (6) condition of maturity (effective age).

It has been said that soil and climate have more notable effects on the amount of life adrift in the water, while the form has more to do with bottom productivity. Such a simple statement cannot be accepted with complete assurance, for Rawson (1953) finds that the deeper the lake the less it has in drifting life (an "inverse relationship between standing crop of plankton and mean depth"). It must be remembered, however, that, because rate of replenishment plays such a great part in actual productivity, the "standing crop" at any one time is not a dependable measure of production.

Immediate interest in the attempted classification of lakes by types stems from two values. There is practical, as well as scientific, concern for intensive studies of the lakes of particular regions, with competent consideration of topography of the lake bed, surrounding soils, climatic conditions of temperature and precipitation, distribution of temperatures and gases within the lake, stratification, if it occurs, and the kinds, numbers, and distribution of plants and animals in the lake. Such studies, carried far enough, will lead to understanding of why the life in any particular lake is what it is and what may be the potentialities of that body of water.

Meantime, without waiting for reliable general formulas, there is a practical value in being able to recognize some lakes as notably dilute in nutritive substances, "plankton poor," and possessed of substantial hypolimnia that are both cold and habitable for cold-water fish throughout the summer. It is useful to be able to place other lakes as definitely fertile, well populated by aquatic plants and free-living microorganisms ("plankton rich"), and thus good homes for warm-water fish, although such lakes may have relatively smaller hypolimnia which stagnate in summer; they may, therefore, be quite unfit for the particular kinds of fish that require cold water during the warm season. Finally, one easily recognizes some waters as deeply stained, definitely acid in reaction, and inhabitable for a comparatively small number of acid-tolerant species.

Another cause of inadequacy in any present scheme of classification is that so many of the bodies of water that we often call "lakes" are not lakes—at least not if we think of a lake as "a substantial body of standing water in a depression of land." Man-made reservoirs and ponds are now increasing in number at an almost phenomenal rate and are becoming more and more significant in the production of fish for sport and for food. Such important bodies of water, in some of their aspects, are considered more particularly in other chapters. Much that is said in these chapters and in chapters 11 to 13 is well applicable to many reservoirs and ponds, which may or may not exhibit thermal stratification or which may have special patterns of stratification.

CHAPTER 5

Stratified Flow[1]

Density Currents

THERE IS ANOTHER SORT OF STRATIFICATION THAT MAY OCCUR quite independently of temperature. This is one resulting from differences in density caused by matter in solution or in suspension. Everyone knows that salt water is heavier than fresh water and that, consequently, the discharge from a river may flow out over the denser sea water. Elementary geographies tell of conditions off the mouth of the great Amazon River. Far out "at sea," well beyond sight of land, the ship sails through river water. Water fresh enough to drink overlies real sea water in the depths. Another striking example of density stratification is in the Black Sea. Deep down, saline water from the Sea of Marmora may flow in over the sill at the Bosporus, while fresh waters of the Danube and several great rivers of Russia and direct rainfall keep fresh the upper waters of the sea. There are, then, two Black Seas, one superimposed on the other: the upper fresh, circulating, and inhabited by freshwater fishes and other animals; the lower, saline, stagnant, and foul.

Again, in wide areas of the ocean, as in the mid-Atlantic, there are great masses of water flowing over or beneath other masses that may even move in contrary directions. Each mass has found the level determined by its relative density resulting from salinity or temperature or both.

1. With full acknowledgment to Bell (1942).

Underflow of Turbid Water

It is only recently that density differences associated with conditions of turbidity have caught the special attention of students of lakes, reservoirs, and rivers. When a turbid stream joins a clearer stream, as when the Missouri unites with the Mississippi, the turbid and the clear waters are not immediately mixed. At the surface they are seen to flow side by side until the heavier turbid water glides beneath the clearer water to give a definite vertical stratification. Mixing occurs gradually and according to the degree of turbulence. Streams that join may differ, not only in the amount of suspended matter, but also in temperature or in chemical content; but, where other conditions are approximately equal, turbidity alone makes a difference in density effective in causing stratification.[2]

Most striking and important are the "density currents" found in reservoirs formed for purposes of irrigation, generation of power, or flood control. Here there may be a large body of clear water into which flows at the upper end a stream that, regularly or occasionally, carries a great amount of matter in suspension. The coarser particles are soon deposited to form a delta at the upper end, which, of course, reduces to that extent the storage capacity of the lake. If there is also much silt and colloidal material in suspension, the muddy water, appreciably denser than the clear water above, continues to flow along the bottom to form a submerged muddy lake in the deepest region. Completely concealed beneath the clear water above, its presence would never be suspected by the casual observer. If, however, the outlet from the lake takes water from near the bottom, a constant flow of muddy water may be seen emerging from what appears from above to be a body of clear water. If, on the other hand, the outlet takes from an upper level, the water discharged is clear while the muddy water remains to drop, in course of time, its burden of suspended water as a deposit of fine silt which gradually lessens the depth and storage capacity of the reservoir. As long as the

2. Differences in density effective in permitting or causing density currents may actually be very slight. A difference of 7° F. (about 4° C.) between two masses of water may give a difference in density 10 times greater than has been found to cause stratified flow. (See Bell, 1942, p. 6.)

muddy water is in motion it may continue to carry at least the finest material in suspension; at rest, it loses almost entirely its capacity to hold particulate matter.

Obviously, then, it may make a difference in the duration of life of the reservoir, as well as a difference in the character of the overflow, if the outlet takes from the bottom, from intermediate, or from uppermost levels. It is only recently that this important principle has begun to be appreciated and to be recognized in the construction of dams. In order to draw water from the bottom, it is not necessary to have the outlet pass through the bottom of the dam. Given a surface outflow from the reservoir, a "curtain" may be erected to enclose the area around the outlet. The curtain is open for the passage of water only near the bottom. Only bottom water enters the enclosed area, in which it rises to flow out over the surface spillway. A seemingly clear lake may, then, have a muddy outflow if turbid water enters at the upper end, disappears from view as an underflow, traverses the whole length of the lake, and rises within the curtained column. A great part of present-day information about turbid underflows has been made available during the past couple of decades by the United States Soil Conservation Service. Some of the basic facts had been known for more than half a century, but the recent experimental and practical demonstrational work has done much to put the conditions into forms clearly visible to the eye and subject to practical analysis.

As a matter of fact, one can readily demonstrate density flows by gently stirring up the fine silt on the sloping sides of a pond or stream and watching the submerged "cloud" of muddy water flow out underneath the clear water and toward a deeper place. In the laboratory it is not difficult to siphon turbid water into a tilted glass container beneath a body of clear water and observe how it flows out under the clear water and down to the lowest part. It is possible to arrange obstructions around or over which the turbid water flows as does the water of a small stream flowing only beneath the atmosphere. Turbid water for the experiment is best made with the finest clay, which will give a fairly enduring suspension.

In the publication of the United States Department of Agriculture, previously cited, Bell describes and illustrates a condition in Lake Mead near its upper end, some 90 miles above Boulder Dam, where the turbid Colorado River water dipped beneath the clear reservoir to flow on down the slope of the bottom. This deep downstream current carried along with it a downstream flow of the clear water just above it, which in turn required a replacing "upstream" flow of surface clear water. Where the downstream surface flow of turbid water, just before it submerged, met the upstream flow of clear surface water, there was formed a broad band of driftwood, brought, in part, in upstream direction from the lake and, in part, in downstream direction from the river. The combined accumulation of flotsam formed a barrier all the way across, so long and so dense as to bar the passage of boats.

Overflows and Interflows

So far we have discussed the underflow of moving turbid water beneath the lighter clear water of lakes. In many cases, however, it is lighter water that is joining a less actively moving body whose water is heavier because of dissolved or suspended matter. The Amazon River, previously mentioned, is a case in point. The lighter Mississippi River water, too, flows out over the heavy saline waters of the Gulf of Mexico. Indeed, in the vicinity of New Orleans "the Father of Waters" is already only an upper stream overflowing the deeper salty water which extends far up the channel of the river. Even the turbid fresh waters of a river are notably lighter than the ocean water.

The conditions that govern density and, therefore, affect stratification are temperature, matter in solution ("salinity" in case of the sea), and matter in suspension. Any one of these conditions may outweigh the others. It is, then, quite possible for a layer of turbid water to flow beneath a layer of clear upper water of nearly the same temperature but above a deeper layer of decidedly colder and heavier water. In this case we should have an *interflow* of turbid water, as contrasted with an *underflow*, such as was described for the Colorado River in Lake Mead, or an *over-*

flow such as occurs when a warm stream flows into (and over) a cold lake or a river like the Amazon flows into and over the sea. When two streams join and one is clear and cold, the other turbid and warmer, the heavier, whichever it is, slips under the lighter while the lighter flows out over the heavier; here there is *both* underflow and overflow.

Recognition of Density Stratification

The density stratification of turbid and clear waters in reservoirs, and they may occur anywhere, may be discovered by taking samples with water bottles lowered to different levels, in much the same way as stratification of warm and colder waters are revealed by taking temperatures at different depths. It has been found, indeed, that the interface between lower turbid and upper clear water is sometimes so sharp that a "bottle," open at both ends, lowered to exactly the right level and then closed by mechanical means, will come up with muddy water in the lower part, clean water in the upper, and only a slight intermediate zone of mixed or slightly cloudy water. Such samplings, systematically carried out, show how a submerged deep turbid stream behaves like a surface stream,[3] rolling into the deeper channels, rising over obstructions and sweeping widely at turns.

In soil conservation laboratories, the flow of turbid water may be watched and photographed through glass-sided tanks to reveal many interesting details of behavior.

"An Underflow in Lake Lee, North Carolina" was described by Jack L. Hough in *Civil Engineering* for January, 1939. Following heavy rainfall, a marked inflow of cold turbid water completely filled the upper arms of the lake for a considerable distance, but then, along a sharp line convex downstreamward, dipped beneath the clear and warm water of the body of the reservoir. A little way down, although the surface water was still clear, the cold turbid water could be brought to the surface with an oar dipped down a foot or more (according to distance from the line of underflow). Motorboats, moving through clear upper water,

---

3. But in "slow motion," because the current is not moving with the relative freedom permitted to a brook under an ethereal medium, but is rather flowing under a watery medium of nearly the same density.

yet stirred up a trail of muddy water in upper reaches; nearer the dam it caused only occasional "boils" of turbid water.[4] An outlet pipe with intake near the bottom of the reservoir discharged muddy waters while the surface spillway carried only clear water, but with increased volume. The underflowing muddy water was pushing clear water out of the lake, while it largely remained to deposit its silt.

Incidentally, the force of density flows is not to be depreciated. Beneath the ocean off the coasts of continents, and cutting into the continental shelf, are gullies and gorges, some even comparable to the Grand Canyon of the Colorado River. Some geologists attribute these to the carving action of density currents of recent stages in the history of the earth or to submarine flows of turbid waters produced by earthquakes. Such drastic work of underflows was mentioned briefly by the present writer in an earlier volume (1949). It had been more fully discussed by Daly (1942), who also cited pronounced troughs in the bottom slopes of lakes, which have been attributed by others to erosion by underflow.

Practical Significance of Density Currents

It has already been brought out that turbid waters entering reservoirs, not only form deltas of the coarser materials at the place of entrance, but also carry the finer materials down into the deeper part of the basin and even all the way to the region of the outlet. If these waters remain at the bottom for an indefinite period, the fine materials gradually settle out as silt. If, on the other hand, the deeper turbid waters are caused to flow out at the spillway, in place of an equal quantity of clear water, the turbid water is *kept in movement* with the result that it carries more of the silt out of the basin. There are conditions in which the turbid water might not be acceptable as a regular discharge, as for a municipal water supply, for example. It could still be discharged in the waste of excess water. The main point is that the tendency of the turbid water, because of greater den-

4. Such crude but convincing demonstration of density stratification may recall to any of us the ready recognition of a type of temperature stratification that is possible in some spring-fed ponds where a bather may float at the surface in a thin upper stratum of warm water or project his feet down into distinctly cool water only two or three feet below.

sity, to remain distinct from clear water makes it possible to plan to keep a substantial portion of such water in continuous movement, at least in times of excess inflow, and thus to reduce deposition of silt, preserve storage capacity, and prolong the life of the reservoir.

As has been indicated, density stratification may result from differences of temperature, as well as turbidity or salinity. Commonly the temperature of the outflow from a reservoir is a matter of indifference; yet there are conditions, as when the reservoir is used for swimming, where higher or lower temperatures in the upper stratum of impounded water is definitely preferred; that preference may well govern the choice of wasting water from the surface or from the bottom.

Stratification by density, whatever the cause, makes possible selective and controllable operations for regular discharge or for the waste of excess waters in times of flood.

Underflow has special significance in replenishment of depleted oxygen supply in some lakes. We have seen how in times of summer thermal stratification the lower lake mass, the hypolimnion, may seriously stagnate while it is cut off from the oxygen of the atmosphere above and, because of darkness, is not reoxygenated by green plants. In such case the underflow of a cold and well-oxygenated stream may bring some refreshment. The underflow of turbid waters may have some objectionable features, but it also can bring needed oxygen. (See Bryson and Suomi, 1951.)

CHAPTER 6

The Basic Nutrients in Water

"Limiting Factors"

WATER AND SOLAR ENERGY, HITHERTO TREATED, ARE BASIC TO OR-
ganic production, but equally so are the raw materials in
the form of dissolved inorganic substances. These include not
only mineral substances, such as calcium, sodium, and iron, but
also atmospheric gases, chiefly oxygen and carbon dioxide, previously considered. Substance and energy are used not separately
but in combinations, and only plants can put them together to
make the original living substance. Given the elementary organic
substance manufactured by plants, animals make recombinations
and additions to form their own specialized body materials. In
some cases animals take inorganic materials at first hand, as we
do with salt and iodine, but by and large they must have plant
substance to start with.

Because water is so nearly a universal solvent, it follows that
all natural water contains a substantial array of dissolved materials. Certain of these are required by all organisms, regardless
of kind, although not necessarily in just the same proportions
for the different organisms. Other materials may be essential for
only particular species of plants or animals. Accordingly, the
available amount of any one chemical substance may constitute
the limiting factor for growth and development of a particular
organism. Such limiting factors hold *a* key (not the only key,
but one of several) to plant and animal distribution and to sizes
of population.

In any quantitative or qualitative study of populations it is helpful to keep in mind Liebig's "law of the minimum." This rule is based on the understanding that each kind of organism requires particular sorts of elementary materials in fairly definite proportions. Thus, while all plants require nitrogen, and usually in combined form, the microscopic plants called diatoms, highly important in all waters, require an appreciable amount of silica to form their glassy shells or skeletons; other plants may need silica only in traces or perhaps not at all. Crayfish have a special need for copper in the blood. Snails require calcium, for the formation of shells, as do freshwater mussels, which also need manganese to serve in their blood somewhat the same function as does iron in our blood. It goes without saying that if any absolute requirement of a particular animal or plant is wanting in a body of water, that organism does not exist there. Assuming, however, the presence in some quantity of every essential material a particular kind of plant or animal may grow and multiply (so long as other conditions permit) until the population has exhausted, or reduced below the minimum, any one of the essential substances. That one substance would then constitute the limiting factor, no matter in what abundance other required substances are present. Should a change occur to increase the amount of the critical substance, production may go on until some other material sets a new limit and thus becomes the limiting factor.

The rule of limiting factors, however axiomatic in principle, is not simple in application. For several reasons the chemical picture in any lake is not fixed but undergoes more or less notable fluctuation. There must be seasonal differences, because, with changes in light and temperature, there will be increase or decrease in rates of growth and mutiplication of plants and animals, and, consequently, in the extent of utilization of the dissolved materials. That is to say, there will be changes in the degree to which materials have been taken out of solution in the water to be temporarily fixed in the bodies of the organism, where they are unavailable for new growth. For instance, the spring of the year brings increasing light, rising temperature and enrichment of the upper productive waters by vertical circulation. All this usually leads to rapid growth and multiplication of microscopic plants. In turn the spring "blooms" of algae result, not only in an increase in oxygen concentration and a change in hydrogen ion concentration, but also in a notable decline in the amounts of "available" nitrogen and phosphorus; that is to say, in the amounts available for new growth. Such changes may be most marked in small lakes, but they are noted also in some parts of the sea.

One change leads to another: the minute plants are eaten by small animals, which may develop large populations; these, in turn, support a growing population of the fishes that feed upon them. Eventually the feces and other wastes of the larger animals, as they are liberated in the water, undergo decomposition to bring about restoration of the content of dissolved substances. Another outburst or "bloom" of microscopic plants may now occur, perhaps in the autumn. Thus there are seasonal cycles of chemical composition of the water, associated with cycles of populations of plants, microcrustacea, fishes, and other organisms. These cycles are related in some degree to the seasonal cycles of light and temperature. The development of the first link in the chain of organisms, diatoms or other plants, *may* be limited by the amount of a particular substance available only in *minimal quantity relative to absolute need for that substance*. The other links in the cycle are dependent upon the first link; and the minimal substance has acted as a general *limiting factor*.

This, however, is not the whole story. The "law of the minimum" is sound; yet its statement easily leads to oversimplification of the basic problems of populations, their successions and cycles. Reproduction and mortality, which determine populations, are not controlled by food alone. Light, temperature, accumulation of waste products of the environment, and other conditions of the environment play their part, as, also, do competition and predator-prey relationships.

Let us assume, for example, that two species have a simultaneous start and use essentially the same nutrients, but that one of these, because of conditions within itself, has a higher rate of reproduction. In the case of the microscopic plants that are the

Pl. 3. *Cascade Creek, Rocky Mountain National Park, Colorado.*

Courtesy of North Carolina Department of Conservation and Development

Pl. 4. *Mountain Stream in North Carolina.*

original producers, a higher reproductive rate may have prompt effects. If cells of one kind of plant divide once a day and another twice a day the latter may within a few days have ten or a hundred times the number of individuals that the other has. It becomes the dominant species, and may soon approach the maximum population possible with the available supply of nutrient materials. Let us suppose, however, that the less fecund species is capable of thriving at a lower level of concentration of the minimal nutrient: it is a more efficient consumer *under conditions of depletion.* When, inevitably, the first species is sloweddown in growth and multiplication, the second species may assume dominance until total consumption has brought the critical nutrient below the lower minimal concentration requisite for its growth and reproduction. Furthermore, with two species having similar needs in nutrients, there may be a difference in resistance to an unfavorable condition of accumulation of metabolic wastes, which could give an advantage to the species that got a poorer start. (See Hutchinson, 1941.)

Predator-prey relationships come into the picture, too. One kind of organism may be consumed to a much greater extent than another. The protozoan Didinium seems to feed almost exclusively upon Paramoecium, which, under given circumstances and because of its fecundity, might have a clear advantage over another species of similar feeding habit but lower reproductive rate. Merely because of the depredations of its predator, Paramoecium may then have to give place to a less efficient species. A certain rotifer is said to feed only upon dinoflagellates—microscopic animals halfway between plants and animals. It has been shown that a certain midge larva will crawl through a blanket of mixed filamentous algae devouring only the threads of a particular species, thus modifying the algal population independently of the chemical conditions (Moore, 1920). The populations of the prey in these cases is limited, not by a minimal nutritive substance but rather by the destructive efficiency of the population of predators.

The law of the minimum is not actually violated under any of the conditions mentioned in the preceding paragraphs; but its operation is greatly complicated and modified by various conditions inherent in the plant or animal or arising in the biological environment and in the complex interrelations existing. Hence truly limiting factors are not usually easy to identify with assurance. The subject is well treated by Odum (1953).

Dilution of the Food Supply

Lakes, ponds, and streams are fed ultimately from surface waters, whether these flow in over the ground from immediate surroundings or arrive only after having seeped into the soil somewhere else to reappear as spring or seepage water. Because all tributary waters have been in contact with a variety of soils and because water is such a general solvent, all natural waters have a great diversity of chemicals in solution, and most of the dissolved materials are nutrients to some plant or animal.

Ordinarily, however, the degree of dilution is high. The concentration of chemical substance surrounding the bodies of plants in water is said to be generally much weaker than in the water of soils accessible to the roots of terrestrial plants and some aquatics. On the other hand, the exposure of plants to the chemically nutrient medium is relatively much greater for aquatic than for terrestrial plants. The roots of a tree must absorb chemicals for the whole body of the tree with its trunk, limbs, and leaves; the whole submerged aquatic plant, roots, stem, and leaves, is in its "soil," which is the surrounding water, free or in the mud of the bottom. Indeed, the most numerous and most significant plants in water are microscopic in size and quite undifferentiated as to roots and foliage; the whole surface of each cell is exposed to the dilute nutrient medium, and the absorptive surface of a minute body is very great relative to its bulk. Aquatic vegetation generally is most favorably formed for the utilization of whatever needed substance is present even in highly dilute solution.

Chemical Needs

Proteins are fundamental building materials in all living matter. Their manufacture requires, not only hydrogen, oxygen, and carbon found in water and carbon dioxide, the raw materials of the even more basic sugars, but also some other substances, including always nitrogen and phosphorus, a small amount of sulphur, and, generally at least, calcium, magnesium, potassium, iron, and manganese. For aquatic animals the water is not in question. *Carbon* is usually plentiful in the carbon dioxide that is liberated as a waste product of the metabolism of plants, animals, and the bacteria of decomposition. The sources and distribution of *carbon dioxide* and free *oxygen* have been considered in Chapters 3 and 4.

Nitrogen is found in all natural waters both as a gas and in various combinations. Usable nitrogenous materials are brought in by tributary waters; they are derived also from organic matter in the water as products of bacterial decompositions and bacterial syntheses. Nitrogen is washed from the atmosphere by rain and snow, not only as gaseous nitrogen, but also, in small quantities, as ammonia, where such has escaped into the air, and as nitric oxide formed by flashes of lightning. The oxide reacts with oxygen (to form nitrogen dioxide) and water to form nitric acid, which readily combines with bases to form nitrates, such as calcium nitrate. In combination nitrogen occurs in water as ammonia, ammonium salts,[1] nitrates, and nitrites, as well as in the forms of partially decomposed and dissolved organic material. In the form of the free gas, *nitrogen* is used only by certain plants, chiefly bacteria and some fungi, and blue-green algae (De, 1939; Fogg, 1942; Duggar and Davis, 1916; Hutchinson, 1941) that have special capacities as "nitrogen fixers" to link free nitrogen with other materials and form useful compounds. Ammonia, although not directly available to many of the larger plants, is used by some microscopic plants, including the minute diatoms; marine diatoms, at least, seem to use ammonium nitrogen in preference to nitrates (ZoBell, 1935). So far as is now known, nitrites are used by plants only to a very small extent, but they are availed of by diatoms (Harvey, 1945). It appears that most of the higher plants use nitrates predominantly in the formation of plant proteins, although they can derive nitrogen from nitrites or ammonium salts. Either directly or indirectly, animals avail

---

1. The gas *ammonia* (NH_3), when dissolved in water enters in part into chemical combination with water and other substances to form *ammonium* (NH_4) compounds.

themselves of plant proteins, digest them, and assimilate the component amino acids to make animal proteins.

Within the water there are continual transformations among the combinations of nitrogen. Apart from the nitrogen-fixing organisms, which link nitrogen with other substances to make nitrates, there are nitrifying bacteria that oxidize ammonia to make nitrites and those that oxidize nitrites to form nitrates. On the other hand, denitrifying bacteria are always reducing nitrates to nitrites, nitrites to ammonia or to free nitrogen, which, for the time, is lost from the organic cycle.[2]

Nitrification requires free oxygen; it is retarded in the deeper waters in times of stagnation in winter or in summer. Denitrification occurs at all times, even at low temperatures and in the absence of free oxygen. Consequently the proportions of the various forms of nitrogen are likely to vary seasonally in association with seasonal fluctuations in the populations of the several types of bacteria, with variations in oxygen content, and with changing populations of animals and plants. The nitrogen cycle in lakes is, therefore, a very complex and inconstant one. Some hold that there is rarely a deficiency of nitrogen in natural lakes; others count it as an essential component of fertilizing materials.

The cycle is made even more complex, because *organic nitrogen,* resulting from the partial breakdown of the proteins of plants and animals in process of decomposition, may also be utilized in nutrition of certain plants and animals. Analyses have shown that a great deal of the nitrogen in lakes is in organic form; but this is discussed below.

There may be conditions under which an excessive amount of ammonia or of nitrates is injurious to some animals in the water, or even to man.[3] Probably, however, it is a fairly general rule that natural fresh waters have a relatively adequate but not excessive supply of available nitrogen in the several inorganic

2. Ruttner (1953, p. 80) says: "It is not known whether reductions of nitrate to ammonia through nitrite, which occurs widely elsewhere in nature, also takes place to a significant degree in the waters."

3. "A problem in water sanitation that has come to light in the past six years is that of nitrate poisoning of infants" (Woodward, 1951). The conditions of such poisoning and standards of tolerance seem not to have been determined; nor are the notable differences in individual tolerances understood.

and organic forms. Emphasis is on the word *relatively*. Where waters are fertilized by municipal sewage or commercial fertilizers, containing substantial amounts of nitrates along with other materials, a notable increase in the population of plants and of some animals often ensues.[4]

Phosphorus as such is a poison and is virtually insoluble in water. It is, however, highly oxidizable. In oxide form in water it combines with bases present to form phosphates, which, with nitrates, are requirements of plants for making proteins. Indeed, phosphates and nitrates are always key substances in organic production. In many ways phosphorus is essential to both plants and animals. As everyone knows, phosphates are highly important ingredients of most commercial fertilizers used on farm soils. In higher animals calcium phosphate is a substantial constituent of bones and teeth; in more complex forms phosphorus plays an important part in the functioning of nerve and muscle tissues. Either directly or indirectly, animals obtain their requirements of phosphorus through vegetable foods.

The dead bodies and wastes of organisms in the upper waters sink toward the bottom carrying downward and away from the zone of production a substantial proportion of the available phosphorus. Consequently the deeper waters often show a higher concentration. At the times of "overturns" in fall and spring, the distribution of phosphorus in upper and lower waters may be equalized. The release of phosphorus in the processes of decomposition occurs more rapidly than does the release of nitrogen; hence the "turnover" of phosphorus takes place more efficiently.

As compared with nitrogen the amount of phosphorus required is small: a common N/P ratio is about 20:1. Phosphates, widely present in natural waters, are brought in by tributary waters and are also released from decaying organic substance within the lake. Apparently phosphorus is utilized by growing organisms almost as fast as it becomes available. The amount in the upper waters shows considerable variation throughout the year, and there are reports of its being present in minimal amounts in times of great development of populations of microscopic

4. But see p. 289.

plants. Some have regarded phosphorus as constituting a limiting factor for the development of populations of drifting organisms. Others have found no definite evidence that this is the case. At least, however, the fertility of a fish pond is increased by the addition of phosphates, along with other materials.

Neess (1946) says:

Phosphorus is undoubtedly the most important single fertilizer. Never present naturally in very great quantity, it is seemingly easily lost from the trophic cycle of ponds. It has frequently appeared to assume the role of limiting factor. . . . According to Demoll (1925) fertilization with phosphorus may be universally recommended even where there is no forehand knowledge of chemical conditions in a pond. So few are at variance with this opinion, that it is unnecessary to pursue the point any further. . . .

In fact, it is well known that phosphorus applied one year is still able to elicit a response in years following (Breest, 1921). . . . Walter did not believe there was any advantage in small applications of phosphorus spread over the entire growing season, but recommended that the whole dose be applied at once in the spring (pp. 346-348). [Others will not agree with this. See Howard D. Zeller in Trans. Am. Fish. Soc., 1952. R. E. C.]

Sulfur, which is essential to the formations of proteins, seems to be always present in natural waters in the amounts needed. It promotes the formation of chlorophyll, although it is not a final component of chlorophyll. In most natural waters the sulfates rank next to carbonates in quantity (see p. 76), being derived chiefly from the oxidation and partial solution of iron pyrites so widely diffused in igneous rocks. An abnormally high proportion of sulfates where neither gypsum nor desert salts are present is indicative of industrial pollution, as from pulp and paper mills or from coal mines (Clarke, F. W., 1924). Most sulfates are fairly soluble in water, but not calcium sulfate, which, nevertheless, is soluble enough to give "permanent hardness" in some waters.

Ordinarily, sulfur in the water is continually undergoing oxidation and reduction. Under anaerobic conditions one of the end products of bacterial decomposition of organic matter is hydrogen sulfide (H_2S), as may become unpleasantly apparent. "Sulfur bacteria" are of several kinds with diverse functions. There are those that reduce sulfates to hydrogen sulfide, and others that oxidize hydrogen sulfide to elemental sulfur and to sulfuric acid, which enters into combination with bases to form sulfates, in which form it becomes available to green plants. Some sulfur bacteria (Leucothiobacteria, Beggiatoa, Thiothrix) deposit sulfur granules within the cell. Others (Thiobacillus) deposit granules of sulfur outside the cell. Some "purple sulfur bacteria," with a pigment called *bacteriopurpurin,* are enabled to use solar energy in photosynthesis. Some of these deposit sulfur intracellularly, and may cause "red water." (See ZoBell, 1946.)

Among the mineral substances required by green plants are calcium, iron, magnesium, potassium, sodium, and manganese. Only some lower algae and fungi seem free of the need of *calcium*. Some Protozoa and crustacea, including the crayfishes, use it in their body coverings. Snails and mussels need calcium for their shells. Boycott (1936) considers 20 parts of calcium per million of water to be the minimum for many species of snails. As a matter of common observation, snails, mussels, and peashells are sometimes found living, and apparently living well, in "soft" water! As Boycott has pointedly remarked, "We must realize that the snail's scale of hardness is not the same as our own." For man "the hardness of softened public water supplies is generally from 80 to 100 parts per million" (Collins, 1937). Water with 20 parts per million of calcium we call definitely "soft," although it is not as soft as rain water. Such water may be sufficiently "hard" for some snails (but not for others), for which 10 p.p.m., or less, would represent softness.

Besides being a necessary component of most plant and many animal tissues, calcium serves indirect uses both within the bodies of plants and in the surrounding water. It functions in reducing the toxic effects of some other basic substances, such as sodium, potassium, and magnesium, when these are present in excessive concentration (Miller, 1938), as well as of iron (Smith, 1950). The bicarbonate of calcium is the most common cause of "hardness" in water, a condition not favored by those who operate boilers, but one with definite biological values. Deficiency in calcium content no doubt limits productiveness for most waters in soft water regions; so that limestone, or other combinations of calcium, are regarded as an essential component of fertilizers for fish ponds in eastern states. European fish culturists suggest the need for 65 parts per million of calcium carbonate, which is about 26 parts per million of calcium (Macan and Worthington, 1951). Distribution of the several kinds of algae is notably governed by the amount of calcium present and its effect on the acidity or alkalinity of the water. Calcareous waters make larger trout.

A special value of calcium is in its effects on bottom deposits. Always dead organic matter tends to accumulate at the bottom, where it is subject to bacterial decomposition resulting in liberation of the raw materials of life for re-use in the organic cycle. With excessive accumulation an acid condition may ensue to retard decomposition: undigested organic matter remains indefinitely to form an undesirable peaty bottom. Addition of a sufficient quantity of lime to the water relieves the acidity and promotes beneficent decomposition. In other ways calcium plays an important part in bringing about the release of potassium and phosphorus to make them available to plants. Calcium carbonate tends also to improve the physical qualities of bottom soils. The important role of calicum bicarbonate as a "chemical carrier" of a reserve stock of carbon dioxide is discussed in other places.

In water with high content of calcium there may occur notable encrustations of marl on any solid objects, such as rocks, roots, the leaves of submerged plants and the parts of mussel shells projecting above the bottom; or there may be smaller or larger pebble-like concretions of marl on the bottom. Such deposits are commonly a product of the activity of algae, particularly the blue-greens. Often marl is greenish in color, or a green tint may be revealed by scraping off the brownish surface coating. A substantial amount of iron may give a red color. The higher alga, Chara, derives its common name of "stonewort" from the calcareous matter within the cells and encrusted on the exterior. Marl is usually found to be mainly pure calcium carbonate, with sometimes a little magnesium carbonate (Welch, 1952). It is more likely to form around, rather than in, the deep central area of a lake where an excess of carbon dioxide promotes the formation of the soluble bicarbonate (Ruttner, 1953).

Potassium, in small part, is required by all plants and most animals. Nothing else can *entirely* replace it. It is readily taken up by plants, both terrestrial and aquatic. In agriculture potassium salts constitute an important part of the fertilizers used to secure better crops. Practical experience in the fertilization of ponds seems in many cases to show that addition of potash increase productivity; but: "Often the results from potassium appear to be erratic and characterized by peculiarities which are not well understood" (Neess, 1949, p. 345). *Sodium* may replace potassium to some extent, and, in proper proportion, it may improve the healthfulness of the media in which plants live. Excessive amounts of potassium or sodium may be toxic.

Magnesium occurs widely; as a part of the chlorophyll molecule, it is necessary for photosynthesis. An exceedingly small amount of magnesium seems to be all that is required. As with calcium, the carbonate is only slightly soluble; but, with carbon dioxide in excess, it is changed to the soluble bicarbonate. In some waters magnesium occurs also as sulfate.

Manganese, besides being necessary in very small amount for most chlorophyll-bearing plants, has been found to play an important part in the physiology of freshwater mussels.

Iron, although not a part of chlorophyll, plays a part in its formation and is, therefore, a requirement of green plants. In small amount it is, of course, necessary for animals that have haemoglobin in the blood, as do the vertebrates and certain worms and insect larvae. The great importance of iron in the biochemistry of waters, soils, and organisms is being increasingly appreciated. It seems to play some part in the metabolism of phosphorus. Pure iron is hardly soluble in ordinary waters, but it is present practically always as salts, such as ferric phosphate or ferrous sulfate, as colloidal ferric hydrate, in suspension or in organic compounds. It has some part in the coloring of waters rich in organic matter. Iron may be precipitated to the bottom as limonite (ferric hydroxide) or, when hydrogen sulfide is present, as black iron sulfide. Some of this deposit may be redissolved with changing conditions. "Iron bacteria" play a significant part in the manipulation of iron in water. In excessive amounts iron may be toxic. In fact, Smith (1950) says that, while laboratory experiments have shown that small quantities of many elements are toxic to algae, iron is the only one of these that is of importance in nature. Toxic effect is found when available iron exceeds 5 mg. per liter (5 p.p.m.), except where there is buffer action of organic compounds of calcium salts.

Silicon, unfamiliar as such, is everywhere about us—as silicon dioxide (*silica*) in sand, and as silicates in clay, granite, cement, glass, and china. The compounds of silicon make up more than a fourth of the solid crust of the earth: for, next to oxygen, silicon is the most abundant element on earth. We think of it as insoluble. Nevertheless, it dissolves to a slight extent; occurring in water chiefly as silica. Because nearly all the waters entering streams and lakes have flowed over or through soils in which the compounds of silicon predominate, all natural waters must have small amounts of silica in solution. Even in the extreme dilution in which it occurs, plants and animals are able to extract it in the amounts required. Certainly, in the course of time, it is taken out in great amounts. The extensive and often quite deep deposits of diatomaceous earth that occur in various parts of the world represent silica that has been in and out of solution in water. Where a lake receives relatively little nutritive material from the outside, and productivity and sedimentation are such that virtually all organic matter that settles to the bottom is fully decomposed, the persisting sediment may be almost purely siliceous skeletal matter. It builds up slowly, but, with the passage of ages of time, it acquires great thickness.

Silica in solution is small in amount, although in some soft-water rivers, such as the Savannah, the Androscoggin, and the Sacramento, the concentration of silica is reported as comparable to that of calcium—or it may be even greater. It is taken out of solution only by living cells; but to certain kinds of organisms it is indispensable. It is particularly needed by diatoms, the minute and widely distributed microscopic plants with delicately engraved and perforated shells, so abundant in waters everywhere. The shells are "of very pure opalescent silica" (Conger, 1941). Some unicellular animals also require it for their housing structures. The skeletons of freshwater sponges are formed of siliceous spicules. Indirectly, at least, silica is very important to higher animals, because diatoms form so prominent a part in the basic food supply of all natural bodies of water. The organic, but not the siliceous part of the diatom, is digested. The higher plants use it to some extent, particularly the grasses, in leaves and stems, where it seems to give some protection against parasites.

The amount in solution has been found to vary with season, with the quantity and character of inflowing waters and with the populations of diatoms. It is believed that in some, however, the silica in solution is never depleted to such an extent as to make it a limiting factor. It would appear that for maintenance of the silica content, the waters must be largely dependent upon addition of new silicates from without (Welch). What is used by the diatoms is said to be put into a form so pure and so resistant to solution that it is largely lost to the organic cycle. This, indeed, accounts for the great and commercially useful deposits of "diatomaceous earth," which, during the ages, have accumulated at the bottom of old lakes to a depth of 50 feet or more. Deposits in some areas once covered by the sea have a thickness of 1400 feet, with diatom shells constituting 90 to 98 per cent of the deposit (Conger, 1941a).

Boron, in "extremely small amounts," is "an essential element for plant growth (Miller, 1938). Various other chemical elements are undoubtedly significant to particular plants and animals, including copper, zinc, cobalt, arsenic, and others. More and more knowledge is being gained concerning the importance of so-called "trace" elements. These, of course, are substances which may occur in such minute amounts as to appear in analyses only as traces, but which are essential to the well-being of all or of particular kinds of organisms. Such, for example, in human physiology are iodine for the proper functioning of the thyroid, copper for the formation of red-blood cells, and fluorine for the healthfulness of teeth. Much is yet to be learned about the parts played by such substances in bodies of water.

The evidence scientifically obtained concerning particular elements, such as phosphorus or silica, as limiting factors under natural conditions, is somewhat conflicting and not too clear in its demonstration. Nevertheless, it is certain that the productivity of a body of water is limited by the general conditions of chemical fertility. This is as would be expected; it is virtually axiomatic. Bricks are not made without clay, nor plants without their constituent chemicals. Lakes receiving drainage only from sterile soils are notoriously poor in populations of plants and animals. Those fed from fertile lands are naturally productive. Can not the infertile ponds, and even the fertile ones, be improved in fertility? The idea is by no means new, but recent years have brought a great deal of experimental work in chemical fertilization of ponds and lakes. The subject is best discussed after consideration of the fish pond.

In the foregoing examination of the basic materials consideration has been given to inorganic substances, with only incidental reference to organic compounds. We are not concerned in this chapter with the actual food intake of the larger animals in the water; that is to say, with the innumerable small plants and animals that drift freely in the water (the plankton), with the great numbers of both that live on or in the bottom, or with the organic debris that accumulates in the bottom from the breakdown of organisms produced in the water or on neighboring lands. Mention should be made, however, of the substantial amount of *organic* substance carried in all natural waters, in the form of colloids or in true solution, and offering potential nutriment. Some of this dissolved organic matter has originated within the lake from wastes of animals or as products of incomplete bacterial decomposition. Another part has been brought in from the land with surface drainage and soil seepage waters or has come in as dust blown by the wind. The amount is relatively great: lakes and ponds generally, although much poorer than the sea in organic salts, are far richer in organic matter. There may be ten times as much non-living organic substance in the water as there is in the living bodies of the plankton; but the degree of concentration varies widely with different lakes and in the same lake at different times (Birge and Juday, 1926).

To what extent the dissolved organic material is availed of and by what plants and animals it can be used are questions to which entirely satisfactory answers are not yet at hand.[5] Proteins in colloidal solution and several amino acids provide food for some animals. Presumably higher animals can use such matter only to a slight extent, if at all, but that is still a disputed question; they may take it by mouth and absorb it through the walls of the intestine, if not through the skin.

We must recognize also the virtually certain presence in natural waters of substances of the general nature of vitamins, hormones, and antibiotics, substances called *"metabolites,"* that, seemingly, are given off as wastes from the metabolism of plants and animals by secretion or excretion (Lucas, 1947). The vitamins, thiamin, niocin, and biotin have been found free in lake water (Hutchinson and Setlow, 1946). Pratt and his collaborators have derived from the green alga, Chlorella, a substance they call *chlorellin,* which is antibiotic in action (Pratt *et al.,* 1949). Some animals, fishes and others, are found to live better in "conditioned water," water in which other animals of the same or distinct kinds have previously lived (Allee, 1934). Some grow better when living in groups than when living singly. Some behave quite differently in waters where wastes have accumulated. Daphnia, which commonly reproduces parthenogenetically, develops males and changes its mode of reproduction when crowded or when placed in water in which Daphnias, or even some other animals, have been crowded (Banta, 1939; Berg, K., 1931).

The metabolites, of whatever nature they are, are not always beneficial; they may be present in excessive amounts, so as to be injurious, to be "antibiotic" in effect. Perhaps what is beneficial to one animal may be antibiotic for another; or what is helpful when present in small amount is harmful in greater concentrations. It has been suggested that "blooms" of certain organisms

5. Rawson (1939) said, "We do not know the function of dissolved organic matter in the biological economy of the lake."

terminate when the dense populations have poisoned their own environment (Patrick, 1948, quoting Akehurst)—which would seem to be a sort of unintentional mass suicide. Fish are known sometimes to avoid aggregations of certain plankters. There is evidence that the destruction of fish in so-called "red seas" is due to substances liberated by plankton algae. Lucas, having in mind the production in the body of endocrine substances, beneficial to some other organ than the ones that produced them, proposes the term *exocrine* as descriptive of the substances liberated to the exterior and beneficial or harmful to other individuals. In this day of penicillin and other substances formed by fungi, and destructive to bacteria, the thought of antibiotics free in the water need not seem farfetched. We know too little now of the exact nature of favorable and unfavorable substances that organisms release into the water. Yet anyone having experience with aquaria or with new small ponds can well believe that there is something in the idea of "conditioning." They seem to do better after a short period of adjustment for the animals and plants in the water. As Allee (1934, p. 42) has said with reference to populations of animals: "Once formed, aggregations of aquatic organisms condition the medium surrounding them by the addition of secretions and excretions, the nature and biological effects of which form one of the most important problems of mass physiology."

Clarke (1924) computed the average composition of river and lake waters of North America, excluding those of closed basins, as given in the following table showing percentage of dissolved salts:

CO_3	33.40 per cent
SO_4	15.31
Cl	7.44
NO_3	1.15
Ca	19.36
Mg	4.87
Na	7.46
K	1.77
$(Fe, Al)_2 O_3$	0.64
$Si O_2$	8.60
	100.00

Substances present as traces, although highly important, are not shown. The chemical diversity of rivers is illustrated by the following five analyses from papers of the United States Geological Survey. The rivers are arranged in order of "hardness" (as $CaCO_3$).

AVERAGE OF ANALYSES OF DISSOLVED SALTS IN 10-DAY COMPOSITE SAMPLES COLLECTED FOR ONE YEAR. (PARTS PER MILLION.)

	Savannah River Ga.	Tennessee River Gilbertsville, Ala.	St. Lawrence River Ogdagsburg, N. H.	Mississippi River Minneapolis, Minn.	Colorado River Grand Canyon, Ariz.
Silica (SiO_2)............	11.	20.	6.6	15.	16.
Iron (Fe)..............	0.05	0.39	0.05	0.07	11.
Calcium (Ca)...........	4.3	19.	31.	40.	94.
Magnesium (Mg).......	1.3	4.1	7.3	14.	34.
Sodium (Na)..........	3.4	} 7.7	6.3	10.	117.
Potassium (K).........	1.2				5.9
Bicarbonate (HCO_3)....	22.	72.	122.	188.	203.
Sulphate (SO_4).........	3.	11.	12.	18.	324.
Chloride (Cl)..........	2.4	3.	7.7	1.6	92.
Nitrate (NO_3).........	0.34	1.2	0.3	1.9	5.
Total Dissolved Solids...........	41.	101.	134.	200.	788.
Total Hardness as $CaCO_3$...........	16.	64.	107.	158.	375.

Source: U.S. Geological Professional Papers 236, 638, 889-E.

CHAPTER 7

Turbidity, Color, Odor, and Taste

Water Not Always Nice

U NFORTUNATELY, NATURAL WATERS DO NOT ALWAYS LOOK GOOD, taste good or smell good— and this quite apart from pollution by domestic or industrial wastes. Turbidity is the most common difficulty. In fact, all waters have at least a degree of turbidity, if they have life at all: that is, if we apply the term turbidity to any condition in which solid particles free in the water make the clarity less than that of pure water; usually, however, we think of turbidity in relation to silt and other non-living matter in suspension. Everyone prefers a reasonably clear stream, but entirely too many of our streams are unreasonably reddish or brownish and low in transparency, although the water itself, after settling or filtration, may be clear. Ponds and lakes may be muddy after rains over lands subject to erosion. There are times, too, when ponds or reservoirs are odoriferous. Even with fairly well-regulated municipal water supplies, consumers have been known to complain of tastes and odors described as "fishy," "spicy," "cucumber-like," or "sweetish," or worse. The comparatively modern practice of chlorination has gone far in relieving this difficulty—and in substituting the odor of chlorine!

Turbidity

Turbidity is caused by particles in suspension, whether silt, colloidal clay, minute drifting organisms, or colloidal organic matter. Because turbidity, or cloudiness, reduces the penetration of sunlight, it makes the zone of photosynthesis relatively shallow and is generally unfavorable to productivity. Nevertheless, there may be conditions in which turbidity offers advantages to particular fishes. Surprisingly, Doan (1940) reported for Lake Erie a distinct positive correlation between seasons of turbidity and the catch three years later of saugers, *Stizostedium canadense.* He suggested that the material in suspension may have adhered to the eggs, preventing stickiness, clumping, and suffocation of eggs, that turbidity could have favored the escape of sauger fry from enemies, and that the surface-feeding young might have found better feeding in the greater concentration of food organisms in a photosynthetic zone that is necessarily reduced in thickness by the muddiness of the waters. Turbidity may well give one species of fish an advantage over others. Meehean (1952) says that turbid waters are not good for bass and bluegill, but are good for white crappie, some bullheads, and catfish.

Wallen (1951) studied the direct effects of turbidity with a diversity of fishes—carp, catfish, sunfishes, bass, bream, and other, particularly with the golden shiner (*Notemigonus crysoleucas*). Using extreme turbidities, beyond those ordinarily occuring in nature, he found reactions of some sort—gulping air at the surface, turning on the side, and others, at turbidities of 20,000 parts per million and higher. "Most individuals of all species used endured exposures to more than 100,000 ppm of turbidity for a week or longer, but these same fishes finally died at turbidities of 175,000 to 225,000 ppm" (p. 24). The fishes died within 15 minutes to two hours, having opercular cavities and gill filaments clogged with silty clay particles. These experiments as to immediately observable *direct* effects, interesting as they are, do not tell us of the possible physiological handicaps to the fish giving no observable reaction. Turbidities that do not cause death or manifest suffering might yet reduce efficiency in respiration and cause waste of energy and retardation of growth.

Naturally, much depends upon what causes the turbidity— whether organisms or silt or fiber, and what kind of silt or fiber. Ellis (1935) has said that particulate matter with hardness greater than 1 by mineralogical standards injures gills and other delicate exposed surfaces of fish, and that ordinary silt will cause a flow of mucus. Actually, we do not know enough about the direct or indirect effects of ordinary degrees of turbidity upon fish. Some indirect effects seem indisputable. Fish extract oxygen from water passed over the gill filaments by action of muscles of the head and by swimming; the breathing processes must be less efficient when the water is "diluted" by inert matter, whether or not the tissues are lacerated or clogged with suffocating silt. This handicap would apply also to all sorts of animals in the food chain leading up to catchable fish. Furthermore, photosynthesis is the basis of productivity within the water and, since turbidity reduces the volume of the zone in which photosynthesis can occur, it lessens the possibilities in production. As Dr. Patrick (1948, p. 500) has observed, "in muddy rivers a very poor diatom flora is present, whereas in a clear river or stream excellent conditions may develop for diatom growth."

Undoubtedly the removal of natural vegetation, with deforestation, improper cultivation of lands and building of highways with inadequate care as to shoulders and banks, has resulted through the years in increased turbidity of streams. Conversely, recent developments in soil conservation are having effects in reducing turbidity of waters and sedimentation in reservoirs. Speaking of sedimentation in the Spartanburg, S. C., city reservoir, fed from the South Pacolet River, Superintendent R. B. Simms (1950) said: "Between 1934 and 1947 the rate of loss was 0.69 percent per year, a reduction of 35 percent in the rate of loss of storage capacity. This was largely due to improved land use and conservation practices put into effect on the watershed above the reservoir" (p. 14).

At least three sorts of turbidity are to be distinguished. Turbidity attributable to dense populations of drifting organisms is indicative of productivity and is generally a desirable condition. It may also hold in check the deeper-living rooted aquatic plants that may not be wanted. Sometimes, of course, these microorganisms give tastes, or odors, that are not wanted in drinking water; but that is another problem to be considered in later paragraphs. Turbidity caused by larger silt particles carried in flood waters or milder surface drainage will soon yield to clarification by gravitation as the particles settle of their own weight. Even though turbidity from this cause is temporary, the sedimentation is objectionable in that it smothers bottom life, tends to fill the pond, and shortens its life as a useful body of water. In natural waters the turbidity most difficult to deal with is that caused by colloidal clay, which does not readily settle out. The cloudiness may endure almost indefinitely, until something causes aggregation of the extremely fine particles to make bodies that will settle.

The problem with clay turbidity is to bring about the coagulation necessary for clarification. The manager of a municipal water supply may use flocculating chemicals, such as compounds of calcium, copper, iron, or aluminum. Alum is a flocculant in common use. Copper or alum is not desirable for ordinary use in fish ponds or reservoirs. There are also organic flocculants. A personal experience of the writer is of interest in this connection. At one time, a good while ago, the Mississippi River below Davenport, Iowa, maintained a milky turbidity for a considerable period of days, while a number of fish ponds supplied with water pumped from the river stayed reasonably clear. A jar of the river water was kept on a window sill to see how fast settling would occur; after many days no change in turbidity was noticeable. A small clump of algae from a pond was then added; on the following day the water in the jar was quite clear. The effect was almost spectacular; but I could not know if the agent of clarification was a product of the plant or the work of filtering organisms introduced inadvertently with the algae.

In recent years much has been learned about natural agents of flocculation. Irwin and Stevenson (1951) in Oklahoma, besides presenting the results of their special researches, give an excellent discussion of the subject with review of the extensive literature. Apparently, the extremely small colloidal clay particles, bearing negative electric charges are mutually repellent, to prevent the desired aggregations. Positive ions are needed to neutralize the negative charges and permit flocculation. They say: "Dispersed clay colloidal particles are negatively charged and any compound that releases sufficient positive ions will cause precipitation. Hydrogen ions are most effective." Green plants and animals liberate carbon dioxide, which reacts with water to form carbonic acid, with liberation of hydrogen ions. The decomposition of organic matter also liberates carbon dioxide and thus provides hydrogen ions. Clarification was effected by addition of substantial quantities of dead vegetation mowed from surrounding fields. Incidentally the added organic matter contributes to fertility of the pond; but one would not want to add so much that the resulting depletion of dissolved oxygen could make a problem of another sort. In aquaria turbidity from excessive bacterial growth sometimes occurs. This may be relievable by removal of the decomposing matter, and, if conditions are not too bad, by introduction of animals that feed by passing water through fine-meshed filters. Such are freshwater mussels, certain types of copepods and cladocera (Daphnia and others). Such filterers must also play an important role in keeping outside waters clear.

In practice turbidity is measured by any one of several different methods. The standard base of measurement is "that condition produced by *one part per million* of silica (fuller's earth) in distilled water." One may make or purchase for use in comparison a set of silica standards. The "platinum-wire method," with United States Geological Survey "turbidity rod" is nearly as simple. The rod to which the wire is attached is lowered until the wire disappears, when a reading of depth is taken. Reference is made to a table in which the "vanishing depth" of the wire is related to turbidity in parts per million. There are various sorts of *turbidimeters,* of which the Jackson candle turbidimeter seems now the accepted standard. For details and guidance in use, reference should be made to standard guides such as Welch's *Limnological Methods* or The American Public Health Association's *Standard Methods for the Examination of Water and Sewage.* The fineness or coarseness of the matter in suspension may be a matter of concern. Directions for ascertaining the "coefficient of fineness" are given in *Standard Methods.*

In waters that are relatively clear, it is customary to make determination of transparency with the use of a modified Secchi Disk, a disk of metal or wood painted with alternate quadrants of white and black. Conventionally, the disk is 20 cm., or 8 inches, in diameter, suspended on a hand line and having a suitable weight attached beneath. The observer measures on the line as closely as possible the exact depth at which the disk disappears from view. This measure of the limit of visibility of the disk answers well for comparison of different waters. Obviously with both the platinum wire and the Secchi disk, the personal equation plays some part in the results obtained. In the cases of the Secchi disk and the platinum wire method, the light penetrating from above must be reflected back to the eye of the observer, thus travelling a double distance. Neither, therefore, is a true measure of translucency.[1]

Color

The visibility of the disk is affected, not only by the turbidity, but also to some extent by the *color* of the water. Color is not usually noticeable in natural waters, except where there is considerable drainage from swamp lands. In extreme cases of swamp-coloring the water may have almost the color of weak tea, and perhaps be as harmless in direct effect. Looking into such a body of water, one may see it as black. The color results from dissolved or colloidal substances extracted from leaves or other decaying organic matter. Tannin, albuminoid ammonia, glucosides and other carbon compounds, iron, manganese, and various chemicals in solution derived from surrounding soils may also give color. (See Whipple, 1933, and Welch, 1952.) Regardless of direct effects, color reduces penetration of sunlight; and, significantly, the wave lengths of light absorbed by the color depend upon the nature of the coloring matter.

Distinction must be made between "apparent color" and "true color." The apparent color is derived in part from the true color, in part from matter in suspension. Thus water that is practically colorless may appear green or reddish or brownish from dense populations of microscopic organisms. Almost any observer has seen ponds appear muddy, when there could have been no mud,

1. For translating the Secchi disk reading into a measure of transparency, Rawson (1950) gives the formula: log. S=.117m—.495. S is the Secchi disk reading in meters; m, the number of meters to which 1 per cent of the light penetrates (p. 50).

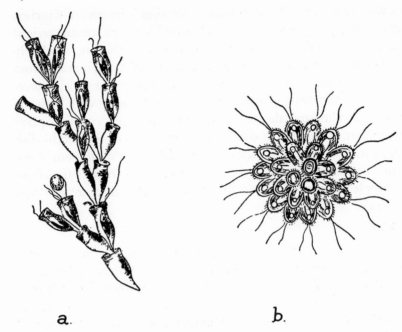

a.   b.

FIGURE 2. Some flagellate algae (or Protozoa) that give tastes or odors to water.

(a) *Dinobryon,* forming a branching colony. (b) *Synura,* spherical colony.

and microscopic examination revealed the presence of myriads of microscopic algae (or protozoans), such as Dinobryon or Synura (Figs. 2a, b), having chlorophyll but with other pigments giving them a yellowish tint. The Mississippi River below Davenport, Iowa, has been seen when its width was dull green in appearance from like swarms of blue-green algae.

Another sort of false color is that of the brown water of bog ponds, which will seem clear of particulate matter and will not settle clear. The color is found to be due, not to matter in true solution, but to organic, colloidal particles which by proper filtration can be removed to leave uncolored water (Welch, 1952, p. 387).

To determine the actual color of the water, organisms and other factors giving turbidity are first removed with the use of a centrifuge. The "true color" of the remaining water, with only matter in solution, is then measured by an arbitrary standard—generally the *Platinum-Cobalt Standard,* described in publications previously cited. A milligram of platinum dissolved in a liter of distilled water gives a color that is taken as the unit of measurement. Accepted standard solutions are made with compounds of platinum and cobalt and hydrochloric acid. The numbered solutions are used for comparisons and record. It should be remarked that this method, while of practical use with waters for domestic use, does not in all cases record actual color to the eye, but rather the concentration of dissolved and fine colloidal materials which commonly impart color to the water. There is also a set of tubes and numbered disks designed by the United States Geological Survey and convenient for comparisons and ratings in the laboratory or in the field.

Odor and Taste

Water may have odors and tastes of real concern to managers of municipal water systems and to consumers. Odors and tastes are not always distinguishable, although salt, iron, and some other substances give taste without odor. Most of us are familiar with iron springs, "mineral springs" they are generally called, or with those having certain salts—waters that have distinct taste but do not smell noticeably. Generally speaking, however, and particularly for municipal waters, "the best way to observe the odor of the water is to taste it" (Whipple). There can be no absolute odor values, because different persons do not always identify odors of water alike, nor does the same person at different times. Nevertheless, odors are recorded by comparison with odor-free water and rough quantitative records are made by tests after different degrees of dilution. The nature of the odor is described by such terms as aromatic (spicy), ripe cucumber, sweetish, candied, violet, chlorinous, sulfuretted, fishy, grassy, and moldy. (See Whipple, 1933; Standard Methods for the Examination of Water and Sewage, 1946; Gainey and Lord, 1952.)

The causes of odors may be microorganisms, decomposing organic matter of the pond or of surrounding swamps, industrial wastes, seeping oils, or materials through which the ground water has passed. Some rooted plants and masses of the colonial bryozoan animal, *Pectinatella,* may also give odor to the water in which they live. Aromatic odors are given by several species of diatom and some protozoa, grassy odors by various blue-green and green algae, fishy odors by diatoms and such green algae as Volvox and Eudorina or by the yellowish Dinobryon or Synura. The diatom Asterionella is a not uncommon offender, causing odors described variously as "aromatic," "geranium," or "fishy." Decomposition of blue-green algae may give a pigpen odor. From the sulfur bacterium, Beggiatoa, and others, comes the odor of sulfuretted hydrogen. Whipple, in the book previously cited, gives an extended discussion of the causes and conditions of odors and tastes.

At a particular time in one of the great cities, there were innumerable reports of bad odor and taste in water coming from the spigots. Particularly notable in the complaints was the diversity of conflicting descriptions of the odor, often as "ripe cucumber," but sometimes as "sweetish" or "fishy." In any particular section of the city, however, there seemed to be less divergence of opinion. This suggested that more was involved than mere personal equations. To some it seemed probable that the offending organism, which in this case was a small colonial flagellate called Synura, gave off different odors at different stages of its decomposition in the pipes. Water reaching one part of the city could have been longer in the darkness of the water mains than that coming to another part, and thus have conveyed the algae remains in a more advanced stage of decomposition. This could have been true, but another likely explanation is based on the fact that the odors of organic substances are known to vary markedly with degrees of dilution.

Synura (Fig. 2b) in minute revolving colonies of some 50 much more minute individuals, or zooids, each with two paddling flagellae and with yellow color bands, is very widely distributed in small numbers; ordinarily it draws no attention to itself, and may be disregarded. Under special conditions that are not too well understood it "takes a romp," as it were, multiplying until the whole water is muddy or soupy with it. Even in fairly moderate populations it is said to give trouble—more often in northern than in southern reservoirs. The same sort of story, but sometimes without the geographic limitation, applies to many kinds of small algae and protozoa that are ordinarily insignificant and tolerable, but that have their times of great nuisance value. When the swarms or "blooms" of such organisms have reached a peak of number, presumably they exhaust some basic requirement of life; they can grow and reproduce no more and can only die and decompose; then the great nuisance! It seems to be true, however, that many of them, including Synura, do not have to die to produce noticeable and objectionable odors. The odors given off in extreme cases may even render water virtually undrinkable. This does not mean that the water is toxic. There does not now seem to be evidence of human poisoning by algae in fresh waters, although cattle poisoning is reported.[2] The difference could be that cattle are likely to drink more freely of algae-laden waters than does man.

Interestingly enough, it has been found that some fish, at least, distinguish the odors of particular rooted aquatic plants, which may well "play an important role in the life of the fish" and "serve as signposts to guide fish into feeding grounds," especially in turbid waters and at night (Walker and Hasler, 1949).

2. But: "In recent years there has been an increase in reports of livestock losses from ingestion of toxic algae" (Woodward, 1951). In brackish water of ponds in Israel, and "especially along the salty shores of the Dead Sea," a phyto-flagellate *Prymnesium parvum,* causes "fish-sickness" to man, but not to the fish, but the alga can be exterminated by use of sulphate of ammonia (Hardy, 1952).

II

RUNNING WATER

CHAPTER 8

The Upland Brook

General Conditions of Life

L ET US LOOK AT THE BROOK AS ONE OF NATURE'S PLANTATIONS, designed, not for a particular crop, but rather for a whole series of crops, both animal and vegetable—or, we might better say, for a great composite crop comprising vast numbers of plants and animals of different kinds. Nature never engages in single-crop farming: she practices diversified farming to an extreme, with a certain measure of crop rotation. Some of the products of brook plantations are of mere microscopic size, such as the one-celled Protozoa among animals, the diatoms and desmids among plants, and the still smaller bacteria. Others are of relatively much greater size and yet not conspicuous to the eye of an observer on the bank: the small crustaceans, insect larvae, and mites; still others are large enough to catch the attention of any passer; these may be mosses, river-weeds, fishes, frogs, turtles, snakes, or otters.

The components of the composite crop are interrelated in very complex fashion, as they prey upon each other, offer subsistence one to another, compete severally for the limited quantity of the available materials of life, or, in the case of green and brown plants, actually add through photosynthetic activity to the sum total of organic matter in the stream. There are, too, reducing agents in the forms of bacteria and fungi that break down organic wastes and lessen the total amount of organic substance in the water, at the same time enriching the water. The animals may subsist upon plants or upon other animals to a great extent but, after all, the community as a whole is dependent for inorganic raw materials upon what comes in from the outside or what, once brought in, has remained for a brief time. In the case of a brook or river, as contrasted with lakes and ponds, what materials of life remain in the water at any particular place for any length of time must be relatively small. The small stream is continually discharging itself into a larger, washing itself out as it were; the larger stream holds its materials a little longer; but it, too, sweeps a great part of its substances on toward the great common depository—the sea. There is not in the stream so nearly a closed system as we find in lakes or ponds. The same water does not pass over the same ledge twice and this is true of the non-living and much of the living organic material within the stream. Materials in solution or in suspension are in passage: to be utilized by plants or animals they must be taken "on the run."

This does not mean that efficient filtration by organisms in upper regions of the stream spells starvation for other organisms farther along the course of the stream. The nutritive substance grasped and used in one zone is later passed on in other forms for life in lower reaches. Besides, new materials enter at every level so that the stream increases in fertility as it runs.

What are the sources of the materials of life in the running brook? These are the springs and ground water, the surface water from hillsides and fields that drain into the stream, the rocks and soil that form bottom and banks of the brook, the atmosphere, and the overhanging trees. Besides, for what organic substance is to be made *de novo* within the stream, dependence is upon what sunlight falls upon and penetrates the surface.

Ground water is rain and snow water that has seeped into the soil, either near by or at great distance, absorbing materials as it goes. It moves slowly, perhaps only a mile or two per year, but eventually finds its outlet in springs, streams, lakes, or ocean, into which it carries its hard-earned load of chemical substances. The water of uncontaminated springs may be clean as respects germs of disease, but it is never chemically pure. It is not surprising then that springs and the runlets from them harbor diverse populations of plants and animals. It is mentioned in another place that from a certain runlet, six feet from its origin, there were found 42 kinds of plants and animals in fairly dense populations.

Contributions from *hillside* and *meadow* vary with the geological character of the land, with its condition of forestation, with its fertility, either natural or resulting from cultivation, with precipitation and run-off, and with other conditions. The additions from the soil and rocks of the *bottom* and *immediate banks* vary: (1) with the character of the bed, whether it is made of igneous or calciferous rocks or of other materials, and its gross structure—of boulders, ledge, gravel, sand, clay, or mud; (2) with discharge; (3) with the gradient of the stream, which, with run-off, determines the velocity of the water and its carrying power; and (4) with the solvent acids, especially the ever-present carbonic acid, received from without or formed within. The *overhanging trees* drop leaves and insects into the streams. Sometimes the overreaching willows fairly drip with plant lice that are gobbled up by the trout.

The contribution of the *atmosphere* is also affected by the gradient and the form of the streambed; for swift water, a swirling current among boulders and waterfalls, gives better contacts between water and atmosphere and effects more complete circulation than do the slower wind-driven currents of lakes. Still waters may be marked by excess or deficiency of requisite atmospheric gases; but it would seem difficult for a rapid mountain stream ever to be far out of equilibrium with the atmosphere floating above it and constantly churned into it. One finds a beautifully clear river in the mountains suddenly transformed by industrial wastes into an almost inky-dark stream laden with fibrous sludge. It appears, and may indeed be, virtually uninhabitable for fish; yet, with all the waste matter carried, the tests for dissolved oxygen may show no deficiency in that respect. The turbulence of a small stream with its effect in mixing is one of the most significant characteristics, particularly that of an upland stream. Turbulence is discussed more fully in the chapter on rivers.

Finally the contributions of the *sun* are heat and light, each an essential condition of life. There is no life without heat and none without light, although light and life are not necessarily *immediately* associated. There are animals and some plants that live in darkness, as in caves or in the depths of the sea, or under stones at the bottom of a stream; yet these all profit from the heat and light of the sun, as they depend upon ready-made organic materials which derive originally from plants living somewhere and sometime in the sunlight. The income of energy from the sun must vary with latitude, altitude, and climatic conditions. In a given geographic location, the absorption of solar radiation is conditioned primarily by seasonal and meteorological conditions, but also by the overgrowth of shrubs and trees, and by the height and steepness of the banks.

A well-shaded stream may be cooler and have less capacity for the growth of green plants within the stream, but, where streams are well fed with organic matter through drainage from surrounding lands, what is called "original production" by green plants *within* the stream is perhaps less significant than in still waters. Nevertheless, the plant life of a mountain brook is more luxuriant than one might suspect, and production within the stream may be very significant. (See Matthews, 1932, and various papers by Butcher.) Inconspicuous as they are, there are yet great numbers of one-celled (or few-celled) plants, or algae, living on the bottom or in the scum on rocks and debris. One may often observe a greenish, yellowish, or brownish tint of bottom sediments, attributable to the dense populations of these minute plants. An actual count of the microscopic algae, were it possible, would give figures of almost astronomic proportions. The thoughtful observer of an upland stream will often be impressed by the quantities of threadlike algae and the mats of moss and river weeds. All of these mean production of organic substances within the stream—production from water, carbon dioxide, and dissolved inorganic materials.

Temperature is of critical significance, both because it limits the total quantity of life, and because it affects the *composition* of the animal community. There are animals that endure a wide range of temperature; there are others whose tolerance is restricted within more or less narrow limits. So, one distinguishes animals as *eurythermal* (broadly tolerant with respect to temperature) or as *stenothermal* (narrowly tolerant). Since the lower limit of the temperature of fresh water, as such, is fixed by nature at about 32° F. (0° C.), and since this freezing or near-freezing temperature generally prevails at some time of the year in all natural waters of temperate regions, the differences between aquatic animals in temperature tolerance have to do more generally with the upper limits. Many animals are therefore restricted to the upper reaches of streams, where temperatures are generally lower. Such stenotherms, the brook trout, for example, may range farther down in shaded streams than in those that are more exposed to the sun and, therefore, warmer. Some eurytherms such as the large-mouth black bass, are restricted to lower reaches because of various influences. They could endure the cooler upper waters but they may be unable to compete with related animals favored by the lower temperatures of the headwater regions. Temperature has also an influence upon rate of living in general and upon particular processes. Consequently it may affect rate of development and duration of the whole period of life, as well as the size and the form of individuals. In some streams we find at different elevations ecological types of mussels, closely related, if not of the same species, but definitely distinguished by size and form. Referring to freshwater mussels, it was said (Coker et al., 1921):

A difference of up-river and down-river habitat is presented by the distribution of two closely related species, the three-ridge, *Quadrula undulata,* and the blue-point, *Quadrula plicata*; the former, a more compressed and rougher form, is found in the more rapid waters of upstream habitats, while the latter, being thicker and less ridged, occurs in the deeper waters of the lower parts of a river system.

As a rule small streams have lower temperatures than the surface waters of lakes and ponds in the same region. They receive cool water more directly from the springs; they are generally better shaded by overhanging trees and by hills. The thorough mixing that results from general turbulence prevents the accumulation of heat at upper levels.

Such, then, are some of the conditions that affect the production of animals and plants in streams. Under the conditions prevailing in any particular place there exist, not one or two or a few kinds of animals or plants living independently, but a closely interlaced community, or series of communities, composed of very many kinds of plants and animals. Each kind plays its particular and perhaps indispensable part in the life of the community as a whole. Each maintains itself and maintains others. Each holds other kinds in check and, in turn, is held in check by others. Each kind fills a particular "niche" in the cycles of life in the stream.

Interrelations of Organisms

We might think of the members of any community as producers, transformers, and consumers, although it is difficult sometimes to draw clear lines corresponding to such a scheme of functional classification. The "producers" in the first place are the green plants, which alone can utilize inorganic materials and the energy of sunlight to manufacture protein and carbohydrate foods (and some vitamins or their precursors) and to store within them the indispensable energy of the sun. The transformers, or consumers of the first order, are the smaller or larger vegetarian animals that feed upon the green plants. These are of many kinds. Considering now only life in streams, they are chiefly some of the protozoa, insect larvae, worms, and mollusks. We do not find in streams many vegetarians of substantial size, comparable to rodents and cattle on land.

Obviously there must be a vastly greater production of producers than of transformers—since the green plants must provide a sufficient surplus of themselves to maintain their own kinds, over and above what is to be used to support the animals that feed upon them. It is to be remembered, too, that each vegetarian animal consumes annually many times its own weight of producers. Then there are intermediate consumers feeding chiefly upon the smaller vegetarian animals, and, finally, the "ultimate consumers," mostly the largest animals which largely depend upon intermediate consumers; these, because of size or defensive equipment, are less likely to be preyed upon within the stream. These, too, consume each year many times their own weight in food and must be vastly outnumbered by the animals that form their prey.

We have, then, what is called the "pyramid of numbers"

(considered more fully in a later chapter.) The broad base of
the pyramid represents the producing plants; the next and narrower section comprises the great numbers of vegetarian animals;
above these in the pyramid come the smaller carnivores in several
sections; at the apex of the pyramid are the relatively few ultimate
consumers. To prevent misconception, it should be stated with
emphasis that sharp lines cannot be drawn between the several
orders of consumers, and that, indeed, there is not even a clear
line between vegetarian and carnivorous animals: many small
animals and large ones too, like man, eat flesh or greens. Nor
does size of body have any necessary relation to level in the pyramid. Some microscopic animals among the protozoa are carnivorous in habit. On land the largest animals are vegetarian: one
thinks of horses, cattle, and elephants. In water, however, it is
generally true that the larger animals are carnivores, feeding upon
animals which are themselves carnivores in habit. Parasites require some modification of statement concerning the pyramid,
since an individual parasite of animals does not require numbers
of prey. On the contrary, a thousand parasites of a kind, and
several kinds, may subsist upon an individual animal. The "ultimate consumers" in this case may well outnumber the animals
upon which they subsist.

We have as yet neglected an important group of organisms—
the "reducers," or the bacteria and fungi that decompose the dead
or waste organic matter, reducing it to the chemical salts that
may again be taken up by green plants. We may suspect that
these play a relatively small part in the swift waters where wastes
are quickly carried on to be deposited in pools or sluggish reaches
or even on the delta at the mouth of the major stream. Places
of primary need for the services of reducers are the deltas at the
bottoms of the sea and of lakes, and wherever organic debris
comes to a final rest.

The "Community" in the Stream

We must not seem to suggest that any swift stream harbors
a single community—or a simple series of like communities. A
brook changes its form and condition from place to place. Waterfalls, riffles, and pools succeed one another in endless variety of

form and sequence. Habitats and inhabitants appear in corresponding variety. There are communities of the riffles, communities of the falls, and communities of the pools. Such communities are sometimes classified rather rigidly and named according to their dominant animal or plant forms; but the communities are not sharply separated. Not only do the physical conditions intergrade, but animals wander or are carried from one locality to another. Nevertheless, there are typical groupings of animals and plants that correspond in a general way with the conditions of the stream.

Different streams present different conditions of chemical content, of basic food supply, of light and temperature, and these differences are reflected in the composition of the organic communities within them. Yet, such is the validity of the rule of coordination between organic life and obvious physical conditions, that, if one knows the fauna of a single swift, rocky brook, one may go into other streams of like appearance in the same region, or even in far distant regions, with some degree of confidence as to the types, if not the species, of animals that will be encountered. A trout stream in New York, a trout stream in North Carolina, a trout stream in Michigan or Montana, each will probably be a Hydropsyche (net-spinning caddis) stream, a Heptagenia (swift-water mayfly), Perla (stonefly), and water-penny (larva of beetle) stream. The species will be different, the proportions vary, and particular types may occur here and be absent there. Nevertheless, one reasonably expects a generally familiar pattern. On the other hand, each stream is, to some extent, a special case, and an actual surprise is always within the possibilities.

Hydropsyche may be found where trout cannot live; water-pennies may have a wider range than Hydropsyche, or vice-versa; and so it is for every member species in the community of the riffle. This does not, however, destroy the validity of the rule of coordination, it merely proves that communities of animals are not sharply bounded, that any one "association," is made up of several species which have different precise requirements as to conditions of living, different "limits of tolerance" of physical conditions, as of temperature, current, oxygen supply, or chemicals. To an extent each species is independent: regarded in one way, the complex community we see might be said to exist because the natural ranges of all of its members overlap at this particular point, or because the several kinds of animals and plants happen to find in this one place the conditions they severally need, and they have been able to make the adjustments necessary to a neighborhood life. This would not be the whole truth by any means. The several species may have a most intimate interdependence: one may be there because of another; none could live as it does if most of the others were not present. As has been said before, each member of the community has some relation to every other; it subsists upon others or it is subsisted upon by its "fellows"; or it merely competes with its neighbors for food or space. Each regulates to an extent the abundance of the others; the actual interrelations form an extremely complex network.

Problems of Life in Streams   *8 4 9 1 6*

It will be understood that the problems of life in running streams are very different from those in ponds and lakes. Allusion has already been made to the lack of an oxygen problem in shallow swift streams where there is continual forced exchange of gases between the water and the atmosphere; only in the larger and deeper pools or the bordering bayous or in the soil under rocks or logs can conditions approaching stagnation ever occur. A second point of difference is that the water in the stream, with its dissolved and suspended material, is nearly always moving on. It is true that, because of the effects of tributaries and of the movement of water by winds, the water in ponds is not always as still as it may appear; but, except on shores exposed to heavy wave action, there is not in the lake so continuous and free a passage of water by the home sites of organisms with limited range of movement as there is in a brook. In ponds and lakes an animal without effective capacity for locomotion must in some way create a current to insure continued renewal of the medium charged with oxygen and food. In the stream the renewal in most places is automatic, at least for animals that feed by filtering or straining.

Perhaps the most distinctive problem of life in a stream, as compared with a lake, is that associated with maintenance of position. "The same water does not pass under the same bridge twice"; and yet the organic community beneath the bridge is an enduring one, persisting as a whole from month to month and even from year to year. The great problem for any member of the community is to stay approximately where it is while the water about it continually moves on. Providing an animal can maintain its position against the drive of the current, the flow of water is advantageous. By continually changing the water immediately around the organism, it brings new supplies of oxygen and food. Current has, however, the effect of limiting the number of kinds of animals that live in a particular place; so that it seems to be a rule that the number of species increases with decreasing gradient of the stream. (See Ruttner, 1953.)

Not all of even a mountain stream is swift water, of course. Riffles and falls may alternate with still pools,[1] but the ecological consideration of the brook as if it were a mere succession of rapids and pools, each discrete and offering its particular conditions of life, is grossly inadequate. Actually the conditions of life are far more complex: even in the swiftest water there may be very great diversity in rate of flow, with falls and raceways alongside of little eddies and sheltered backwaters below stones or in moss where the current is almost nil. A substantial part of the life in "rapids" is not actually touched by water in rapid motion. We cannot, therefore, classify the population merely as inhabitants of riffles or dwellers in pools. Apart from the fact that some active animals go back and forth between rapids and pools, we find within the riffles many animals that possess slight capacity for resistance to current but have a distinct knack in finding shelter from it.

Among the hazards of life in streams are those of ice-formation and floods. A swiftly moving brook is not likely to freeze solid,

1. So generally is this the case that we may overlook the possibility of a stream without pools. The River Rimac in Peru falls over 16,000 feet within a distance, as the crow flies, of less than 100 miles. At an elevation of about 10,000 feet, I followed the small river for a considerable distance without finding a single spot where a small trout could have found even momentary rest. In spite of its favorable conditions of temperature, oxygen content, and insect life such a stream would not seem to qualify as a trout brook!

but ice forms at the sides or where the waters are least turbulent. When it breaks away it is carried by the current to cut and slash at animals adhering to the rocks in riffles. Where the current is too strong for the formation of surface ice, "slush ice," or "frazil," forms as innumerable free crystals carried by the current and sometimes so abundant as to give a turbid appearance to the water. Cold cloudy days with an upstream wind are said to be most favorable for the formation of slush ice. "Anchor ice," resembling frazil is said to form on the bottom, particularly on dark objects in shallow open bodies of water (Meyer, 1928).

The greatest of all occasional hazards to animals in streams is that of floods following heavy precipitation in the watershed. Torrential flows may literally scour the bed of the stream, moving sand and rocks and mechanically erasing valuable populations of living animals on the unmoved rocks and logs, or cutting away banks inhabited by burrowing animals. Where the gradient is strongest, as in high mountains, it requires very little increase in velocity of flow to cause a rolling of gravel that may be disastrous to fixed animals. Not infrequently, an entirely new bed is carved through adjoining land. The new and barren bed will be seeded in time; but thriving communities of sedentary animals can come into existence only gradually and with the lapse of months or perhaps years.

The deplorable hazard of pollution is the subject of another chapter.

Modes of Life in Streams

In respect to plant life in small streams little need be added to what has been said on an earlier page or to what will be given in the following chapter on rivers. It should be said, however, that the smaller the stream the greater is the proportionate part played by the films of diatoms or other algae on rocks and logs, by the blankets and tresses of mosses on rocks and roots in shallow water, and by the marginal vegetation, such as the dense borders of forget-me-nots, conspicuous along the sides and in the waters of some mountain streams. Even the damp moss on rocks overhanging the brook harbors certain kinds of copepods, some of which drop into the water (Coker, 1934). The overhanging willows and alders afford homes for aphids and other insects that at times literally rain down into the streams to afford food for fish and other aquatic animals.

A principal "community" of still water is virtually wanting in the brook. This is that of the drifting life, the small plants and animals with no great powers of locomotion and no means of attachment to fixed objects. Such an association of organisms is most important in ponds and lakes. In small streams drifters are broken loose from the bottom or washed in from without, but their lives in the flowing water are likely to be short as they are dashed against the banks, washed roughly over the rocks, or strained out of the water by the filtering mechanisms of caddisfly larvae, blackfly larvae, or other drift-catchers.[2] The life in the small or shallow stream is predominantly sedentary. The more conspicuous animals may be the strong swimmers, but the greater number of animals and the greatest volume of life is on the bottom, and sides, or on any sort of fixed objects.

Outstanding features of stream animals are: streamlined forms or flattened bodies;[3] means for clinging, burrowing, or otherwise withstanding current; equipment for catching food as it passes, for straining the water, for scraping the living film on solid objects or for seizing other organisms. Even some of the minute diatoms attach themselves by gelatinous housings and some desmids live in attached tubes, as do some rotifers and midge larvae. In summarizing his studies of the food of insects in trout streams, Muttkowski (1927) remarked: "Environmental conditions in trout streams are strenuous"; "aquatic insects in rapid streams are op-

2. "It was Schroder (1899) who, as a result of his work on the phytoplankton of the Oder River, proposed the theory that the amount of plankton in a river is in inverse proportion to the slope of that river." Other conditions affect plankton productivity, but "The velocity of the current . . . is one of the main limiting factors in plankton production, and many investigators have pointed out that rich plankton crops coming from the upper part of a river may be destroyed by passing through a series of rapids or sharp falls and that stream velocities may assume destructive proportions. . . . If other conditions are equal, the productivity of a stream is proportionate to the age of its water and inversely proportionate to its velocity." (Reinhard, 1941.)

3. Flattening of the body, be it noted, has three effects: the low body offers less resistance to the current; the broad underside gives greater surface for adhesion; closeness to the substratum keeps the animal out of the strong current, since the velocity of flow next to the bottom is the least.

portunists"; they "take whatever comes along, be it plant, detritus, or animal matter." In a very rough way the life in streams can be considered in eight categories.

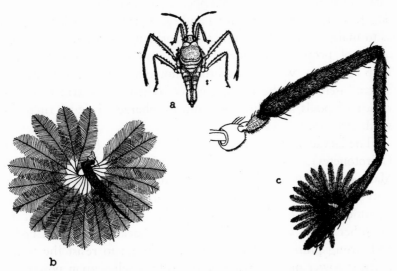

FIGURE 3. (a) Broad-shouldered water-strider, *Rhagovelia* (enlarged), that runs on the surface of swift water and paddles or swims at the same time. The "swimming plume" of each long middle leg is folded back into a deep notch, only a claw showing. (b) A leg is shown with swimming plume and a claw expanded. (c) The plume with one claw is also shown in detail. ((a) from Hungerford, 1914; (b) (c) from Coker, Millsaps, and Rice, 1936.)

1. Obviously typical of swift streams are animals with strong powers of locomotion. Among fish, trout, darters, black-nose dace, and some suckers seem to find their way farthest up the highland streams; but many other fishes, minnows, sunfish, bass, and catfish, are common inhabitants of brooks. The crayfish is another example of this group, for, although they frequently crawl, they can with strong strokes of the tail fin move backward through the water with great velocity. Small "broad-shouldered water-striders" (Fig. 3a) of the genus Rhagovelia have on the ends of the middle pair of legs those remarkable "swimming plumes," which they thrust through the surface film, so that they actually swim or paddle with one pair of legs while at the same

time they are running on the surface with the other two pairs. The accompanying figures (3b, c) show how the terminal pad (pulvillus), characteristic of the legs of so many insects (the suction pad that enables a grasshopper to climb on a plateglass window), is so extremely modified and specialized in this little insect as to make the fanlike plume that works under the surface as an organ of propulsion while the body and the limbs in general keep dry above water. The broad-shoulder water-striders, not to be confused with the larger slender-bodied water-striders (Gerridae) of pools and slow streams, are characteristic of riffles in small streams.

The larvae of the "howdy" mayfly, Isonychia (formerly called Chirotonetes), requires special mention in this connection. Many of its relatives are typical "stream-adapted" mayflies, whose thin flat bodies and broad flat limbs are closely pressed against the under sides of the stones they scrap for food; Isonychia, on the other hand, with high and rounded back, streamlined body, and strong plumed tail fin, pursues its prey; to resist the transporting power of the stream, apparently it relies upon powers of locomotion and bracing, rather than upon form of body. "This nymph," according to Dr. Morgan, "lives in the tumbling waters of stony creeks, among which it leaps and dashes with amazing agility. There it braces itself, tail down and head up, and holds its front legs outward to catch its food from the current."

Not all swimmers are equally swift, but, since not even the strongest swimmers are adapted to stem the current continually, the pools and eddies are common homes of the swift as well as of the slow.

2. Other inhabitants of brooks rely less upon strong swimming powers than upon flattening of the body and ability to cling to uneven surfaces of rocks as they creep or scurry about. The extremely flattened slow-moving flatworms, or planarians, although with no powers of locomotion except ciliary action and slow contractions and extensions of the body, are yet at home with relative safety on the surfaces of rocks in swift water.

Active creepers are the mayfly nymphs alluded to, by ways of contrast, in the preceding paragraph, and the stoneflies. Among mayflies the strongly depressed Heptagenias, and, among stone-flies, Perla and Peltoperla, are good representatives of the clinging but actively motile animals in swift waters. Here again we have great diversity both of species and of capacities to cling (Figs. 6a, b). Among mayflies, nymphs of the genus Iron are characteristic of very swift waters in mountain streams and even of waterfalls. Body and gill plates are modified to form a sort of suction disc. In one species, *I. rubidus,* body and gill plates are extremely flattened to offer least resistance to the pressure of swift water. In another, *I. confusus,* the body is less flattened but the over-lapping plate-like gills are so arranged that, with the hinder part of the body, they form a particularly tight suction disc to supplement the holding power of the claws at the tips of the flattened legs. Rhithrogena, which also makes an adhesive disc of its gills and body, may cling so strongly that the collector has difficulty in separating it from its rock (Eller, MS). Other mayflies and stone-flies are at home in the more protected places that occur even in rapids, as are some fishes. Water-mites may abound in sheltered places.

The extreme among mobile clingers is afforded by the net-winged midge larvae known as blepherocerids. These little larvae have the remarkable capacity to live under waterfalls. The impact of water falling directly from a height of several feet may keep the rocks polished clean and make impossible the survival of other larvae. In spite of the uninterrupted battering of water upon their backs, the blepherocerids not only survive and keep from being dislodged but actually run actively about with wriggly sidewise movements. How do they do it? They have no legs; but on the underside of the body are six little suckers in a single fore-and-aft series along the middle line of the body (Fig. 4); each sucker is most elaborately designed for greater efficiency as a hold-fast. Around the smooth stiffened rim is a circlet of fine bristles, and there are glands that secrete a sticky substances to give better adhesion between the rim of the sucker and the surface of the rock. Thus the space inside each suction-disk is made water-tight and air-tight. In the middle of the top of this space there is a short piston-like structure capable of being moved in

FIGURE 4. Waterfall midge larva, seen from above (a) and below (b) (much enlarged).

The cross section of the body (c) shows a "piston" above the suction chamber and muscles by which it is raised. At the right (d) is a greatly magnified section of suction disk which shows clearly the plunger and muscles attached to it. ((a) (b) (c) from Kellogg; (d) drawn by W. K. Hubbell from Thienemann.)

a vertical direction by muscles that extend from the upper end of the piston to the integument of the back of the larva. The contraction of these fibers elevates the piston with vacuum-producing effect, giving a relatively powerful suction grip. Half the number of suckers is adequate to hold the larva in place, despite the strong force of the water. In its peculiar form of locomotion the larva releases the hold of the three forward suckers, swings that end of the body to one side, grips anew with these, then releases the other suckers and swings the hinder part of the body into line with the forward part or beyond. The rapidly repeated alternating sideswings of forward and hinder parts of the body make a droll sight; but they enable the larva to move about with surprising agility and security under the heavy downpour of the waterfall. The strange pattern of movement and the highly specialized mechanism[4] that makes it possible are probably unique among animals. It is particularly described here as one of the most notable illustrations of the capacity of organisms in evolutionary history to become highly specialized in structure, function, and habit in order to live under conditions that are intolerable to animal life generally.

3. Although no sharp line can be drawn, it is convenient to make another group of the slow creepers and gliders, among which may be listed the brook snail, Goniobasis (Fig. 18), which has gills and a horny shoe or plate (operculum) to close the opening of its shell, and some lunged snails (Fig. 17) without the

4. Well described and illustrated by Thienemann, 1926, pp. 9-12.

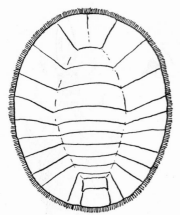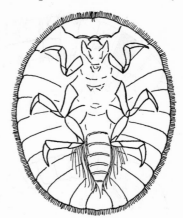

FIGURE 5. "Water penny," the larva of a small beetle, *Psephenus,* seen from above and below. It adheres tightly to stones in swift water. Actual length of larva about 1/4". (Drawings by W. K. Hubbell after Imms.)

operculum. Another good example is the "water penny," or limpet-like larva of the beetle, Psephenus (Fig. 5); it has no resemblance to an ordinary insect larva; but when, with the blade of a knife, one pries it loose from the rock, the inconspicuous jointed legs of a beetle larva can be observed underneath the greatly widened, protective, and sucker-forming covering of the back. Caddis larvae, such as Helicopsyche, with its portable house in the form of a snail shell, Glossosoma (Fig. 7), with its broadly flattened case formed like the shell of a turtle, Leptocercus, with cornucopia-like case of small sand grains, Neophylax in a flattened tube of fine sand grains with ballast rocks cemented to the sides, and the flat worms (planarians) creep slowly on the rocks, chiefly on the under sides, and are obviously of this group. For those who may regard a flattened body as a condition of sedentary life in rapid water, the cumbersome house of Goera and the thick bodies of the stonefly Pteronarcys, mentioned in the preceding paragraph, to say nothing of the mayfly, Isonychia, offer intriguing problems of dynamics. Here also are some protozoa, including the creeping or "flowing" amoebas.

4. In a fourth group we find animals that, by one means or another, form temporary attachments or construct refuges but which may detach themselves for movement to another place.

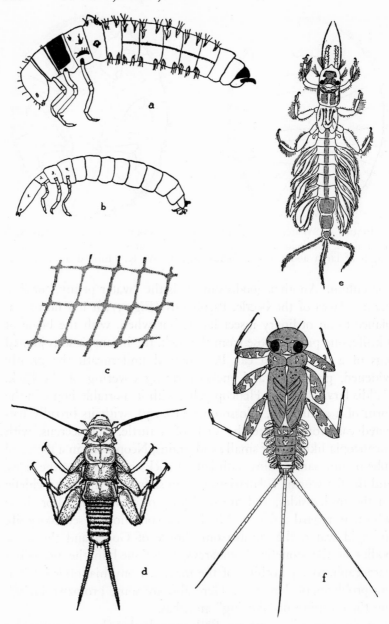

FIGURE 6. Some insects of streams.

(a) Case-making caddis larva. (b) Free-living caddis larva. (c) Some meshes of a net of caddis larva (*Hydropsyche*), which is spread against the current to catch small articles of food carried by the stream. Greatest dimension of a single mesh less than 1/100″. (d) Stonefly nymph with greatly flattened body for life in swift water. (e) Nymph of mayfly that burrows in the bottom. Note the prominent tusks from the mandible. More often found under sluggishly flowing water. (f) Creeping nymph of mayfly with flattened body, common in swift streams. ((a) (b) (c) by Harriet Taylor; (d) by Louis Jacobson; (e) (f) by Carolyn Coker and W. K. Hubbell.)

The downstream face of a dam, as well as the surfaces of rocks and logs in a stream, may be blackened by an almost continuous coating of black larvae forming the so-called "black moss." These are the dark worm-like larvae of the blackfly, or buffalo gnat, Simulium, which in the adult flying stage are often such pernicious pests. Blackfly larvae are said to require a flow of at least 0.3 m. per second (Allee and Schmitt, 1951, p. 377), or about two thirds of a mile per hour, a strong current for a small stream. The larva is a quarter to half an inch long, the gnat still smaller (Figs. 7g, 8). A pair of prolegs (unjointed larval legs) at each end of the larval body is modified to form a strong sucker. With the rear sucker alone, the larva maintains position in very strong current; or it may hold with both suckers in swifter water. With the two suckers it may creep about, loping like a leech. It has little capacity to swim; yet, if dislodged from its base, it is not carried far by the current. It retains attachment through silken threads spun from salivary glands so large that they extend from end to end of the body. Along such threads it creeps back to the original position or to another near by. Microscopic plants, such as diatoms, and other minute articles of food are captured by large spreading fans of fine hairs on projections from each side of the head. Conical vase-like pupal houses, spun later, are firmly attached to the substratum. The winged gnat that finally rises to the surface, runs on the water to some solid support up which it climbs to dry its wings in preparation for flight. During a short life out of water it feeds by sucking juices from plants or animals (or fishermen), mates, and deposits eggs in gelatinous masses on plants or other objects in the water.

The small larvae of midges, non-biting mosquito-like insects, are found in all types of waters, even in swift water where the coiled gelatinous strings of eggs are common on stones. Many of them build temporary soft tubes spun from salivary glands and usually covered with dirt. The little streaks of mud on stones in flowing waters are almost always the houses of the slender and delicate midge larvae. Others lurk in the moss and weed on the rock or live in tubes on the bottom. Some Tanytarsus, also called Rheotanytarsus, build firm cases, attached securely to the sub-

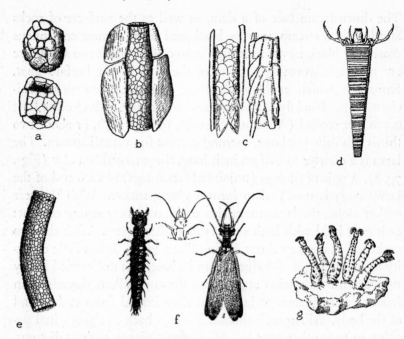

FIGURE 7. More insects of streams.

(a) (b) (c) (d) (e) Cases of caddis larvae, "stick-bait," *Glossossoma, Goera, Pycnopsyche, Brachycentrus, Psilotreta* (from Lloyd). (f) Helgrammite or "crawler," Dobsonfly larva *Corydalus,* larva and adult (from Needham and Betten). (g) Blackfly larvae, *Simulium* (from Miall).

stratum by a stalk and provided with slender horns across which a net may be spread (Fig. 8).

The little hydra, with simple sack-like body having an adhesive base and a circlet of slender tentacles at the free end, is sometimes abundant in swift water. The base is detachable, as may readily be observed in an aquarium, when small bubbles form beneath the base to cause its separation and sometimes to make the body rise rapidly to the surface.

Even the casual observer of the rapidly running brook may be impressed by the great number of apparently cup-shaped openings leading into the covering of moss on the upper surfaces of the weed-covered rocks. Each cup is really a trap of silken material spun by species of caddis larva belonging to the genus Hydrosyche (Figs. 6a, c). The larva itself may not be attached but lurks

Pl. 5. *Colawah River, Olympic National Park, Washington.*

PHOTO BY JACK DERMID
Courtesy of North Carolina Wildlife Resources Commission

Pl. 6. *Eroding slopes that pollute rivers.*

Pl. 7. *Eroding road banks that pollute rivers.*

PHOTO BY JACK DERMID
Courtesy of North Carolina Wildlife Resources Commission

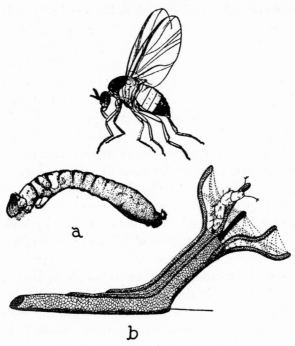

FIGURE 8. (a) Blackfly or buffalo gnat and larva (from Metcalf and Sanderson). (b) Stream-adapted larva of midge, Rheotanytarsus, with fixed 5-prong case, the larva engaged in spinning between prongs a salivary net for capture of food carried in the current (after Walshe).

in the weed or in crevices from which they have access to the trap they have spread for other larvae or items of food. There will be dozens on a small area of rock surface and perhaps thousands in view from a single vantage point. One of our students found as many as 135 of one species and about 100 of another species, in an area eight inches square. With the nets spread so as to catch any small particles of food brought down by the current, the Hydrosyches must play no little part in the general biology of the stream. Other Hydrosyches are found anywhere on the surfaces of the stones, wherever the nets can be spread against the current. The little "glove finger" caddis (Polycentropus) living within a tube of finely spun material on the under sides of rocks, seems to feed in essentially the same way.

The pupae of other caddis, such as Rhyacophila and Psilotreta, should be mentioned. The large and bright green larva of *Rhyacophila fuscula,* while it feeds and grows, wanders freely in the weed; later, it forms a corral of little stones, within which it spins a "house" of webbing in which to live with a degree of protection during the period of its metamorphosis into the winged caddisfly. The larva of Psilotreta, during its growing period, is housed in a cylindrical or conical case of sand grains until the time arrives for pupation. It then cements the cylindrical case on to the surface of a rock and closes each end with a flat pebble. There are favored places for attachment; so that one often finds clusters of cases presenting the appearance of a miniature wood-pile. The difficulty of grouping the inhabitants of streams by habit is illustrated by the fact that the larva of Psilotreta, generally found in not too rapid water, would have to be placed in group 3 and that of Rhyacophila in group 6 below, although in both cases the pupae may be placed in this or the following group.

5. In a fifth group we have adherent organisms with permanent attachments, including among plants some diatoms, the filamentous algae, the freshwater relatives of sea-weeds (Batrachospermun and Lemanea, Fig. 9), the mosses and the river-weeds, Podostemum (Fig. 14). Among animals in streams only the freshwater sponges and Bryozoa seem to qualify as fixed residents of any given spot; but even these have preserved the capacity to release small portions of their bodies in the specialized form of *gemmules* for sponges, or *statoblasts* for the moss-animalcules (Figs. 14i, j), which can drift away to develop into daughter colonies at another place. These are not eggs or larvae; they are rather to be regarded as "internal buds"; but they do save the colonies from complete destruction when changes make uninhabitable the location of a colony that is quite unable to move as a whole.

6. Still another habit-group of animals is represented by the shelter seekers, which includes the "moss fauna" and others; it may be difficult to draw a line between these and the slow runners and creepers of groups 2 and 3 above. Several kinds of small fish find shelter below stones in pools or in small hollows. The

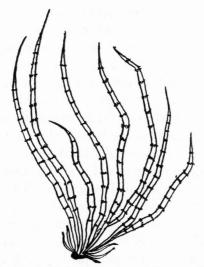

FIGURE 9. A small tuft of *Lemanea,* one of the very few representatives in fresh water of the family of red "seaweeds" (after Ward and Whipple).

helgrammite ("crawler," dobson-fly larva), cranefly larvae, the large stonefly nymph, Pteronarcys, and a number of caddis species, as well as isopods and some midge larvae are examples. Careful washing of a mass of dead leaves or of debris caught between stones in rapids or piled along the shore will yield a large number of individuals and species. Every angler knows helgrammites (Fig. 7f) are best collected for bait by holding a net against the current and dislodging rocks and debris above it. Moss and river weeds growing on rocks in the swiftest current may harbor a remarkably populous community. In a brook near Chapel Hill, North Carolina, a blanket of weed from a ledge in a rapids yielded on examination fifteen species of animals visible to the naked eye, with a combined population of 502 animals per square foot. The measured sample with densest population yielded 1206 animals per square foot.[5] The count did not include any of the undoubtedly much greater number of animals that could have been found with the microscope. Animals in the moss blankets find a good feeding ground, concealment from enemies, and shelter from the impact of currents.

5. Observations of J. Paul Reynolds as a graduate student.

7. A rather distinct habit group is formed by the many animals that seek shelter by burrowing into the bottom. One of the best places we have found for the beautiful burrowing mayfly nymphs was in the gravel of a riffles in a mountain brook. Perhaps this was an unusual occurrence and due to the presence of an artificial lake a little way above. Some kinds of fresh-water mussels anchor themselves in the bottom in the midst of rapids; but in my observation they are found, when in rapids, chiefly in the shelter of stones that partially break the current. In the bottom under the quieter waters and along the shore, one may find dragonfly, mayfly and horsefly larvae, leptid dipteran larvae, fresh-water mussels and peashells (sphaeriids), and earthworms. The trails of dragonfly nymph may be frequently seen as narrow furrows in the soft bottoms of the quieter reaches of the stream, for they are great travelers and quite predatory. It is said that they even eat each other. Trout and dragonfly nymphs are not only competitors for the same kinds of food, but they prey upon each other, as the nymphs seize the very young trout. If the stream is badly polluted, the larvae of chironomid midges, with tails down in tubes in the soft bottom, may cause bright red patches on the silt bottom of less rapid parts of the stream. The red color is attributable to haemoglobin in the plasma of the blood, which enables these so-called "blood-worms" to utilize the limited supply of oxygen available where much organic matter is undergoing decomposition. The longer tubificid worms live under similar conditions; their haemoglobin-rich bodies waving in the water have a duller red color. See the chapter on "Stream Pollution."

8. There is a great diversity of animals that make use of the stream, with all degrees of dependence upon the stream or the life in it. Mention has already been made of the broad-shouldered water striders of rapid water. There are also the larger ordinary water striders and whirligig beetles of the surface film and certain spiders that run on the surface and dive for food or for nesting. There are turtles and snakes that are not at home away from water, and aquatic mammals such as the otter, mink, and muskrat. There are toads, frogs, and salamanders that deposit eggs in streams and complete early development there—besides such per-

manently resident salamanders as the "mud puppy," Necturus, and the "hellbender," Cryptobranchus. Other animals make more or less regular forays into the stream: the kingfisher bird, the raccoon, and bears. The waxwing birds, hovering about a stream, the phoebe, with its nest under the bridge, and some of the bats illustrate another sort of relation to the stream, as they snatch in mid-air the flying insects that have emerged from larval life in the water and that, if not caught too soon, would leave eggs in or on the water for the beginning of a new generation of stream inhabitants.

Finally, mention must be made of those terrestrial organisms that do not enter the stream by intent but that nevertheless constitute a substantial source of food for animals of the stream. Among such are grasshoppers, plant lice, bees, and many others. Professor Forbes, our first intensive student of the food of fishes, regarded these as of great importance. "Terrestrial insects," he said (1888, p. 483), "dropping into the water accidentally or swept in by rain, are diligently sought and largely depended upon by several species" of fishes.

It should be obvious that the groupings we have made in rough fashion do not constitute a formal classification. The groups, as described, are not all-inclusive, nor do they lend themselves to any sort of precise application. Where would one place the leech that creeps or swims or attaches itself to fish? The armies of parasites that live in or on all sorts of animals play a significant part in the web of life within the stream and might make another group.

Recognition of the imperfection and inconsistencies of any attempt at classification may well give emphasis to the elaborateness of the web of life in the stream. The brook may appear all the more clearly as an exceedingly complex plantation with an enormous number of species of pasture plants and livestock. Some of the animals are strong swimmers or runners; others are built to offer little resistance to current as they cling and crawl. Still others, with more elevated backs, hold fast in one way or another as they creep or dart about. Some have the capacity to cement themselves or their houses, but yet are able to break away. A very few make attachments for the duration. Many are adept in finding shelter wherever it may be. There are also animals that divide time between stream and land. Finally a great body of parasites manage to shift to their vertebrate or invertebrate hosts the responsibility for resistance to currents.

The aphorism that "nature abhors a vacuum" gives popular expression to the ever-prevailing "organic pressure" that has resulted in the population of every nook and cranny on earth that offers the slightest possibilities for existence. To the ecologist, every kind of organism may be regarded as playing some special part, as filling a "niche"—meaning, not just a nook in space, but rather a function in the whole web of organic life.

Stream Improvement

It is in the nature of man to work to improve both his own personal surroundings and the environment of the animals and plants that he values. Our whole agricultural development is the outcome of that urge for betterment. To the waters comparatively little intelligent and practicable effort has been directed. As a matter of fact, there is little we can do, or, at least, know how to do, to increase the productivity of the larger bodies of water— oceans, lakes, and rivers. Yet rivers, as will be seen later, have suffered from the mismanagement of agricultural and forest land and highway borders, and, notably, from preventable pollution. Ponds and small streams are another story. The latter need the same sort of environmental protections as the river, but in many cases they are also susceptible of internal improvements that are entirely practicable.

Streams are so diverse in their characteristics and in surroundings, that no hard and fast rules can be of general applicability. Each stream is a case to itself, requiring special study and experimentation. The general principles of stream management may, however, be outlined. More detailed suggestions are to be found in the recent book of Rounsefell and Everhart.

In the past there seems to have been widespread but illfounded faith in what is called "stocking" or "restocking" by the addition of more fish. Apparently it is only under exceptional conditions that stocking leads to substantial benefit. Originally the "trout streams" of Colorado were without trout; their introduction was highly successful. This is true also for other states and for Andean streams of Argentina and mountain brooks of New Zealand, which now maintain populations of non-native trout. The rivers of California were originally without shad or striped bass (rock-fish), which, on transplantation from the east, took hold in good form. Our eastern rivers were once without the European carp or its equivalent. The results of the introduction of carp are too well known to require comment, and the actual benefit derived is still a matter of opinion and subject for heated argument. European brown trout and western rainbow trout in southern Appalachian streams are esteemed supplements to the native populations of brook trout.

Another type of stocking is that of adding catch-size trout to mountain streams just before the opening of the fishing seasons. The idea here seems to be, not an addition to the permanent populations of self-supporting fish, but rather that of offering a degree of sport to the great numbers of persons, laborers, clerks, or presidents, who can spare only a day or two for the healthful recreation of "sport fishing" and who will enjoy that exercise only if there is something ready to be caught, however tame may be the prey. Some such streams after periodic stocking are reserved for angling by women and children. In special cases, then, there have been possibilities in establishing new kinds of fishes in waters that were well adapted for them but in which nature had not placed a parent stock. There are found to be possibilities, too, in making temporary additions to natural populations of adults that could not find support in the water into which they are placed, but which may survive long enough to take the hook of eager fishermen.

What we are concerned about just now is the practicability of increasing the populations of native fishes in the streams we have. We can make new ponds indefinitely, but the number of streams is fixed by nature. Can we improve them, by making it possible for them to produce more fish of catch-size than they do under natural conditions—or, rather, under conditions that currently prevail, partly from strictly natural conditions and to no little extent from the environmental tamperings that have followed the development of an agricultural and industrial civilization?

In the first place, there is much to be accomplished indirectly through the improvement of agricultural and forestry practices, and highway maintenance with general lessening of soil erosion. There is little sound excuse for the destructive turbidity of so many of our smaller and larger streams, or for the extreme and disastrous fluctuations of flow that are so destructive to stream life. Water conservation in the soils is beneficial to farmers, foresters, and fishermen. Water conservation by proper impoundments may serve all, including the angler who wades the stream with rod and reel. A recent *Bulletin of the Sport Fishing Institute* tells of an interesting "Adopt-a-Stream" program:

The League of Ohio Sportsmen has initiated an important conservation program. Each club has been urged to "adopt" a portion of a stream, and to work in collaboration with the farmers and the conservation agencies in bringing about improvement of the watershed. Emphasis will be on keeping the silt on the land and out of the streams. It's a habitat improvement program for both fish and game.

What can be done within the stream? For too long a time there was an almost universal tendency to underestimate the propagative capacity of native fish. The general demand was for adding more fry or fingerling to the brook (or pond) without thought of what the new fish would do after they were put there. What can they do but feed at the same table with the fish that are bred in the brook? With due allowance for exceptional cases, it may be assumed, as a general rule, that the indigenous fish multiply and grow as prolifically as the food available and other conditions permit. If the fish are too few, the first thought may well be that subsistence is deficient. If the fish are too small, one may naturally suspect inadequacy of food or overcrowding. One does not relieve starvation by adding to the number of feeders, which is essentially what "stocking" is. Undoubtedly there has been great waste of money and effort in the maintenance of fish hatcheries and distribution of their output in ways that could do more harm than good.

The general result of careful scientific studies has been well summarized by Dr. Shetter (1950):

In view of the experimental evidence recorded in the literature and the facts discussed above, it must be concluded that the planting of fingerling brook trout in streams which produce numerous brook trout fry is an inefficient management procedure. In all probability any such hatchery fingerlings which arrive at the legal size of 7 inches do so at the expense of an equal number of naturally-reared brook trout. It would appear that emphasis in trout management should be placed upon increasing the natural carrying-capacity of the habitat, rather than upon trying to force the habitat to support two legal brook trout where there is space and food for only one. Since the productive capacities of trout waters are definitely limited, lower creel limits will also aid in spreading the available supply among more anglers.

The only instances where fingerling plantings of brook trout in streams might appear to be justified are: (1) where angling pressure has been so heavy that insufficient brood stock is left; (2) where the breeders of a stream system have been removed by some natural catastrophe; and (3) where suitable spawning conditions do not exist and cannot be created at a reasonable cost. (p. 92)

In efforts toward stream improvement for optimum fish yield the primary aim should be to increase the basic feed of fish that live in the stream. It may be emphasized again that the main food supply of stream fish is not in the free water (which holds so much in ponds) but at the bottom and sides. It is in the sedentary life, composed of clingers, creepers, and burrowers; these can exist only where there is something to cling to or to dig into. What is generally needed, then, is greater stability of bottom, less drifting sand and shifting mud, more anchored rocks, logs, and roots. Naturally, the first two desiderata are to be supplied chiefly, if indirectly, by procedures of control of the environment near and remote, as has been mentioned. In most moving waters, particularly the larger streams, a primary need is for more objects of attachment, things that will not be carried away by the current. For the fish, themselves, resting and breeding places are essential. For some fishes unduly high temperatures, resulting from elimination of shade or from wastes, are undesirable.

The values of direct action for stream improvement cannot be appraised in commercial terms: Whether the expense is justifiable or not depends upon the values attributed to sport fishing and the recreational benefits derived from it. Costs are defrayed in some instances by private clubs; in others from public funds, derived through a tax on the immediate beneficiaries. The way in stream improvement seems to have been led by the State of Michigan (see Hubbs, 1930), but it has been followed in several other regions. Mechanical improvements within small streams may be effected by installing artificial obstructions in the form of sunken and anchored logs, by building short wing-jetties of plank piling, posts, and logs, by strategical placing of boulders or concrete blocks, or by various other sorts of deflectors, which, in effect, increase the extent of riffles and pools and bases of attachment for insects and other feed organisms. They may take the form of stabilizing banks by use of wing-jetties or logs, or by terracing and planting. In some stretches, planting along the banks may provide additional shade and give protection against undesired rise in temperature of the waters. In at least one instance new fishing waters were "created" by making a diversion dam to direct part of the water through an old ox-bow channel (Clark, 1948).

New waters are frequently created by dams built for one purpose or another. The effect of a dam on the productivity of a stream depends in no little measure on the purpose of the impoundment and on its management. If the effort is to keep the reservoir full at all times this may cause extreme fluctuation in rate of flow below the dam. Conceivably in a time of great drought and reduced inflow, the outflow could be stopped completely. When the impoundment is used primarily for regularization of discharge, by catching flood waters and releasing them gradually, as in flood control, fluctuations of the stream below the dam may be notably reduced, to the great advantage of aquatic insects growing in the stream. In such case, the level of the reservoir itself would be subject to wide fluctuations to the detriment of its direct productivity. A study of Stevens Creek in California revealed that "Production of bottom organisms, both in number and weight, was much greater in the area below the dam than above" (Briggs, 1949). Incidentally, about "80 percent of the total production originated in riffle areas."

CHAPTER 9

Rivers

Their Importance

MORE WATER FALLS UPON LAND THAN CAN BE ABSORBED BY THE soil. Naturally so, considering that the whole surface of the earth contributes to the vapor in the atmosphere, that only a small part of the earth's surface is land, that changes of temperature are more sudden and sharp over land, and that high altitudes favor condensation. The water not evaporated is carried in ground-water drifts, perhaps to reappear in part as bubbling springs or to work with great slowness toward streams or the sea; or it runs on the surface in rills and land gullies, ditches and drains, brooks and creeks, to gather in rivers, the great avenues of transportation of water from land to sea.

The significance of rivers to human life can hardly be over-estimated. Even now, when man-made highways and railroads have reduced the value of waterways for travel and transportation of goods, the rivers still bind most of the cities to them by offering, not only waterways for shipping, but also the required volumes of water for domestic and industrial uses and convenient passage-ways for the removal of great quantities of used water. Hence arises the ever-present problem of how to use the river for diverse purposes and yet keep it fit for all the desired uses—how to eat the cake and still have it!

Among other great values of rivers is their use in necessary recreation—for swimming, boating, and fishing, uses that are frequently lost, wholly or in part, when untreated wastes are discharged into the streams. Nor are the aesthetic values to be depreciated: appraised only in the crudest terms of dollars and cents, a clean river is a community asset. Measured by the standard of uplift in spirit and health, the river rates even higher as a public treasure with values that reach far beyond a local community. It is again true, however, that a particular value may be reduced or entirely lost in consequence of other uses to which the stream is put. Many cases could be cited of rivers to be avoided because of disagreeable odors and colors, or of flotsam and jetsam.

The potential uses of rivers, then, are for transportation, or travel, for sources of water for municipal or industrial uses, for recreation, health, and beauty. Another and generally conflicting use is for cheap disposition of domestic and industrial wastes; this use cannot be altogether escaped. Liquid wastes are the inevitable accompaniment of community development; the laws of gravity insure that liquids in volume will inevitably find the river. The larger and more industrialized the community the greater is the volume of potential pollutants of the streams. The problem is, not to keep used waters out of the river, but to render them innocuous before permitting their entrance into the natural avenues of discharge. We cannot go back to the days when rivers were unaffected by man. Unhappily, then, we may have to decide what is the best possible use for a particular stream, thinking of the greatest good to the greatest number.

Characteristics of Rivers

Rivers, as contrasted with lakes, have characteristics that derive from their basic function as conveyors of the surplus water of precipitation from land to sea. These are: (1) the continuous *one-directional movement* of the waters, with flow in the longer rivers even from one climatic zone to another; (2) notable *variations in velocity* with changes in volume; (3) extreme *fluctuation in level, or stage, and in width,* according to conditions of precipitation and run-off; (4) conditions, not ordinarily of stratification as in lakes, but rather of *continual mixing* or *turbulence,* it being understood that the term "turbulence," as used in discussion of natural waters, does not imply violence of movement, but applies to all sorts of movements that involve mixing[1]—in a stream turbulence prevails always, its degree varying with the velocity of flow and with the shapes of sides and bottom;[2] (5) continued or occasional *turbidity,* the causes and effects of which are discussed elsewhere; and (6) following from the changes in velocity, a relative *instability of bottom;* and (7) the most significant fact that the river is an *open system.*

1. The generally one-directional movement from source to sea or estuary is neither uniform nor without minor local reverses. Almost anywhere there may occur eddies of smaller or larger scope that cause movements contrary to the main course of the stream, or from surface toward the bottom or the reverse. It is, however, a *generally* dependable rule that "the same water does not pass under the bridge twice."[3]

2. Velocity of flow is affected by many factors, chief among which are: the *discharge,* or the quantity of water passing through any cross-section in a unit of time; the *slope,* or the inclination of the surface in the direction of flow, which roughly parallels the *gradient* of the bed of the stream; the *form-ratio,* or the proportion of depth to width of stream; to some extent velocity is affected by the *load* of suspended and rolling materials. Matter in suspension tends to increase density and viscosity, to add to the driving force, and, contrariwise, to absorb energy and decrease the rate of movement. Probably the general net effect of turbidity is to retard the flow. Turbid water, being heavier,

1. "In nature, laminar flow is rarely or never encountered, but instead, *turbulent flow* or *turbulence,* prevails. By *turbulent flow* is understood a state in which random motion of smaller or larger *masses* of the fluid is superimposed upon some simple pattern of flow . . . masses of different dimensions . . . pass from one layer to another." (Sverdrup, et al., 1942, p. 90).

2. "Even with the smoothest and most symmetrical boundaries obtainable, flowing air or water will always change over from a smooth, or 'laminar,' state to the thoroughly erratic turbulent state when its velocity gets high enough." (Corrsin, 1950). The boundaries of a river are never smooth or symmetrical.

3. After comparison of plant growth in ponded and running water, Butcher (1946) said: "It would seem from these results that there is a fundamental difference between still and running water based on the difference of movement alone. Nor does it appear to be simply the strength of the current, as one has never observed such fundamental difference in the slowest and fastest portions of the river." The basic difference is not in light, temperature, oxygen, or rate of movement, but rather in the fact that the movement of water goes on all the time.

tends to underflow clearer water that it joins. Temperature, too, has its effect, since warm water is more fluid than cold water.

With the same fall a larger river flows faster than a smaller one, because there is less friction with banks and bottom in proportion to volume of water. So we observe without surprise that with increased discharge a stream flows faster. With a given discharge, the velocity is greater where the stream is narrower without compensation in depth, where it is shallower without proportionate increase in width, or where the gradient of the bed is greater. Most significantly, velocity is not uniform from bank to bank or from surface to bottom. Everyone understands that banks and bottom tend to retard the flow: the main current is removed from the banks, at a distance varying with many circumstances. It is not so well known that the atmosphere has also a slight braking effect. Surprisingly enough, friction with the atmosphere has such effect that the greatest velocity of flow is found to be generally not at the surface but somewhere below, at a level said to vary usually between one-tenth and four-tenths of the total depth, and depending partly on whether the stream is deep or shallow. It is at a lower level when the wind is against the direction of the current than when the wind is with the flow. The rate of flow at any place is not always as regular as appears to the observer. Nearly all streams show some *pulsations* in velocity (Meyer, 1928).

There are various methods of measuring velocity in a stream. Timing the floating chip can measure only the surface flow. This crude method was improved by the use of "floats" made to stay at a given depth, with a rod reaching up through the surface for observation. At best one could only get average velocity over a given distance. Much better are mechanical current meters, which can be held at any desired place and depth. Current meters may have a screw propeller (Haskell type), or they may have cups revolving about a vertical axis (Price type), with a mechanism to record the number of turns in a given time. There are conditions under which the Pitot tube is most useful: basically this is merely a bent tube with a long arm held vertically and extending above the surface of the water. The height to which the water in the vertical tube rises above the surface of the stream is governed by the pressure at the mouth of the short arm aimed against the current at any desired depth; pressure varies, of course, with the strength of the current. The Bentzel velocity tube, measuring rate of flow through a vertical U-shaped tube, is another current measuring device. For details of design of such tubes and for other methods of measurement of velocity, one may refer to standard works on hydrology or limnology methods, such as those of Meyer (1928) and Welch (1948).

3. The level or stage of the river varies, of course, with the volume of water entering the stream. At any given place the fluctuations of level depend also in part on the form-ratio, and on slope and velocity, but more particularly on the cross sectional area at that place.

4. Probably no feature of a river merits more emphasis from the standpoint of its productiveness than the fourth characteristic listed above—that of turbulence. The conditions are entirely too complex and diverse for any satisfactory analysis. Let us look for just a moment at some of the complicating influences. As the stream follows its course, through straight stretches and around easy or sharp bends, over a broad bed or through a narrower section, in slow motion here and faster there, a particular particle of water, or of living or dead matter free in the water, is continually changing position with reference to other particles around it on all sides and with reference to banks or bottom. Every bend and shift in direction or slope, every ledge, log, rock, or root, every slight irregularity of bottom or sides makes for turbulence. Anyone looking on a river observes the eddies, whirls, little vortices and upwellings that mark its surface here and there. But, besides the observable vortices with vertical axes, there are invisible vortices with no superficial signs. The drag of the bottom on the deepest water leads to movements in the forms of submerged vortices with horizontal axes. (Gilbert, 1914, p. 249). Similar and weaker vortices in opposite rotation must occur near the surface. It is due in part to such concealed vortices that the greatest velocity in a stream is not at the surface but somewhere below.

PHOTO BY HILEMAN
Courtesy of National Park Service

Pl. 8. *Red Eagle Lake, Glacier National Park, Montana.*

Pl. 9. *Pollution of river below paper mill.*

PHOTO BY JACK DERMID
Courtesy of North Carolina Wildlife Resources Commission

Courtesy of North Carolina News Bureau,
Department of Conservation and Development

Pl. 10. *Greenfield Lake, Wilmington, North Carolina.*

Pl. 11. *Typical everglades scene, Florida. Wright or saw cabbage palm in background.*

PHOTO BY G. R. GRANT
Courtesy of National Park Service

For our purposes we do not need to analyze or to understand fully the causes and behavior of such rotational movements. What concerns us is the end result—the general mixing effect of all the gyrations occurring and the consequent fact that organisms in the water remain at no particular level. It may be assumed that the turbulence phenomena mentioned have much to do with the fact that rivers in motion do not usually develop a population of drifting organisms comparable to that of a lake. A drifting organism can have no fixed home area with reference to the bottom. Drifting life, constituting the "plankton," is brought into the main stream of a river by drainage from marginal pools, backwaters, and swamps and in other ways; but the capacity for survival of the introduced organisms and for their reproduction in the river is limited. The more sluggish the stream, the longer they may survive; in general, the introduced organisms are gradually lost in the downstream course of the river.

5 and 6. The qualities of turbidity and instability of bottom are considered in other places (pp. 78 and 131).

7. A lake or a pond is more or less of a "closed" or self-contained system. Except for certain additions and subtractions through inflow and outflow, the materials of life remain within it and may be used over and over again, so far as the means of circulation prevent permanent loss to a growing bottom deposit (Chapters 3 and 4.) In contrast, life at any place in the river must avail itself of what is there only temporarily. Nutritive material may remain for a time, lodged somewhere or embodied in a plant or an animal. Eventually, in one form or another, it passes on and, once departed downstreamward, it cannot directly return. The river is an "open system"; it continually receives new water and nutritive substances from without and passes them from one potential home of organisms to another. Even what develops within must go toward the sea, either in continuous movement or step by step.

The Changing River

What has been said in another chapter about the brook or upland stream applies equally well to the upper reaches of substantial rivers, other than those that originate in the great plains. Even in the higher altitudes, relatively slow-moving, quiet, pool-like stretches may alternate with reaches of fast, shallow, turbulent flow over rocky beds. Rapids, or even occasional falls, may be encountered. As the stream passes on through the piedmont or foothill region, the stretches of slow movement become longer and the depth greater, although rapids may still interrupt the smoother course. The broad Mississippi had notable rapids at the level of Rock Island, Illinois, and again above Keokuk, Iowa. There are long stretches of smoothly flowing water above those breaks in the generally gradual slope.

All along, the tributaries bring in additional matter in solution and in suspension, each "joiner" adding in its own characteristic load. More or less permanent turbidity may prevail. Beyond the "fall line," the river debouches on the coastal plain, flows in steadier but often winding course through the sedimentary deposits, to change perhaps to a meandering alluvial stream and to end as an estuary or arm of the sea. The situation grows in complexity, as, more and more along its course through the coastal plain, the river receives contributions from, and makes contributions to, a diversity of backwaters, in the forms of swamp-pools and ponds, and so-called "lakes" in old, abandoned stream channels. In the end, the great rivers become tidal estuaries, where conditions of sea and river are mixed in varying patterns. In these final reaches, we may encounter periodic reversals of direction of flow caused by the tides.

Obviously the chemical conditions and, more particularly, the physical and biological conditions undergo pronounced alterations corresponding to the changing geographic environment and the diverse and varying supplements from the tributaries. The lake has a relatively fixed environment. The river reflects uninterrupted change of environments; this has its effect on whatever lives in the river. Only by combatting the current can a fish, for example, keep within a favored region; even then, the environment is altered from day to day with the fluctuating stages. Animals and plants that are fixed on the bottom feed and breathe from changing water. Drifting microorganisms, a basic food supply, go with the water they are in, but, as previously mentioned, are subjected to continual stirring of the medium and shifts of position with reference to the bottom.

It is obvious, then, that in the study of rivers we face a lot of complexities and instabilities. What is worse is that comparatively little scientific attention has been given to this field of hydrobiological research. Still waters "stay put"; the changes within them are gradual and often cyclic. It is easier, or more immediately rewarding, to study lakes than to investigate the flowing waters that change from mile to mile and from day to day. Most of the studies of rivers in this country have been prompted by concern over pollution. The studies have been directed at waters in an unnatural state. We need more knowledge of what takes place in rivers in a relatively natural state. What the late Professor Stephen A. Forbes said for Illinois long ago (1919) still holds true fairly widely.

That the condition of the river and meandered lakes could be greatly improved by carefully considered management as a public fisheries property there can be little doubt, but the problem of methods of operation and policies to be adopted in such a case is a new one, for the solution of which there are no precedents. As a fisheries property the waters of the state are an unsubdued and neglected wilderness, and the investigator in this field must be prepared to do a pioneer work (p. 156).

In recent decades a good deal has been done, that we do not attempt to review here; but the field of river studies is still relatively open.

It is well said in a book appearing since this chapter was written: "There could be no more fascinating subject than rivers. They are so different from one another and so different in their several parts." (*Water*, by Thomson King, Macmillan, 1953).

River-lakes or Reservoirs

More and more the natural courses of our rivers are being broken by artificial impoundments. Above dams built in the interests of power, navigation, or flood control, great ponds are formed which have many of the characteristics of natural lakes, but which differ notably from typical lakes in the extent of renewal of water by the streams whose courses they break. Other reasons for impounding are for municipal water supplies, irrigation, logging, or improved sanitary conditions.

The impoundment, or "river-lake," is commonly called a "reservoir." Such an impoundment may sometimes, however, result from natural causes. In the course of the Mississippi River, Lake Pepin, more than 20 miles long, two and a half miles in width and some 30 odd feet in depth, exists because the deeper water of the Mississippi is effectively dammed by the delta of Chippewa River entering from the east. The Chippewa is smaller than the Mississippi but its fall is about ten times that of the Mississippi in that region. Consequently, its deposits of sand and other materials accumulate faster than the larger but weaker Mississippi can remove them; an effective barrier or dam of natural origin is maintained.

Most river lakes are of artificial construction, and they yearly increase in numbers and importance. Indeed, some rivers are now changed greatly in character. An originally swiftly flowing stream, with rapids and falls, broken only by occasional natural pools, is transformed into a chain of man-made reservoirs (Pl. 13).

In general, these reservoirs, whether natural or, as commonly, man-made, are of great biological significance. They serve as settling basins, relieving the river of its load of sediment; they increase substantially the acreage of productive water; they afford conditions of relative stability favorable to the growth of aquatic vegetation; they permit the maintenance of a more enduring population of plankton; they offer safer nesting places for most species of fish. The reservoir becomes an area of accentuated internal production: the river, entering above, continually brings in new raw materials; the river below is freed of silt and enriched by the outflow of microorganisms developed in the relatively still water. As settling basins, the reservoirs retain for re-use much of the decaying organic material. On the other hand, their inevitable function as settling basins leads to their gradual filling, as occurs generally in lakes and ponds, but sometimes in impounded waters at a much more rapid rate. It is remarked in another connection that with some reservoirs there are possible practices of controlling

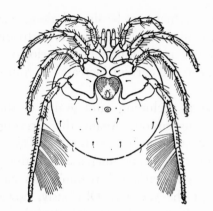

FIGURE 10. Water-mite, *Hydrachna,* viewed from below (from Cook and Mitchell).

the outflow so as to keep the turbid entering water underflowing through to the outlet, rather than to waste the clearer upper water. A particular difficulty encountered with reservoirs having storage functions, as most of them do, is in the extreme fluctuations of level incident to use of the stored water for power or irrigation and sometimes damaging to the life within the reservoir. On the other hand, and somewhat in compensation, the fluctuations of reservoir level tend to regularize flow in the river below.

Finally, it may be noted that new reservoirs are different biologically from old reservoirs. The new reservoir has submerged land and the organic growth on it. It has the quality of virgin territory for the production of aquatic life. For a few years it may be conspicuously productive. After a period of years the body of water attains a state of relatively stable equilibrium, with generally reduced productivity at a more enduring level (see p. 282).

Content

Even under the best conditions, rivers carry much more than water (see p. 128). Quantities of material from the land are carried by traction, in suspension or in solution. Relatively heavy materials, such as coarse sand, gravel, or even boulders are moved by traction, rolling, sliding, or leaping ("saltation") along the bottom. The stronger the current, as in time of flood, the larger are the bodies that may be shoved along, the greater is the amount of loose material that is moved downstream. The driving force of water varies as the square of the velocity. In short, doubling the velocity of the current increases its transportation force about four times.

Lighter material, including sand grains of sufficiently small size, are held in suspension. Again, the carrying power varies with velocity, but at a much higher ratio. The carrying power for suspended matter, greatly increased by the phenomena of turbulence previously mentioned, is sometimes stated as the fifth or sixth power of the velocity. Obviously, however, this ratio must depend largely upon the special conditions of turbulence. Temperature is also a factor in sedimentation, for warm water is less viscous; it offers less resistance to sinking particles.

Still finer material in a chemical and physical form called colloidal, or sometimes jelly-like and perhaps combined with water, are also carried in suspension and may be held almost indefinitely. Finally, much is held in true solution, including almost any sort of mineral dissolved from rock or soil, as well as the products of decomposition of vegetable or animal matter.

Solid particles rolled on the bottom, the "bottom load" of the river, or carried in the current, are sometimes quite significant. They may crush or abrade small plants and animals on the bottom, wrench loose and carry away bases of attachment, or otherwise make for instability of bottom. Thus they may vitally affect the bottom communities, upon which the productivity of a river so largely depends. The terrific force of water moving at increased velocity is often shown most vividly and disastrously by its work in flood seasons on banks, bridges, and buildings.

Minerals in solution, so far as they are derived from the soils, are not likely to be harmful to organic life nor to decrease the supply of free oxygen in the water. Most of them are actually useful to the plants and animals of the river. The products of partial decomposition of plants and animals may serve in part as food supply, but they may also, as they undergo further decomposition, deplete the limited supply of dissolved oxygen. When present in excessive quantity they may also discolor the water and interfere with the penetration of sunlight necessary to photosynthesis.

An advantage that rivers have over still waters is in the generally satisfactory content of dissolved oxygen in the flowing water. In the case of a shallow, swift stream in the mountains, even a heavy load of organic industrial wastes may effect no net oxygen depletion for the water above the bottom, although it may have bad effects in other ways. While oxygen in quantity is being used in decomposition, the mechanical disturbances of riffles and rapids can bring reoxygenation at a rate faster than the processes of depletion. This would not be true in a stream of slow movement. Yet, when a virtually septic condition occurs in a sluggish and heavily polluted stream, the passage of water over falls, as those of a dam, may so reoxygenate the water, that, for a distance, it is a tolerable home for some fish. If undigested organic wastes are also carried over the dam, the oxygen depletion accompanying decomposition is gradually resumed until the stream farther on becomes again unsuitable for fish, as it was above the dam.

In the absence of pollution almost any river will, through the mechanics of flow, be kept well-oxygenated, except in the deeper places of sluggish streams. In the same way the free carbon dioxide content is kept more or less in equilibrium with the atmosphere. The acid-alkaline reaction (hydrogen-ion concentration, measured by the pH) depends chiefly on the chemical nature of the drainage area.

In this connection, however, it must be pointed out with emphasis that in ordinary tests of the free oxygen content of streams, too much attention is concentrated on the *flowing* water; too little is generally given to the relatively static water immediately overlying the bottom. In rivers the principal feed for fishes is in the organisms of the bottom where water movement is sluggish. The important animals there may be only indirectly affected by the mass of strongly moving water above. The lower Missouri River, on the other hand, with its high velocity and shifting substratum has a paucity of bottom fauna and little internal production. The chief food of fishes is the organic matter from the land, which is washed in in substantial quantity. Berner (1951) refers to the washed in material as "syrton." Of the food found in the stomachs of fish examined, 54 per cent was produced outside of the river.

The effects of domestic and industrial pollution on oxygen supply and in other ways are considered in a following chapter.

Sedentary Life

There is life in the river from its very source, but the quantity and composition of the flora and fauna changes materially along its course. It seems clearly established that "Water immediately emerging from the ground contains enough plant food to support a large population" (Phelps, p. 236). From the bottom of a rivulet about six feet from its source, a spring in the side of a clay bank, there were taken 42 species, 17 plant and 25 animal, with a total of 640 individuals per milliliter. All along the course of the stream there are additions of species (and some losses) and contributions of food materials, as well as of useless and sometimes injurious matter and, of course, of oxygen-consuming matter.

Further along, with increasing contributions of nutritive substances, there is greater organic productivity, until a maximum is reached. The upper, but not the uppermost, regions of a river are often indeed the richest in production of animal life in *proportion to volume of water*.[4] The stream is shallow, light is available everywhere, the conditions for oxygenation are especially good, and the current is adequate to prevent the deposition of organic and oxygen-consuming silt. The lowermost part of the river may be poorest relative to volume of water. This sort of sequence may, of course, be subject to modification anywhere by conditions resulting from human populations or industries.

4. The Ohio River basin has been most carefully studied by the U.S. Public Health Service. Phelps (1944, p. 237), says: "But figures could be cited to show that most of the rivulets and small creeks entering the rivers of the Ohio Basin have smaller and less varied populations per liter than the rivers themselves, that most of the rivers entering the Ohio have greater and more varied populations than the Ohio, and that the Ohio has a greater and more varied population than the Mississippi below the mouth of the Ohio. Thus the population peaks for the Ohio Basin tend to be in such rivers as the Licking, Great Miami, and Scioto. In the only one of these which has been extensively surveyed, the Scioto, the population peak was approximately in the middle third."

Living things in a river are in three main categories: the fixed or sedentary organisms, the drifting life, and the active swimmers. Naturally a flowing stream, with all its vagaries of discharge and level, is not generally a favorable place for the growth of rooted plants. In a current the rooted plants require strong stems and leaves and good anchorage. Even then they may be carried away in times of flood. Filamentous algae, such as Cladophora may endure substantial losses of material with their capacity for rapid replacement through growth (Butcher, 1933). There may, however, be scattered areas protected much of the time from strong current and scouring. In such places some of the higher plants find suitable homes. Of course, in impounded zones, which now abound in most rivers, and in what may be called the collateral waters—pools, ponds, bayous, and swamps—almost any kind of higher aquatic plant may grow in abundance. Among such are the surface-covering duckweeds, the anchored waterlilies, lotus, water shield (Brasenia), and pondweeds (Potamogeton) with water-proofed floating leaves, the submerged hornwort (Ceratophyllum), and crowfoot (Ranunculus). Water celery or tape-grass (Vallisneria), with its long flexible leaves, withstands strong current. There are, too, the emergent smartweeds (Polygonum or Persicaria), the river bulrush (Scirpus) and numberless others. Much of what is said about plants of lakes in Chapter 12 is equally applicable to the backwaters, bayous and more sluggish parts of rivers.

Swift rocky streams have a limited variety of the larger plants. The microscopic diatoms and some algae may occur in great numbers in the films on rocks and sometimes give brownish or yellowish color to the bottom. Most diatoms of swift water have special adaptations for withstanding current; these may be gelatinous stalks or beds for anchorage (Patrick, 1948, pp. 496, 497). Filamentous algae of several kinds, such as Cladophora, may be conspicuous in long tufts streaming from the rocks. The stonewort (Chara), with encrustations of carbonate of lime, is mentioned for certain swift rivers in hard-water country. An alga, Lemanea, of the group of "red seaweeds," grows in small erect tufts of stems on the rocks of some rapid waters.[5] A few of the mosses (Fontinalis, Hypnum, and others) may be conspicuous, Fontinalis, the "spring moss," often showing as long masses trailing from the rocks. Sometimes predominant in swift water is a flowering plant, quite moss-like in appearance, which clings tightly to the rocks while branching extensively and sending up some erect stiff parts. The flowers, when present, are quite inconspicuous. The thick spreading masses of this "river weed" (Podostemum, Fig. 19e) may harbor a diversity of aquatic insects and other invertebrates.

The role of plants in oxygenation is not so important in a river as in still water. They contribute to the animal life of the stream by acting as organizers of living matter. They also afford bases of atttachment for algae and protozoa and serve as refuges or "shelter" for aquatic insects and other invertebrates that might not otherwise live in such numbers in swift water. It is the life on the bottom or on plants or roots projecting from the bottom that is of greatest importance in a stream. The large rooted plants, said Butcher (1933), "act as a habitat for animals and algae and *largely* determine the fertility of a river" (italics mine). He was referring, of course, to the relatively small rivers of Britain, rather than to such large rivers as the Mississippi, Illinois, or Danube rivers.

Animals of a stream must be able to maintain positions in spite of the current. If not strong swimmers, they may have flattened or streamlined bodies with broad surfaces for adhesion or strong claws for clinging (nymphs of mayflies and stoneflies, snails, flatworms). They may have spinning glands to make threads for attachment (larvae of blackflies or buffalo gnats); or they may have strongly adhesive brushes of hairs (the byssi of peashells). They may have suckers or sucker-like bodies (some mayfly nymphs, "waterpennies"—parnid beetle larvae—Fig. 5). They may burrow in the bottom (some mayfly nymphs, dragonfly nymphs, and peashells). Whatever their adaptation for with-

5. Others of the group Rhodophyceae (embracing, chiefly, the "red seaweeds") that are characteristic of flowing fresh water are Draparnaldia and Batrachospermum (frogwort).

standing currents, they have to subsist upon what the river affords. So far as they do not feed upon each other they must be able to catch what passes. They may have, as parts of their bodies, filter fans (blackfly larvae—Fig. 8); they may spin nets to spread against the current (caddis larvae—Fig. 7); they may have scraping devices (snails, some mayfly nymphs). In general they are predators or detritus-feeders.

Sedentary animal life exists in rivers in great profusion of kinds, notwithstanding the obvious vicissitudes of life where depths and velocities of water change continually and sometimes in extreme degree, and where abrasive action and sometimes actual scouring may prevail. As has been described in the chapter on the upland brook, a lot of insects and other invertebrates have special adaptations for maintaining a hold against weak or even violent currents and under waterfalls. The presence of protozoans in rivers may be taken for granted, since some kinds of unicellular animals of microscopic size will be found wherever there is natural water that is not too hot or too strong chemically for the existence of life. Fixed masses of sponge and the rapacious hydra are often common in rivers. Roundworms, flatworms, attached rotifers, and the fixed moss animalcules (Bryozoa) may be prominent. Earthworms of some kinds and their smaller relatives are at home in the sand and gravel among the rocks. Leeches are widely distributed. There are snails, both gilled and pulmonate, on the rocks and elsewhere, and peashells (Sphaeriidae) in the sand and gravel. Freshwater mussels in great diversity of species, well anchored in the bottom, occur even in some soft-water streams, but are most abundant and thick-shelled in the harder waters of limestone regions. In the Mississippi River Basin and parts of the Great Lakes Drainage, mussels of many species occur so abundantly and have shells of such size and quality as to support an industry of button manufacture.

Among insects, the stonefly nymphs with few exceptions, and blackfly larvae occur only in running water. This is true also of dobson-fly larvae (helgrammites—Fig. 7), and their relatives, the fishflies (Sialidae). There are, too, a great variety of mayfly nymphs and caddisfly larvae. Water-striders and whirligig beetles on the surface film are frequently evident to the casual observer. Midge larvae are extremely numerous in most swift or slow waters. No one needs to be reminded that gnats and midges are often abundant in proximity to streams. The insects on the wing are pests, but their larvae are basic food for fishes. Professor S. A. Forbes of Illinois, through a period of years, made extensive studies of the food of freshwater fishes. He concluded that "minute slender dipterous larvae [of midges and related kinds] are of remarkable importance, making, in fact, nearly one-tenth of the food of all fishes studied" (Forbes, 188, p. 483).

In the more sluggish parts of the river resident life is not so evident as in the riffles. Yet the softer bottom may harbor a rich fauna of burrowers, notable among which are freshwater mussels and the burrowing mayfly and dragonfly nymphs. The nymphs of burrowing mayflies, and some of their close relatives that only sprawl on the bottom, have a special straining apparatus of hairs to filter drifting food from the passing current. Often the young nymphs of mayflies occur in large numbers and metamorphose almost by the calendar to give clouds of literally millions of short-lived flying insects; after molting again, they mate and deposit eggs in the water. Life out of water is only a matter of hours or of but a day or two. Sometimes the cast skins and dead bodies on the surface form conspicuous broad floating bands that follow the main channel of the stream; the bands, as well as the clouds of mayflies in the air, may be seen even from a distance. At such times fishes gorge themselves upon both the larvae rising from the bottom and the flies falling from the air. Needham (1921) has said: "Among the burrowers none are more abundant or more important than the young of the mayflies. Indeed, there are hardly any aquatic organisms of greater economic value, for they are among the principal herbivores of the waters, and they are all choice food for fishes" (p. 269).

Various other writers have attested to the great value of mayflies as food of fishes. Forbes (1888) after extensive studies, reported: "In fact nearly a fifth of the entire amount of food consumed by all the adult fishes examined by me consisted of aquatic larvae of this order, the greater part of them larvae of dayflies

(Ephemeridae), principally of the genus Hexagenia [the burrowers]" (p. 484).

It is not surprising that mayflies should have been among the first lures employed by anglers, or that so many of the artificial "flies" should have been modeled upon mayflies of various kinds.

It must not be understood that the bottoms of streams generally are notably populated. Great extents of some streams, particularly the Missouri River and some in the coastal plain, have bottoms of sand or mud that shift with the changing velocities of flow. Sedentary animals can maintain themselves only in protected places and on fixed objects, such as anchored logs, the roots of trees, and occasional rocks. It is basic procedure in stream management for improved productiveness to add to the number of such fixed bases of attachment, as well as to make more pools and sheltered spots.

The sterility of unstable bottoms may, perhaps, be overemphasized; it is said that, even in shifting sand, some organisms, such as burrowing mayflies, manage to live deep enough to keep in place and thrive despite the instability of the sand above them.

It is noteworthy that so many of the small animals, insects, moss animalcules, mussels, and peashells, have strainers for capturing the minute food carried in the current. The strainers may be outgrowths from the body in the form of ciliated tentacles, or combs of hairs or setae; they may be fine-meshed traps manufactured from special glands, as in the case of the net-forming caddis larvae. The food carried by the current may be small organisms dislodged by the current, organisms living freely in the water, or organic debris, either developed in the stream or washed into it.

Generally speaking, the insects and other denizens of fast-flowing water cannot be too discriminating in feeding. They must take what comes, as it comes, or as it can be found without risk or loss of position.

Drifting Life

The organisms living adrift in the water are called, as for lakes and ponds, the *plankton* (or, strictly speaking for flowing water, *potamoplankton*); those merely washed in and carried temporarily constitute the *tychoplankton*, which is not unimportant; while the silt, sand, and finely divided parts of decomposed organisms are termed *detritus*, which may be *inorganic* or *organic* and serviceable food material for small animals.

It has already been said that the river, because of the mixing and stirring phenomena, associated with normal drag of bottom, banks, and atmosphere, with bends and twists, and with changes of breadth and depth even with uniform discharge, is not a favorable place for indigenous plankton populations. It would seem quite obvious, indeed, that animals or plants carried passively in the current are always moving on, and their offspring as well. The potential effect of current on drifting life becomes impressive if we imagine a copepod in a stream flowing at the rate of two miles per hour, or 48 miles per day. The rate of development from egg to mature breeder varies with temperature and food; but, if we take a reasonable developmental period of 15 days, it is evident that the copepod hatched at one place in the stream might arrive at maturity more than 700 miles farther down the river, where all physical, chemical, and biological conditions are greatly different. In actuality the travel downstreamward might be interrupted some by temporary sojourns in the eddies and pools that break the uniform flow of the river. The copepods of one generation or another, however, must get a long way from the ancestral home. A true community of drifting, self-reproducing organisms can be expected only in a slowly flowing stream, such as the Volga, "in which even the high water of spring requires almost two months to reach the sea" (Ruttner, 1953).

Generally, the stock of plankton at any given place in a river may be assumed to have come from places higher in the river's course, from tributaries, perhaps to some extent from the occasional semipermanent eddies, or, as strays, from a resident bottom population. At any rate it seems generally accepted that typical river plankters are a few species of bacteria, blue-green algae, diatoms, yellow-green flagellates, and true-green algae, and, among animals, principally protozoa and rotifers.[6] Nevertheless, there

6. The diatom *Synedra acus*, var. *angustissima*, the green flagellates *Euglena viridis*

may be in a large river a fairly dense population of adventitious plankters in transit. Any kind of alga or protozoan found on the bottom or in side waters, may, regularly or irregularly, be taken up and carried in the flowing water and some of these while adrift may reproduce prolifically to make important drifting populations. This might be particularly true where fertility is increased by organic pollution. Where the Mississippi carried pollution from the Tri-cities (Davenport, Moline, and Rock Island), I have seen it deeply colored for its whole broad expanse and almost soupy with the blue-green Aphanizomenon.

Ordinarily, rivers carry much that is not "characteristic" of streams. Daphnias and other small crustaceans and rotifers are continually drifting in from back waters and tributaries. The chance invaders may live and reproduce for a while; but they disappear gradually to be replaced by others from new sources. We need to know more as to duration of life and capacities for sustained reproduction of the larger plankters in rivers. Whatever its source and persistence, rivers have a variable but sometimes substantial load of drifting life and debris. The Potomac below Washington sometimes swarms with Cladocera and other plankters. "Indeed the Volga, the Thames, the Illinois and the San Joaquin have been shown to have well-developed plankton floras" (Patrick, 1948, p. 500). Among important and extensive studies of the plankton of American rivers are: the classical study by Kofoid (1903, 1908) for the Illinois River, the monograph by Allen (1920) for the San Joaquin and its tributaries, the studies of the Mississippi by Galtsoff (1924), Wiebe (1928) and Reinhard (1941), and that of Chandler (1937) on the fate of lake plankton in streams.

After extensive studies of rivers of Britain, Butcher (1932) said that the plankton "is only a pale image of the benthos [the bottom or attached life] from which it was almost entirely derived." His observation, "It seems obvious that there are no truly pelagic forms in flowing water," is plainly sound. Nevertheless,

---

and *E. pisciformis* and the yellow-green Chrysococcus are characteristic of rivers rather than of still waters (Phelps, p. 239-40); Chrysococcus occurs free-floating or on wet rocks. Others, such as the green *Pleodorina illinoisensis,* are ascribed to the plankton of rivers (Ward and Whipple, p. 268).

this does not quite give a complete answer to the question of plankton in rivers as they are, with all their pools, eddies, and side waters. Even in rapid streams there are pools of relatively quiet water in which "a small but changing population of zooplankton could reproduce sufficiently to contribute a significant population to the main stream" (Pennak, 1943).

To what actually lives in the water, there is added, as potential food for fishes, the insects that alight upon the surface or fall from overhanging trees. Sometimes the shrubs overhanging a trout stream fairly drip with insect larvae. The ancient and enduring practice of dry-fly fishing rests upon the assurance that fish devour, not only aquatic organisms, but also the denizens of the atmosphere.

Swimming Life

To the great majority of people the chief interest in rivers centers on its productiveness in fish and the related recreational values. In the river there are other "swimmers," such as frogs and the tadpoles of frogs and toads, turtles and snakes, mink, otter and muskrat; but practical interest is in the fish favored by anglers.

If fish in flowing water were quite passive they would all eventually be swept out of the river at its mouth. They must of necessity be more or less habituated to swim against the current. In technical language, they must be positively *rheotropic*.[7] Even to stay in one place, when in current, a fish must swim upstreamward as much as it would otherwise be carried downstreamward. It may be asked how a fish in moving water "knows" the direction of the current, or, more correctly, how it can receive the stimuli requisite to proper orientation and activity. We ourselves are constantly moving through space with great speed, but with general unawareness of that fact—and with total inability to resist the movement. It is only by observation of bodies outside of our particular system that we can be made aware of our movement along with the surrounding atmosphere and land. So the

7. From Greek *rheos*, current, and *trope*, a turning; rheotropic means turning involuntarily with the current. Another term used is *rheotactic*, from *rheos*, current, and *taxis*, order; the fish orders, arranges, or orients itself by the current.

fish must be stimulated for orientation and activity by objects outside of its moving system—objects such as the bottom, the banks, and the trees that may be in view. There are experiments to indicate that this is so.

To say that a fish in the river is positively rheotropic does not mean that it continually battles the current. As everyone knows, a fish may swim in any direction, remain sometimes at rest in the quiet water, or even be passively carried down by the stream. Nevertheless, if it is not to be irretrievably lost to the sea, it must at times be a current-fighter and predominantly so. The failure to sense this basic fact leads sometimes to misconceptions. Where fish gather at the base of a dam or falls, it may sometimes mean that a strong and necessary upstream migration is blocked by the dam, as is the case of salmon. In other cases it can mean only a congregation of local fish at a fixed barrier checking the fish in normal rheotropic activity. In short, the fish concentrated below the falls may be those that would not have gone far in the absence of a block and that might have returned in course of the day or week. Carp, drum, and catfish may be prominent in such aggregations, although they are not notably migratory species. Or, again, they may be attracted to the foot of the dam by the extra food brought over from the impounded waters above.[8]

Recent studies of the movements of fishes in streams have led to the conclusion that most fish keep to their own preferred homes covering only a short range, that "once a fish becomes established in an area it will remain there for most, if not all, of its lifetime" (Gerking, 1953).

In *The Fisherman* for October, 1951, Emmet Gowen gives a vivid account of the aggregations of large catfish and hickory shad in the "boils" below the turbine exits in the surging tail waters of Kentucky Lake on the Tennessee River. Assuming with probable correctness that the fish are attracted to this place by

8. Such aggregations of fish below a dam were discussed by the present writer (1929) in relation to fish of the Mississippi River; the question of fishways had been considered earlier (1917). The very different conditions of Pacific Coast streams have been presented by several specialists in a symposium (Sumner, 1940). A recent most useful treatment of need and of plans for fishways is found in Chapter 11 of Rounsefell and Everhart, 1953.

food brought down through the turbines, he aptly terms the location "catfish hotel," where "board and lodging" are free for catfish.

Chief among strictly *anadromous* (meaning "up-running") fishes, which may be effectively blocked by dams from reaching their proper spawning grounds, are the salmons, and the trouts (sometimes), the shad, and striped bass or "rock." Even these, in the sea, may keep in their own coastal territory when not in spawning migration. (See Raney et al., 1952.) To facilitate the upward movement of such fishes, it is often required that dams be equipped with "fishways," or "fish ladders," providing a series of practicable steps for fish to use in passing from the stream below to the pool above the dam. Except where fishes of pronounced migratory habit, such as those just mentioned, are to be provided with passage, the utility of fishways is at least questionable. Obviously, too, the fish must be induced to use the practicable passageways offered; they must be directed positively toward the lower entrance of the fishway. If the fish is guided in his movements by the strongest current, it may well be led away from the fishway toward the main spillways where ascent is impossible; the fishway is useless. It is a matter of design. However easy the path of ascent, once the fish has entered, the ladder serves no purpose unless the fish, which is reacting to strong current, is attracted to its foot. This condition is not always easily met.

In contrast to the anadromous fishes, which must ascend rivers to spawn, there is the one catadromous fish, the common eel, which attains its growth in the interior waters, but, on approaching maturity, the females at least, must *descend* the river to enter the sea and spawn far out in the open ocean. Low dams and falls seem to offer little obstruction to the downstream movement of eels or to the upstream migration of the young "elvers." Since the Keokuk-Hamilton Dam was built across the Mississippi River, the catch of eels in the upper Mississippi has declined notably, whether or not the decline is attributable entirely to the mechanical obstruction.

The significance to fish of the dam in a river course is not all on the negative side. The impounded waters, with conditions favorable for food production and for spawning, may increase the total population of fish in the river system. Furthermore, the reservoir water flowing over the dam or through the turbines may substantially enrich the stream below for some distance.

In the uppermost parts of a river the number of kinds of fish may be small. Sometimes little is found but trout, dace, darters, and some suckers, with perhaps madtoms (small catfish, Schilbeodes), and miller's thumb (Cottus). In the lower course diversity of species increases greatly, with persistence of some of the same kinds and with minnows of diverse species, carp, buffalo fish, drum, suckers, catfishes, sunfishes, crappie, basses, sturgeon, garpikes, and many other kinds. In the lowermost estuarial sections of the river one may encounter marine species, particularly those adapted to varying mixtures of salt and fresh water. To some bacteria and plankton organisms that are carried by the current the salt water is lethal.

For any river of immediate interest it is desirable to know what is its population of fish. The practical fisherman may be content to know what fish he can catch; one may, however, want to consider the possibilities of improvement in yields or appraise the effects of changes of any sort resulting from pollutions or from measures taken for stream improvement. In any such case quantitative determinations are needed, but difficult to obtain. One may drain a pond or use poisons to obtain every fish to be counted with approximate accuracy. In the river one must resort to sampling by hoop nets, traps, or by the use of poison (rotenone), or other methods of destruction in limited areas. (See Stroud, 1953.) At best doubts arise as to the effectiveness of the sampling and only rough approximations to quantitative accuracy are possible. The catch by any method of fishing is never a reliable criterion of actual abundance of particular species, and most methods of capture are to some extent selective with reference to species, size, or sex.

CHAPTER 10

Stream Pollution

Sources of Uncleanness

NO RIVER IS PURE IN A CHEMICAL OR A STRICT BIOLOGICAL SENSE. It would be no place for fish, if it were. Our concern with any stream is not to keep it strictly "pure," but to keep it *clean*. By "clean" we mean: well oxygenated; free from silt, unnatural colors, odors, or tastes; and untainted by germs of disease of man or animal or by substances toxic to man, beast, fishes, or the living food of fishes. Because living things and the natural processes of decomposition occurring in a river compete for the free oxygen in "solution," it follows that, when we call for adequate free oxygen, we are demanding freedom from an excess of decomposable matter. A reasonable addition of organic waste from farms or cities, so far as it can be decomposed without weakening the desired oxygen balance, actually enriches the stream. An *excessive* amount lowers the free oxygen content and reduces the stream's productivity for what we want.

Fortunately, as has been mentioned on a preceding page, a typical river in the natural state presents no oxygen problem. But streams in regions inhabited by civilized man are often not "typical" in that sense. We want civilization; we want it highly industrialized; but we do not want to pay an unnecessarily high price in stream modification.

Inevitably a stream receives contributions of some kinds in all its course from source to mouth. Without such additions it would be a poor stream. We are justifiably concerned only if bad things are introduced or even too much of a good thing. Really toxic substances are likely to come only with industrial wastes, or from artifacts, such as abandoned but unsealed mines. Some natural additions and industrial wastes may be of a character to befoul the bottom or otherwise make it unfavorable for life. Other natural pollutions, industrial effluents, and domestic sewage may be potential nutrients for plants and, thus, indirectly, for animals. Much of this is, however, in forms too complex for use by plants. It has to be decomposed. The word "decomposition" may have no implication of elegance; yet it is an essential phase of the cycle of life. Without it much dead organic matter would be regularly lost from the cycle; the supply of building material for plants and animals would everywhere be continually diminishing.

The chief agents of decomposition are bacteria and fungi. Fortunately, the purest stream has its ready stocks of these useful organisms and of the oxygen they need for their work. For the relatively quiescent bacteria "work" is to keep alive and to make their own body substance for growth and multiplication. To accomplish this they break down complex organic materials into parts such as they require, and other parts that green plants may use. Their own bodies may serve as food for small animals. They have the capacity to multiply rapidly in adjustment to increasing amounts of the basic materials that constitute their nutriment. In doing so they use more and more oxygen. Under ordinary conditions the beneficent processes of decomposition attract no attention; the trouble comes when the need for decompostion results in overtaxing the capacity of the stream for renewal of free oxygen. There may follow, then, not only the loss of free oxygen, but also the beginning of anaerobic decomposition with liberation of objectionable gases.

Rivers derive originally from atmospheric precipitation. What are the common sources and sorts of additions to rivers and their tributaries? We may consider as possible sources of contamination: the atmosphere, forested areas, swamps, farms, highways, cities and towns as communities of people with domestic wastes, and, finally, industries in cities or without.

1. From the atmosphere come water, dissolved elemental gases, chiefly nitrogen, oxygen, and carbon dioxide, and some ammonia; all are helpful or innocuous. From it come also, along with inorganic dust, the spores of bacteria and fungi and other air-borne organisms, much if not all of which the stream readily utilizes to advantage.

2. From forested hillsides and plains comes surface or seepage water, carrying mineral and organic matter, in particulate form or in solution, contributing to fertility of the river. The stream lover should be an advocate of forestry development. Without our forest or grass cover there may come into the stream too much unwanted sand, clay, and gravel.

3. Back-waters and swamps might be considered parts of the river, but their contribution to the main stream is distinctive. They afford more favorable conditions than do the flowing waters for development of the small, drifting plants and animals whose overflow into the streams with rising water level bring enrichment in basic food. Incidentally, they are often nurseries for young fish, some of which escape into the river. Our concern with them now is as *possible sources of natural pollution*. Swamp waters are often deeply colored with extracts from the roots, trunks and leaves of trees and shrubs, and from humus. In many regions, and particularly in the southeastern coastal plain, some rivers, lagoons, and ponds are deeply dyed to give "black" waters. The coloring matter is probably not in itself harmful to any great extent,[1] except as it interferes with the penetration of sunlight needed for basic productivity within the stream.

4. From farms come the same sorts of matter as are added by forests, plus a significant part of the fertilizer which the farmer inevitably loses from his enriched lands. On the whole, the better the farming, the richer is the stream. But from farms may come also domestic sewage and animal wastes, with perhaps occasional germs of disease of man or beast. Such germs find in the flowing oxygenated water an unfavorable habitat and are likely to be lost

---

1. Boatmen along the coast claim that "black" water keeps better in the barrels on shipboard. If this is because it checks the growth of bacteria or other organisms, it cannot be favorable to stream productivity.

soon in the natural process of "self-purification." It is for this reason that the bacillus *Escherichia coli* (a common intestinal inhabitant of man) is so good an indicator of pollution: because it does not live long in the river, its presence indicates a relatively *near and recent* source of pollution. Since it occurs in domestic animals as well as in man, the sanitarian places different values upon it as a test organism, according to whether the source could have been a farm or a city.

The poorly managed farm, with inadequate land cover of vegetation and with eroded slopes, adds more in forms of sand and sterile clay, contributing to turbidity with reduction of light penetration, to silting and smothering of bottom organisms, and, with more rapid run-off, to exaggerated fluctuations of water level. Soil erosion is often spoken of as if it were a mere matter of loss of soil. That loss is serious enough; but erosion means also turbidity of streams and deprivation of sunlight for potentially productive plants in the stream; it means sedimentation of reservoirs, unstable and less habitable bottoms in rivers, and the hampering of navigation.[2] Soil erosion is stream pollution in a big way. The promoter of good farming, the soil conservationists, the power plant owner, and the fisherman have a common interest in better farm and highway practices.

5. From highways come oils and tar, but any considerable amount of this type of pollution is only occasional and may be unavoidable. From highway drainage comes also a variable but often substantial amount of clay washed from shoulders and embankments. To a great extent this is avoidable; it is wasteful of shoulders and roadside banks and harmful to rivers. There would seem to be no good reason why so many of our main river courses should be so continuously turbid. Little or nothing can be done about some of the banks of rivers themselves, but the extensive washings from roadsides should be reduced everywhere by seeding

2. "The adverse effects of soil erosion have been greater in some cases than the damage caused by either sewage or industrial wastes. It is most unfortunate that the same consideration and publicity have not been given to soils and natural pollution, which both have considerable effect on aquatic life and significant effect on our health and welfare" (Seckinger, 1950, p. 32). See also United States Forest Service and the Soil Conservation Service (1946).

and use of brush and straw on new banks. In highway engineering surface protection is extensively practiced but as yet is by no means sufficiently widespread. *No roadway, however "secondary" it may be, should be considered completed or acceptable as long as it has eroding banks.*

6. From towns and cities come ordinarily domestic wastes that add materials of potential contribution to fertility along with some disease germs. Here a first consideration is that of relative quantities. What is the content or organic wastes, what is the volume of water receiving it, and what are the conditions of circulation in the river that has to take care of the wastes? Other considerations will, of course, follow. Let us look at two glaring cases.

It may be assumed that no city in the hemisphere discharges more sewage than New York. That great metropolis has been aptly described as "an island entirely surrounded by sewage." Phelps (1947, p. 24) quotes Richard H. Gould as saying:

New York Harbor is one of the most astonishing of the natural agencies for the disposal of sewage that I know. I never cease to be amazed by the fact that some ten millions of people can discharge their sewage into its waters and still live on its shores in relative comfort and apparent good health. This is possible only by the combination of a large stream flow from the Hudson River and a fairly rapid and extensive circulation of tidal currents.

Ketcham, Redfield, and Ayres found in the New York bight such a rapid flushing resulting from tidal action that "not more than about ten day's contribution of any pollutent, dissolved or suspended in the water, will accumulate in the area at any one time" (p. 24). The city may maintain generally "normal" health conditions; nevertheless, the water surrounding Manhattan is not nice water and there are at least some responsible intimations that health conditions would be better without the close proximity of open sewage-laden waters (Phelps, p. 25).[3]

The Illinois River actually experienced a great increase in

3. The conditions described seem to prevail around New York in spite of the fact that the city does have some sewage disposal plants and sludge vessels for transportation of sewage sludge to sea.

yield of commercial fishes after the Chicago drainage canal was led into it. It was, however, the lower portion of the river that maintained the big fisheries; the septic upper section for many miles was neither good for fish nor pleasant to live by.

Quite apart from the effects of domestic sewage in dissemination of water-borne disease germs, such as those of typhoid, cholera, and dysentery, are other strongly objectionable consequences.[4] Unsightliness, bad odors, and general "dirtiness" follow with any substantial addition of domestic wastes. Furthermore, so far as the content of the effluents are decomposable, and most of them are, there is always the danger of destroying the desired "oxygen balance," with consequent reduction of productivity and sometimes with liberation of noxious odors.

Speaking of the Potomac River, Seckinger, in the paper previously cited, said:

The sanitary quality of the river water in the upper Potomac River Basin (Luke-Cumberland area) had degraded by the end of World War II to septic or cesspool quality. In the Washington Metropolitan Area the sanitary quality of the river water had degraded to an oxygen content of less than 2 parts per million at low flows. The oxygen content has subsequently reached a minimum of less than one half part per million. Degradation of lesser degrees occurred in many of the tributaries (pp. 25, 26).

7. Industrial effluents may be grouped rather roughly in four general categories: (1) those, relatively rare, that contain actually toxic substances, such as, sulphuric acid, lead, phenol, and some mine wastes; (2) those that, although not harmful in themselves, cause undesirable colors, odors, or tastes; (3) those that add readily decomposable matter in such quantity as to overtax the streams; (4) those of such a character (cellulose, ligneous matter, oils) that biochemical digestion occurs only slowly, while, meantime, the refuse beclouds the water, smothers bottom-living animals, abrades the gills of fishes or is harmful in other ways; and (5) heat—the temperature of a river in Ohio, whose waters were

4. "Health authorities in the West and Southwest are well aware of the high incidence of enteric diseases in the areas where sewage-polluted water is used for irrigation" (Woodward, 1951).

diverted for cooling and returned at higher temperature, approached 140° F. during December, 1949 (Thomas, 1951). With development of atomic energy there may be added other categories—radio-active materials and, with copius discharge of cooling water, significant elevation of stream temperature.

Toxic substances and color-giving materials require little argument. We know we do not want them in the river at all. They should be kept out, if physically or economically possible. This applies also to smothering, abrasive or turbidity-producing material, and to excessive organic matter.

In some cases, when it is not economically possible to prevent an objectionable degree of pollution, decisions are forced as to which is the more valuable to the public, the clear stream or the industry. There are a few instances where reluctant but considered decisions have been made to abandon particular streams to service in the disposal of wastes. Even in such cases, however, it is important that the river should not have a greater load of wastes than it can take care of within itself (Phelps, p. 187). The principles of stream classification are discussed by Hubbard and others in Second Southern Muncipal and Industrial Wastes Conference, 1953.

Polluting Substances

The organic substances involved in pollutions are chiefly carbohydrates, proteins, and fats. As far as the breakdown of carbohydrates is concerned, the story under favorable conditions is one of relatively simple oxidation. With enzymic assistance the sugars and starches are reduced with oxidation to carbon dioxide and water; too much leads to exhaustion of free oxygen, anaerobic decomposition, and liberation of methane. Among carbohydrates the celluloses of plant cell walls, a main ingredient of wood pulp and paper mill wastes, offer more difficulty. Paper itself digests readily, but some of the celluloses are attacked with greater difficulty and the oxidation is slow. The ligno-celluloses of wood are resistant to most agents of decomposition found in water: wood entirely submerged in water may indeed last almost indefinitely. In marshes and bogs it may be reduced only to peat or lignite, and perhaps, ultimately, with the intervention of other reactions, to coal (Phelps, p. 120). If the cellulose pulps, fibers, and sawdust decomposed rapidly, with heavy withdrawals of oxygen, they would put a load on the stream that would actually be less objectionable than they are. As it is, the fibers settle on the bottom or catch on the rocks to smother bottom-living organisms or prevent their lodgement and growth. Meantime, the material in suspension causes turbidity or may have lacerative effects on the gills of fishes, while its extractives and the processing chemicals discharged with it discolor the water.

In some cases undesirable flavor of the flesh of fish is attributed to the waste from pulp mills, either some part of the liquid effluent or decomposition products of the disintegrating waste pulp fiber.

Protein digestion in the stream proceeds by somewhat the same steps as in the human intestine, but the bacterial agents carry the breakdown further, reducing the amino acids and amine compounds to ammonia which other bacteria oxidize to nitrites and nitrates which are good food for plants. While ammonium compounds are useful to plants, ammonium carbonate is toxic to most aquatic animals. In unpolluted waters ammonia and ammonium compounds are generally present in amounts smaller than 0.1 p.p.m. The maximum consistent with favorable conditions is stated as 1.5 p.p.m. (Ellis, 1935, pp. 9, 10). Where conditions are anaerobic, the liberation from proteins of sulfur and iron compounds may have ulterior objectionable effects.

Fats, oils, and tar wastes, being slowly decomposable, may at first form films on the surface of the water, which interfere with the absorption of oxygen from the atmosphere. Oils form so thin a film that a very little of it may cover a great area of water. They may also make coatings on objects on the bottom in which some diatoms thrive, while insect larvae and other food of fishes are smothered.

Entirely apart from organic wastes as disturbing the oxygen balance, blanketing the bottom or sides, or lacerating the tissues of aquatic organisms, there may be actual toxins in some effluents —metallic poisons (lead, copper, zinc, mercury compounds, arsenic), dyes of some kinds, some cyanides, sulfur derivatives of proteins, or gases such as carbon monoxide, ethylene, or benzene. The amounts of some of these that cause injury may vary with the stream. Thus it is said that in one stream copper to the amount of one part to four million was found to be toxic to most aquatic animals, while in another, having different salts in solution, a concentration four times as high was tolerated by the same species (Ellis, 1935, p. 10). With some such poisons an addition in quite small amount that is not harmful at first may become so in time from the cumulative effect of continuing discharge. This is the case with poisons that neither decompose nor pass on.[4a]

Strangely enough, although nitrates, as nutriment for plants, are basic to organic production, there is such a thing as "nitrate poisoning."

In discussing natural, sewage, and industrial pollutions references have been made to the deleterious effects of turbidity and discoloration, which interfere with the penetration of sunlight and thus with the renewal of free oxygen by green plants. A condition of turbidity may be caused, not directly from introduced particulate matter in suspension, but sometimes indirectly as a consequence of reactions taking place in the water. Just as an example, it is said that ferrous iron, derived from copperas discharged from paint factories or steel works, tends to flocculate around living things in the waters, such as drifting diatoms. The overweighted little plants settle to the bottom; but, meantime, the water is beclouded by their fluffiness (Olsen and Brust, 1941).

Natural waters contain in small amounts and in diverse proportions salts of various kinds, chiefly chlorides, sulphates, carbonates and phosphates of sodium, potassium, calcium, and magnesium. The several concentrations change in small degree as varying additions are made by tributaries, as the materials are used by organisms, or as some are precipitated in relatively insoluble forms. Carbon dioxide, a continuous product of the res-

4a. Literature on the toxicity of industrial wastes has been digested in several publications, including a "Critical Review" by Doudoroff and Katz, 1953, and a "Selected Review," 1952, distributed by the United States Department of Health, Education and Welfare, from Washington or from its laboratories in Cincinnati, Ohio.

piration of both plants and animals—and a notable product of aerobic decomposition—is also the food of green plants while sunlight is available. With water it tends to form carbonic acid. It combines with carbonates to make the easily soluble bicarbonates; it can be withdrawn from the bicarbonate to leave the relatively insoluble carbonate. As in one way or another it goes into solution and out, the acidity or alkalinity of the water is changed. Consequently, for many reasons, hourly, seasonal, and irregular fluctuation in the balance between acids and alkalis is the normal condition. There are, however, changes due to wastes from chemical or other industrial plants, changes that are definitely inimical to aquatic life. Determinations of "specific [electrical] conductance" is one means of tracing pollution by ionizing substances.

The reaction of the water as to relative acidity and alkalinity is measured as *hydrogen-ion concentration,* expressed inversely as pH. (The lower the pH reading the higher is the hydrogen-ion concentration or the acidity.) In itself the hydrogen-ion concentration seems to have ordinarily no marked significance. It depends upon what causes the change from that normal to the stream. Even brook trout are said to show voluntary tolerance to waters giving pH readings of 4.6 to 9.6. Yet pH determinations are important in the study of pollution. As Ellis (1935) has said, "It has been found advisable to view with suspicion any stream waters having a hydrogen-ion concentration outside of the limits of pH 7.0 and pH 8.5, unless it could be definitely shown that the deviation was due to natural causes rather than pollution through human causes" (p. 5). Notable acidity might result from pollution of chemical works, fertilizer factories, bleaching plants, creameries, battery factories, unsealed coal mines, or other causes.

The Critical Problem of Oxygen Supply

In studies of pollution, apart from its relation to spread of disease, the effects on dissolved oxygen supply receive primary consideration. Free oxygen is constantly withdrawn from the water both by living animals and by agents of decomposition. The supply of this dissolved oxygen is replenished intermittently by plants in photosynthesis, while sunlight is available, and continuously (or as may be required) by absorption at the surface and the general mixing that goes with turbulence in the stream. The interchange between surface water and atmosphere is, of course, reciprocal. An excess in the water is given off to the atmosphere: it is a matter of relative partial pressures of the gases in the water and in the air above. The greater the volume of deeper water, and the less the mixing, the more important is the part played by photosynthesis and the greater is the need for penetration of sunlight, which depends upon clarity of water. This means that contaminations causing color or turbidity hamper oxygen renewal. In streams with significant current and without contamination, there is not likely ever to be too much animal life for the oxygen supply—as there is, not infrequently, in ponds.

So long as the processes of withdrawal and renewal are in equilibrium, the "oxygen balance" is maintained. Where, however, there is considerable addition of decomposable matter from sewage or industrial wastes, dissolved oxygen may be withdrawn more rapidly than it can be replaced. The oxygen balance is destroyed; the capacity of the stream to support desirable organisms is lessened. In extreme cases there is not even enough oxygen for respiration of bacteria of "direct oxidation" (the aerobes). Fortunately for the ultimate breaking down of excess organic matter, there are bacteria that can live and work even under these conditions. Such are the anaerobes, which are capable of finding the oxygen needed for respiration within the molecules of polluting materials, as from carbohydrates and nitrates.[5] These, then, operating on the intramolecular supply of oxygen, may reduce the decomposable materials to the forms of raw materials for plant life and to escaping gases—hydrogen, or, more commonly,

5. Actually there is no clear line between aerobes and anaerobes. The contrast is, rather, between aerobic decomposition (by "direct oxidation") using the free oxygen dissolved in the water and anaerobic decomposition ("intermolecular" or "intramolecular" oxidation) operating in the absence of free oxygen. Some bacteria may work either way, using free oxygen while it lasts and then finding the oxygen for their own oxidative processes by breaking into organic compounds containing fixed oxygen. They may get their oxygen from nitrites, nitrates, or carbohydrates, or even from carbon dioxide. The gases liberated may be carbon dioxide or hydrogen, but in nature the hydrogen combines with carbon to form "marsh gas" or methane (CH_4). More objectionable is the hydrogen sulfide made by sulfur bacteria (Beggiatoa) with the sulfur from protein decomposition.

hydrogen sulphide, or methane (CH_4). The food materials resulting from anaerobic breakdown can be used by plants after being carried by the stream to regions where free oxygen is again available. The anaerobes have worked inefficiently, considering the proportion of the wastes that have been made into bacterial bodies, compared with the amount of substance broken down for the raw materials they use in making bacterial substance and the oxygen they use for energy requirements. At least, however, they have been efficient in relieving the stream of a part of the burden of oxidation by use of free oxygen. With conditions as they are, the anaerobes and the noxious-gas producers are highly useful; deplorable, however, are the conditions that call for their service. If streets must be littered with refuse, buzzards may be useful. Cleaner streets without buzzards are preferable.

There can be all degrees of disturbance of the oxygen balance. The oxygen supply may be enough for the most exacting species of animals; it may be too little for any but the most tolerant animals and for some aerobic bacteria; it may be so greatly reduced that anaerobic decomposition is notably predominant with the accompaniment of bad odors. Seasons and weather also play some part. In warmer weather, decomposition is more active and withdrawal of oxygen more complete, the warm surface water absorbs less oxygen from the atmosphere and the oxygen requirements of fish are higher.[6] A load of pollution that was not bad in cool weather may with rising temperatures become notably objectionable. Flood stages flush out the stream, dilute the sewage, and give it wider distribution. Dry weather reduces the volume of flowing water and diminishes the area of absorbing water surface; thereby the total stock of oxygen is decreased, while the concentration of organic wastes in less water is increased. A stream that for a long time has safely carried a certain load of wastes may, during a period of heat, drought, and low stage, have its oxygen balance fall below the critical level. Sudden and catastrophic effects may follow. Once the bottom and swimming ani-

6. Generally fish require at least 5 p.p.m. although some will endure lower concentrations at least for a short time. Rounsefell and Everhart (1953) suggest that the figure 5 p.p.m. may be a little too high. The amount of free oxygen needed to prevent nuisances is said to be about 2 p.p.m. (Eldridge, 1942).

mals have begun to die, the oxygen requirements for decomposition rise in ascending scale. Under such conditions a section of river that had long served with seeming adequacy for the disposition of wastes may within a few days suffer the loss of every living animal that has found no means of escape.

In consideration of free oxygen in polluted streams, two important considerations are often overlooked. For one thing, we should be concerned, not about the concentration of dissolved oxygen that causes the death of fish, but rather about the concentration that first brings difficulty in respiration and that is physiologically upsetting. For instance, it seems generally accepted that a level of dissolved oxygen of about 5 p.p.m. is necessary to support most warm water fishes and other aquatic animals upon which fish depend (Ellis, 1935). The fairly tolerant carp has difficulties when the oxygen is reduced to 4.3 p.p.m.; yet it may live for a short time in water with less than 1 p.p.m. The conditions for carp should be regarded as critical when the level falls below 5 p.p.m. Brook trout live best in cool water with 10 or more p.p.m.—approximately the saturation level at low temperatures— and show discomfort at levels below 7 p.p.m. Any continuing reduction of oxygen supply in a trout stream should cause concern. As Japanese writers (Nitta et al., 1953) have recently pointed out, we should consider, not just the dose that is lethal to fish, but rather the dose that is "unpleasant" to them, as indicated by their presence in numbers smaller than is normal in the situation. An illuminating comparison is made with man, who lives in an atmosphere of approximately 21 per cent oxygen, collapses when the content is reduced to about 6 per cent, but begins to have respiratory difficulties at about 18 per cent (Ellis, 1935).[7] Thus, an oxygen level that does not cause the early death of fishes may yet be incompatible with an active life; it may also lead to emigration or it may weaken the resistance of the fish to disease or to enemies. Of course, acclimatization plays some part. Just as human beings become adjusted to life at high altitude where reduced oxygen pressure prevails, so fish also may become physiologically

7. Assuming a normal atmospheric pressure.

adjusted to water with a somewhat lower content of free oxygen than is normally required.

An important point, often overlooked, is that generally the critical condition with respect to oxygen balance is not in the free-flowing water where samples for testing are most easily taken; it is, rather, *close to the bottom* where the food of fishes is mainly found. A flat-bodied mayfly nymph, clinging to the surface of the stone or stick on the bottom, is actually dependent on the lowermost millimeter, or so, of water where current is negligible and the oxygen is renewed mainly by the photosynthetic activity of bottom algae or by the slow process of diffusion from above, rather than by the mechanical mixing of turbulence, more effective in the water above. The nymph may be on the underside of a rock, where current, dependent upon eddy movement, must be very slight. Another kind of mayfly nymph, or a midge larva, is buried in the bottom, having a respiratory apparatus designed to draw water from the bottom-most layer. Because much organic waste tends to lodge on the bottom, the competition for the limited oxygen supply is greatest there between bacterial decomposition and insect larva. Consequently, it may well be that, even in a stream where oxygen supply by ordinary tests seems adequate, there may yet be such a small supply of free oxygen in the critical bottom-most millimeters of depth as to preclude the life of insects upon which fish depend for food.

It should be kept in mind that in a channel of flowing water the molecular film of water adhering to the sides and bottom of the channel may be regarded as stationary. Immediately successive layers have extremely slow movement. Velocity, turbulence, and mixing increase away from bottom or sides of the channel; but so much of the sedentary life of the stream is in the relatively sluggish water.

Temporal or spatial variation in rate of flow are also significant at any level. Overloading of a stream with organic wastes is first evidenced in slack-water stretches (Phelps, p. 107).

A Biochemical Test

Since decomposition occurs in all streams even under natural conditions and since a degree of contamination is now nearly universal, there may be need with any stream to know its load of decomposable matter and its capacity to deal with that load, to oxidize it readily. Only extreme cases of pollution are detectable by the eye or nose. We want to know just how much oxidizable matter there is at any point and how much yet remains to be oxidized at other points farther along in the stream. A good yardstick is the *biological oxygen demand,* usually termed by abbreviation the B.O.D. "This has become the most useful single determination in the routine examination of sewages and the effluents of sewage-treatment plants, of industrial waste waters, and even of the streams themselves in the study of stream pollution." (Phelps, 1947, p. 62).

The B.O.D. measures, not the requirements of oxygen for complete chemical oxidation of all the organic matter present, but rather the oxygen needed for *bacterial decomposition* to a stage of stability with respect to bacterial action. No matter if a polluting substance could be burned, or otherwise oxidized, in the laboratory, yet, if in the river it is not oxidizable by organic agents of decomposition, it makes no noteworthy demand on the oxygen supply, the demand that is measured by the B.O.D. Familiar to most of us, probably, is the old log at the bottom of the swimming hole, upon which bathers of successive generations have stood. It is still oxidizable in that, if laid on the bank to dry out, it can be burned. In the water it is poor food for bacteria: its B.O.D. is almost nil, hence it has persisted.

In practice, records of B.O.D. are qualified as to time and temperature. Tests are commonly reported as the oxygen lost by a given sample during a five-day period at 20° C. (68°F.). If the five-day B.O.D. is below 3 p.p.m., only a low degree of pollution is indicated; if it is between 3 and 5 p.p.m., substantial pollution is shown; a loss of more than 5 p.p.m. (B.O.D. 5) indicates serious pollution. In natural waters, of course, temperature, as well as concentration, is variable and time is unlimited. Properly understood, however, the B.O.D. is a highly useful instrument of measurement.

In making the B.O.D. test duplicate samples of water are

taken. Usually these are diluted with distilled water (to insure an adequate supply of oxygen), and one is tested immediately for oxygen content. The other, in properly sealed containers, is kept in an incubator at 20° for a period of five days. Its oxygen content is then determined. By comparison with the first analysis the loss of oxygen is ascertained, with appropriate correction for the dilution factor; and this is the B.O.D. as qualified. (See: Phelps, 1947; *Standard Methods,* 1946; Gainey and Lord, 1952.)

The B.O.D. test, properly interpreted, is good for information on load of readily oxidizable matter and on capacity of the stream as a whole. Of course, it tells nothing about other harmful effects of pollution, and, ordinarily, little about conditions affecting the food of insects on the bottom.

The actual rate of decomposition of ordinary sewage is found to vary with the concentration, with temperature, and with time. Thus it is found that at 20° C. (68° F.) approximately 1/5 of the material left each day is oxidized in the next twenty-four-hour period. If, from the original 100 per cent, we subtract 1/5 each day, we would find about 33 per cent left after 5 days (80-64-51-41-33), or about 99 per cent consumed in 20 days.

In actual experience a lot of complicating factors enter. The rate of oxidation of one material may be dependent upon the presence of something else. Bacterial bodies require more than just sewage of some sort; they may need ammonia and certain mineral salts, which, in fact, are generally present. Again, there must be the right oxidizing agents for a particular substance. Cellulose, a chief component of the wood fibers of pulp and paper mill wastes, is acted upon chiefly by cellulose-fermenting organisms, which may or may not be originally present in adequate quantity. With time they develop in numbers, but the short period B.O.D. test can be misleading.

The Biological Test

Quite a different way of appraising pollutional conditions is found in what may be called the "Biological Assay." Because both animals and plants differ widely among themselves in tolerance of oxygen levels, the dominant flora and fauna of a region may give evidence of the degree of organic pollution. In the course of a stream below a source of heavy sewage pollution there is a fairly distinct succession of dominant species graduated in accord with tolerance of low oxygen levels. Emphasis must be placed upon the word "dominant." That an animal lives in polluted water does not mean that it cannot also live in clean water.` In the good water, however, it has innumerable competitors that are intolerant of pollution. The relatively few kinds of animals that are not adversely affected by conditions of heavy organic pollution can multiply almost without check where they enjoy conditions of exceptionally rich feeding along with freedom from so many kinds of competitors and predators. Populations of extreme density may result. The successful animals must, of course be those that feed upon bacteria, fungi, or the raw organic wastes, except for the few that feed upon the others. They must be "saprobic," meaning adapted to live under putrid conditions. They must be able to do with little dissolved oxygen or be extremely efficient in extracting what little there is; or else they must be able to reach the surface for oxygen from the atmosphere. Perhaps the true green alga (or protozoan, as you will), *Euglena viridis,* called a characteristic sewage flagellate, can keep close enough to the surface for absorption of sunlight and production of its own oxygen supply.

Quite a number of Protozoa, amoeboid, flagellate, and ciliate, swarm in highly polluted water.[8] The colonial kinds, such as Epistylis, form a fluffy growth on solid objects that, to the naked eye, looks like a fungus growth. There is even a rotifer, *R. actinurus,* that is reported to live in septic waters. Most rotifers require better conditions; but, on the whole, rotifers have some tolerance for pollution; few species are restricted to clean water.

There are true worms of the family Tubificidae (tube-makers —Tubifex, Limnodrilus) whose blood is red with haemoglobin to make them highly proficient in getting oxygen where it is least in quantity. The bodies of these "sludge worms" are greatly

8. Among such are Carchesium, Vorticella, Epistylis, Bodo, Oikomonas, and Paramoecium putrinum (Allee and Schmidt, 1951). Many others are listed by Whipple (1933).

extensible, capable of stretching to ten or more times their contracted length; doing so, they wiggle an inch or two of the hind
end of the body with a corkscrew movement that pulls water
downward and enables them to capture the traces of free oxygen
in water normally well above the bottom (Prosser, 1950, p. 262).
At the worst they can desert their tubes to rise to the surface for
atmospheric oxygen. In strongly oxygen-poor water there is often
such a density of population of these worms that, where the bottom in shallow water can be seen, it presents a solid color of dull
red. A very few other worms, and even some leeches, are ascribed
to septic water.

A little less tolerant are the so-called "blood worms," which
are not worms at all but the larvae of certain kinds of midges
(Chironomidae, or Tendipidae) that also have haemoglobin in
the blood. They, too, can leave their temporary tubes in the bot-

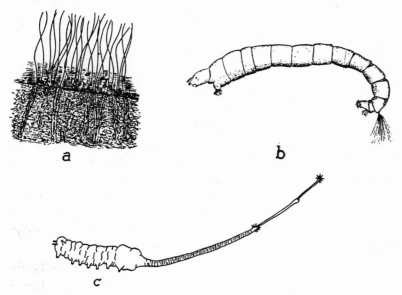

FIGURE 11. Some indicators of strong pollution.

(a) Tubifex worms, or "sludge worms," with heads down deep in tubes in the
sediment and hind ends waving in the water above (not enlarged). Dull red in
color. (b) Chironomid midge larva or "blood worms," greatly enlarged. They are
bright red in color, live in tubes in the bottom and perform much the same function
as the sludge worms. (c) "Rat-tailed maggot" of foul waters; this is the larva of the
"flower fly," Tubifera (Eristalis); the telescopic breathing tube is only partly extended
(after Pennak).

tom to rise to the surface. Shorter and stockier than the tubificid worms, they sometimes give a brilliant red color to large areas of bottom. That the apparent color of the bottom is due to living organisms (Tubifex or Chironomus—now called Tendipes) rather than to mineral substance, is evidenced when one gives a slight jar to the bottom by stamping on the shore and observes that the color vanishes; the color fades to view as the worms or the midge larvae retract into their tubes. Gradually the color reappears. Other chironomid larvae are bluish or clear and more demanding in respect to free oxygen. It has sometimes been said that, before analysis of oxygen content is made, one can tell if the supply is good or bad by collecting samples of the mud and observing if the midges that are found in numbers are red Chironomus or a clear species like a Tanytarsus.

There are other insect larvae with well protected bodies, which live independently of oxygen supply in the water. They secure atmospheric air either by making periodic trips to the surface or by extending a respiratory tube to the atmosphere to draw air down into the well-submerged bodies. A striking example is the "rat-tailed maggot," or larva of the drone fly.[9] Its long breathing tube, continuing the hind end of the body, is of two sections, one telescoping within the other; the tip, extended a considerable distance to the surface, is protected from water by a circlet of hairs. Rat-tailed maggots may live in conditions of extreme putridity. Strangely enough, the winged insect that emerges from the deepest filth hovers among the lovely flowers of the garden, where it is familiar as the "flower fly," "hover fly," or "drone fly." It owes the last mentioned common name to its resemblance to a bee without a sting. Less elegantly, it is also called "sweat fly" (Fig. 11).

Air-breathing aquatic beetles and some air-breathing beetle larvae seem fairly indifferent to pollution. Other beetle larvae require oxygen-rich water.

Among molluscs, only a species or two of peashells (Sphaeriidae—Musculium, Sphaerium) are highly pollution tolerant. Other clams of this family, as well as the freshwater mussel gen-

9. *Tubifera (Eristalis) tenax* of the family Syrphidae.

erally, require fairly clean water. In moderately polluted waters some of the air-breathing snails[10] are sometimes found in extraordinary numbers, blanketing entirely the exposed surfaces of rocks, as well as abounding under water. They find rich feeding in the water, but come to the surface for breathing and storage of air. Even the gill-breathers, Campeloma and Viviparus, are reported by Richardson (1928) and others to be somewhat pollution tolerant. The same sorts of snails may be found in clean water, but they would have there no such monopoly on food or freedom from predators. Speaking of pulmonate snails and air-breathing insects taken under pollutional conditions, Richardson (1928, p. 404) said: "The normal preference of all these surface and edge forms is for clean water, and they are wholly lacking in index value in connection with the study of stream pollution."

The fish fauna is often a good indication of degree of pollution. Trout are, of course, restricted to water of near saturation with oxygen at low temperatures. Bass, sunfish, and pike are somewhat less exacting. Some catfishes, sticklebacks, and particularly the carp, are more tolerant; the eel is said to have one of the lowest requirements of free oxygen. Fish in oxygen-poor waters may often be seen rising to the surface and gulping in air with the top water.

Organisms and "Zones"

Many investigators have attempted to identify successive zones in a polluted stream with respect to the conditions and to the types of life that are dominant in them. Because polluted streams differ so much among themselves, and because both the stream volume and the sewage discharge are so variable, there cannot be expected to be very close agreement among investigators as to the definition of the zones that each finds convenient. Doubtless for heavily polluted waters all would agree that there are the following zones:

Zone of Recent Pollution, where there is much organic matter, decomposition is only beginning and free oxygen is still plen-

10. Claassen (1927) mentions Physa, Planorbis, Lymnaea. Because they come to the surface for air, they are "well adapted to live in situations where the food supply is rich regardless of the oxygen content of the water."

tiful. As oxidation takes place actively, this zone shades gradually into a

Zone of Active Decomposition—a true Septic Zone if the pollution is heavy enough for virtual exhaustion of the free oxygen. At the worst places here not even sludge worms may live. As the decomposition proceeds to relieve the stream of its overload of decomposable matter, there comes the

Zone of Recovery, in which the stream begins really to cope with the task of renewal of oxygen faster than it is removed; conditions progressively improve until there is the

Zone of Cleaner Water (which may have less fertility than the preceding zone, and be less productive).[11]

It is the Zone of Recovery that offers most difficulty in subdivision. Some writers have divided the region between septic and clean water zones into so-called "polluted" and "contaminated" zones. Others whom, for convenience, we shall follow later, divide the zone of recovery into two subzones, using names indicative of milder pollution. Campbell (1939) gives just the four zones listed above. Brinley (1942), disregarding the Zone of Recent Pollution, divides the recovery region into a Zone of Intermediate Pollution and a Fertile Zone, which is followed by the Game Fish Zone and a Biologically Poor Zone or Poor Fish Zone. The last mentioned zone would seem to be one where, as in high trout streams, the fish depend to a great extent on insects falling in and hence readily "rise to the fly."

It is not the purpose here to contribute to classification of schemes of zoning but rather to give some indication of how the known tolerances of particular kinds of plants and animals may be used in appraisal of pollutional conditions. In the following pages the zone names used are (1) Zone of Recent Pollution (following Suter and Moore, 1922, and Campbell, 1939) (2) Septic

---

11. Butcher, as quoted by Macan and Worthington (1951, p. 227), recognized for the Trent River in England four zones: (1) "the zone of foul pollution," dominated by sewage fungi with some plants and a few tubificid worms; (2) "the zone of pollution," with sewage fungi and tubificids abundant, some red chironomids and many algae; (3) "the zone of mild pollution," with large numbers of isopods and all species of algae in abundance; and (4) "the repurified zone," with flora and fauna similar to that above the source of pollution, and with *less algae* than in the preceding (more fertile) zone.

Zone (3) Strongly Polluted Zone (4) Mildly Polluted Zone and (5) Zone of Cleaner Water. These names are not original and are not proposed for general acceptance.[12] They merely serve present convenience. We do not consider particularly the "Poor Fish Zone," simply because that does not seem a natural sequence in polluted streams. Once a stream has been heavily polluted by organic matter, has overcome the pollution and become cleaner water, it is not likely to be notably biologically poor—or to be "Katharobic," as Kolkwitz and Marsson pointed out (1909, p. 130, 131). Use of the term "contaminated" for "mildly polluted" is avoided, because "contaminated" may have a special significance in sanitation. Well-oxygenated "cleaner water" may yet be *contaminated* if it carries a few germs of disease.

1. Little need be said in this connection about the Zone of Recent (or Immediate) Pollution. The introduced organic wastes

12. Richardson, who made extensive studies of the Illinois River when extremely polluted by Chicago sewage, used terms of essentially similar meaning.

For greater detail in analysis and in ecological or chemical classification, the interested reader is referred to such standard works as the following:

Whipple, 1933. More than a thousand species of plants and animals are listed with indications of their assignments by various authors to the several ecological zones proposed by Kolkwitz and Marsson: *Polysaprobic, Alpha-Mesosaprobic, Beta-Mesosaprobic* and *Oligosaprobic* (roughly corresponding with zones 2, 3, 4, and 5 described in this chapter), and the *Katharobic* Zone for waters notably clear of decaying (saprobic) matter, such as a good trout stream. The Zone of Recent Pollution, No. 1 in our series, the zone where nutriment is plentiful and oxygen is as yet little depleted, seems not to be recognized in the classification used by Whipple or Liebmann; but it should not be overlooked.

Liebmann, 1951. He presents in considerable detail and with many illustrations the distribution of organisms according to the system of Kolkwitz and Marsson (1908, 1909), its revision by Kolkwitz (1933), and a further revision in the light of many later studies.

Schmassman, 1951.

Lackey, Chapter 7 in Phelps, 1944. (Septic Zone, Zone of Recovery, Clear-Water Zone.)

State Water Pollution Control Board (California), 1952. (Not ecological.)

Patrick's system (to be discussed below) based on number and kinds of organisms present, corresponds roughly with that of Kolkwitz and Marsson, based on sanitary wastes and oxygen depletion, but may have wider applicability. As she names zones and their equivalents, "roughly," they are: Very Polluted (Polysaprobic); Polluted (Alpha-mesosaprobic); Semihealthy (Beta-mesosaprobic); and Healthy (Oligosaprobic and Katharobic)—(Patrick, 1953).

Useful in biological assays are memoranda by Dr. H. W. Jackson, tabulating organisms by tolerance to organic pollution, and issued from the Robert A. Taft Sanitary Engineering Center, Cincinnati, Ohio, United States Department of Health, Education and Welfare.

are not oxidized forthwith. Green plants persist. There is both oxygen and organic wastes, food for scavenger animals, including some fishes. Fish may crowd about the outlet. Fish may be actually attracted, or else indifferent, to waters of extreme toxicity from gases such as ammonia, carbon monoxide, hydrogen sulfide, and benzene (Shelford, 1917; Wells, 1918). Bacteria and fungi are developing strong populations, as well as the sewage protozoa. Decomposition is predominantly aerobic.

2. Where pollution is heavy, the increasing activity in bacterial oxidation leads to great depletion, if not complete exhaustion, of the free oxygen. There is free liberation of carbon dioxide and hydrogen sulfide, with development of predominant anaerobic decomposition. This is the Septic Zone, which, of course, shades into the zones immediately preceding and following. Diatoms and the higher plants are wanting. Characteristic are bacteria, including iron and sulfur bacteria, and "sewage fungi," which are likely to be fungus-like bacteria. True fungi usually require some free oxygen. A few blue-green algae may thrive.[13]

The small animals that feed upon bacteria and fungi are in dense populations. There are Protozoa of many kinds, including the green *Euglena viridis*. One or two species of rotifer may thrive, as previously mentioned. The rat-tailed maggot, and possibly some aquatic beetles may nearly complete the fauna. If oxygen depletion is not complete, sludge worms abound; with extremely septic conditions even sludge worms may be wanting; red midge larvae, or blood worms, may be numerous; but these indicate the beginning of recovery (Campbell, 1939). The possible abundance of sludge worms in such a situation may be conceived from Richardson's report of as many as 350,000 per square yard, equivalent to 270 per square inch! (Richardson, 1928, p. 411). In another place (p. 445) he estimated that there were 1300 pounds of tubificid worms per acre.

13. Some examples of lower plant organisms, most of which may be called "sewage fungi":
Bacteria—Sphaerotilus
Iron bacteria—Cladothrix, Leptothrix
Sulfur bacteria—Beggiatoas, Thiothrix
True fungi—Leptomitus, Achlya, Mucor, Saprolegnia (the last mentioned commonly on organic bodies)
Blue-green algae—Aphanotheca, Arthrospira, Oscillatoria (several species), Spirulina.

Speaking of the sludge worm, Limnodrilus, Purdy, as quoted by Whipple (p. 345), said: "Apparently they *prefer* an environment of heavy pollution." He added:

The possible and probable importance of this worm in the economy of stream pollution is three-fold, first, its *ability* to work in a nauseous environment which seems to repel most other forms of animal life. They are pioneers, so to speak, in a virgin soil. Second, the *large amount* of work done by them as a result of their great numbers and their continuous activity; and, third, the *kind* of work done and the net results in terms of stream purification. The *subsurface* mud is elevated and dropped into loose piles of pellets on the surface.

A merit of the sludge worms and, to a lesser extent, of the blood worms, is that they turn the bottom sludge over. With heads deep down they take material that is out of reach of the surface bacteria, convert what they need into their own meat and pass the remainder up through their bodies to drop it on the surface.

3. The septic zone shades into a Polluted Zone. Active oxidation still prevails, and the free oxygen, at least at night, is below 5 p.p.m.; but green algae begin to appear and to play some part in oxygen renewal. Dense growths of bacteria persist; fungi assume more prominence. Among blue-green algae there may be additional species of Oscillatoria and some others. A few kinds of diatoms and certain green algae[14] are important. Higher plants are still wanting.

New kinds of Protozoa are encountered and many species of rotifers. A freshwater sponge or two, round worms (nemas), and even one or two species of moss animalcules (Bryozoa— *Plumatella fungosa*) may appear. Sludge worms may still be greatly abundant, but there can be several other kinds of aquatic oligochaetes (Aelosoma, Dero, Nais, and others) and a true earthworm, as well as one or two kinds of leeches. The red midge larvae, or blood worm, vie with the sludge worms for prominence, but there can be a few other midge larvae that are not red.

Among crustacea, about four species of Daphnia, two copepods, and an isopod are listed as definitely tolerant. Several addi-

14. Such as Chlorella, Prasiola, Ulothrix, the desmid, Cosmarium.

tional kinds of insect larvae begin to show: those of the soldier fly, sewage fly (or moth fly), alderfly, and black flies,[15] although most of the black flies are associated with clean water. At least one water strider (Velia), running on the surface, is reported as tolerant of strong pollution. So also, surprisingly, is one mayfly nymph (*Caenis fumosa*). Air-breathing snails of one or two species may be highly abundant. Whipple lists two of the gilled snails (*Campeloma subsolidum, Viviparus contectus*) as reported from the polluted zone. At least one of the peashells shows the capacity to live in water of very low oxygen content. In reference to a particular peashell, *Musculium-transversum,* Richardson (1921) commented: "It was something of a surprise to us to take the largest hauls of this stoutly tolerant little shell among the sludgeworms and larval midges of the filthy channel-bottom . . ." (p. 38). In another place (1928, p. 445) and at another time he found that "the Sphaeriidae averaged well over 5,000 pounds per acre"!

4. With increasing recovery a zone follows that is some-times described as Mildly Polluted, "sub-pollutional," or "semi-healthy." The breakdown of the polluting organic matter is ap-proaching its end. Dissolved oxygen is above 5 p.p.m. Bacteria and fungi are less prominent. There may be several kinds of blue-green algae that are not found above. Quite a diversity of diatoms and green algae find tolerable conditions of living. A substantial number of higher plants can maintain themselves where the water is sufficiently sluggish in movement—hornwort, pond weeds, water lilies, and some floating duck weeds.

Conditions now meet the tolerance of many more kinds of Protozoa and of freshwater sponges. This does not mean more in-dividuals, but, rather, a greater diversity of species, with smaller numbers of each kind. At least one species of Hydra is re-ported. Flatworms, less tolerant than roundworms, now come into the picture. Nearly all kinds of rotifers, as well as gastro-

15. Soldier flies—Stratiomyidae
     Moth flies—Psychodidae
     Sewage fly—Psychoda alternata
     Alderfly—Sialis
     Black flies—Simulium

trichs, thrive in the mild pollution. More species of annulate worms and leeches are to be encountered. The tolerance requirements are met for more species of snails, peashells, and even for an occasional freshwater mussel, and for more kinds of Cladocera (Daphnias, etc.), copepods, many ostracods, and some amphipods. Mites of several species may occur. Among insects, we find some of the less tolerant larvae of midges and mosquitoes and larvae of some kinds of dragonflies and caddisflies. Among the first of the caddises to appear are some Hydropsyches, which spread their fine-meshed nets against the current to filter out particulate organic matter carried by the stream. A limited variety of fishes may live well in this zone—eels, carp, some suckers, sticklebacks, creek chubs, and top minnows. Some of these work well up into the zone of blood worms to feed upon them.

Gradually the stream's self-purification with respect to the added matter is concluded. We have again "clean" water, or as some would prefer, Cleaner Water, generally well oxygenated and clear. This does not mean that there is no decomposition. That occurs in all streams. Even in the clearest mountain brooks, some anaerobic decomposition may occur, as in muck under stones. What is meant is that, in the water generally, even close to the bottom, the balance between removal and renewal of free oxygen is now maintained. Free *oxygen* is present, even at night, in quantity greater than 5 p.p.m.—or, maybe, up to saturation. Bacteria and fungi continue present, as almost everywhere, but not in notable quantities. In the flora, green plants predominate, both algae and such higher plants as are adapted to the natural conditions of the stream.

Most of the animals of the preceding zone continue in some numbers in the clean water. There are few species of Protozoa that are listed as *restricted* to clean water.[16] The ciliates decrease with increasing purity of water. The favored territory of rotifers is passed: seemingly only a few species are restricted to clear water, although many live there in some numbers. This is good water for flatworms, hydra, water mites, and crustacea of any

16. Particularly some Difflugia, Chlamydomonas, Gonyaulax, Mallomonas, two or more species of Mastigamoeba, and a number of Euglenas, but not many ciliates.

kind adapted to the temperature, current and other physical and chemical conditions of the stream. The development of a diversified fauna of mollusks is indicative of the restoration of natural conditions, particularly the presence of many gilled snails, freshwater mussels, and certain kinds of peashells. A typical upland brook insect fauna of stonefly and mayfly nymphs and larvae of caddis and dobsonfly (the "crawler" or "helgrammite"—Corydalus) proves good water. The presence of the game fishes native to the stream is also evidence of the virtual disappearance of pollutional effects. Most restricted by oxygen requirements are the trouts, requiring virtual saturation at low temperature.[17] Indeed, a fifth category in ecological classification is set up to cover "the flora and fauna of springs and pure mountain streams," the favored home of trout.

It must always be recognized that decomposition, oxygen withdrawal and renewal, and the whole complex of changes involved in "self-purification" are continuing processes; and that they are subject to unremitting fluctuations. Lines of demarcation can be drawn only to suit the convenience of investigators in interpreting and describing the uninterrupted chain of physical and biological events. Spatial demarcation of the assumed transition bands will shift greatly with changing conditions of sewage discharge, river flow, and temperature. Temperature changes permit the shift of motile animals between zones of different concentrations of sewage. The less the flow of water the greater is the concentration of sewage coming in at a fairly uniform rate. The warmer the water the less is the amount of oxygen it will absorb and the more active are the bacteria in using what little there is. Thus, fish and some snails that are excluded from one area in summer may move into it in winter, even into one where tubificid worms are dominant in the sludge (Allee and Schmidt, 1951, p. 664).

Furthermore it is to be remembered always that just *one day* of lethal conditions is enough to denude the stream of intolerant

17. But, seemingly, even brook trout may endure a low concentration of oxygen for brief periods. Jahoda (1947) reports fingerling trout surviving in a cold New Hampshire stream where the concentration of oxygen went as low as 1.1 p.p.m.

organisms; and, also, that it is the summer low-water period that is critical for fish populations (Brinley, 1942).

The biological assay has, then, no claim to exactness in interpretation. Neither, however, have the other tests, such as, oxygen analysis, B.O.D., or chemical tests. The values of all are affected by the same basic variants. Because of these and other circumstances, there cannot yet be agreement as to delimitation of zones or as to identification of some organisms with respect to degrees of tolerance of pollution. Much more research is needed.

The use of floral and faunal criteria generally requires considerable experience on the part of the surveyor who will rely only occasionally upon the index value of particular species, and, more often, upon the associations of species and relative abundances above, within, and safely below the stretches suspected of being seriously polluted. Actually, there are now few organisms that, as individual species, can be relied upon for index value; but there are some. When Tubifex worms are found in conspicuously dense populations, the meaning is unmistakable. Again, if sulphur bacteria are abundant, sulphur contamination is unquestionable, whether or not sulphur in the water is revealed by chemical analysis of samples of water taken on particular days or at particular hours.

At one time the swift and rocky Tuckaseegee River in North Carolina, where heavily polluted and conspicuously discolored with straw board wastes, showed continuous oxygen saturation; fish, confined in cages sunk in the water, lived well for weeks. At the same time free fish avoided the whole zone of strong pollution, which was marked also by almost complete absence of the insect larvae that existed in normally rich populations immediately above the mouth of the polluting effluent. Presumably, something was wrong in the bottom-most layers of water, which was not revealed at all by the oxygen tests. The absence of food, and perhaps other effects of the pollution could have caused exclusion of fish. At any rate, the biological picture, told an unimpeachable story; surely, it pointed to the need for more refined techniques in physical tests.

We have dealt principally with effects of organic pollution

on the supply of free oxygen and the evidences afforded by the distribution of living things. We have considered also to some extent toxins, turbidity, discoloration, laceration, and smothering. Oxygen depletion is usually the chief concern with sewage pollution. A secondary effect of reduced oxygen supply and the resultant bacterial and fungus domination must not be overlooked: a slight injury to a fish, one that might easily heal in good water, may in fungus-laden water lead to infections that sap the vitality of the fish or cause its death. Again, whether or not the pollution actually kills the directly or indirectly useful animal, it is harmful if it sets up conditions that are unfavorable or "unpleasant" to them. Furthermore, it is important to keep in mind that conditions readily endurable by the adult may yet hamper the production of useful populations if injurious to eggs and larvae.

In any discussion of particular species associated with different degrees of pollution, we encounter some inconsistences and a want of certainty as to what the presence in moderate abundance of this or that organism means. Perhaps the most satisfactory criterion of pollution is that proposed by Dr. Ruth Patrick (1949), who demonstrated that the number of species of plants and animals, together with numbers of individuals, can be used as basis for judging degree of pollution. Great diversity of species, with only moderate populations of each kind, is the expectancy under healthful conditions. The presence of only a few species with great populations of each implies that many species have found, or would find, the existing conditions intolerable and have been eliminated. Only the more tolerant species remain; these, so largely freed from competition, may multiply to form populations that are quite beyond the ordinary. A notable effect of the pollution is, then: "a reduction in number of species and a great abundance of those remaining."

Because most studies of pollution have been concerned mainly with sewage, the various designations of zones have been based too generally upon the amount of bacterial activity and its effects. Often, however, the pollution is from toxic wastes that induce or permit little activity of bacteria. With her basic premises of number and kinds of species and numbers of individuals, Pat-

Courtesy of North Carolina Wildlife Resources Commission

Pl. 12. *Emergence of mayflies, Lookout Shoals Lake, August, 1948.*

PHOTO BY HEMMER
Courtesy of North Carolina News Bureau,
Department of Conservation and Development

Pl. 13. *Chain of reservoirs on Catawba River near Charlotte, North Carolina.*

Pl. 14. *The farm pond affords water for irrigation or for fire protection.*

PHOTO BY JOHN W. BUSCH
Courtesy of Soil Conservation Service, Raleigh, N. C.

rick's system of zones or grades of pollution (1949, 1953) is applicable where either toxic wastes or sewage gives occasion for concern.

It is too early yet to talk about the effects of atomic energy developments on pollution with radioactive substances or on effective changes of temperature of streams into which are discharged the great volumes of cooling water. Rivers below atomic energy plants receive substantial amounts of radioactive elements, some of which are found in far greater concentrations in the bodies of aquatic animals and plants than in the water itself. Algae can build up phosphorus concentrations to 500,000 times the level in the surrounding water. But as yet "no harmful effect of the Hanford operations has been found in Columbia River algae —or in plankton and fish" (U.S. Atomic Energy Commission, 1952, p. 89). The Atomic Energy Commission is, of course, actively sponsoring research on the biological effects of radioactive materials and on the safe disposal of radioactive wastes.

Discussion of the possible effects of sewage pollution in the spread of human disease must be left to professionals in public health and medicine. The interested reader will find a wealth of information in various publications of the Public Health Service, Division of Water Pollution Control (Federal Security Agency), such as: "Clean Water Is Everybody's Business" (1950), "Suggested State Water Pollution Control Act and Explanatory Statement" (1950), and "Water Pollution Control. Excerpts from *A Water Policy for the American People*" (Report of the President's Water Resources Policy Commission, 1950). The first paper mentioned quotes Surgeon General Leonard A. Scheele as follows: "A sanitary environment is the foundation of a sound health structure. A major task in creating a sanitary environment—and one of its most neglected aspects—is the development of a Nationwide program to reduce the pollution of our water resources."

III

STILL WATER

CHAPTER 11

The Lake or Pond as a Place of Life

The Lake and the Outside World

LET US LOOK AT A CONFINED BODY OF WATER AS A PARTIALLY closed system with a complete community of plants and animals. Each organism is continually taking into its body water and other substances and giving off water and wastes. Actually animals give out more water than they take in, and plants less than they absorb, because animals liberate water from compounds that were manufactured by plants from water and carbon dioxide. The plants take in both free oxygen and free carbon dioxide held "in solution" in the water but give off an excess of oxygen. The animals use oxygen and give out carbon dioxide. This is all as in a "balanced aquarium." The plants grow and multiply, using the energy of sunlight, water, and inorganic materials in solution. Eventually a great part of them are consumed by animals, either in the living state or after death and comminution or partial decomposition. If completely decomposed, the bodies are reduced to inorganic forms available only for the sustenance of other plants. The animals feed upon plants and upon other animals as they grow and multiply. The wastes, including the dead bodies of both plants and animals, serve to fertilize the water and the bottom and to promote the growth of more plants and more animals. So it goes on in cycle after cycle.

Within this more or less self-contained world, there is, then:

production (by green plants) of organic materials, including carbohydrates, proteins, fats, and vitamins; *conversion* of the materials formed by plants into tissues of animals of successively higher levels or of larger sizes; and there is *reduction,* or destruction, either partial or complete, of animal and plant matter by bacteria of decomposition, which is only conversion downward to or toward the bottom of the food chain. Decomposition is merely a reversed form of production and conversion; although we may disparage it as "rotting," it is just as necessary to the organic cycle as is any other link in the whole chain of transformations that forms the great organic cycle, without which all life would come to an early end. The decomposition of organic matter should really have in our minds all the beauty of the sprouting seed and the growing plant. But it does not!

We recognize immediately that even the most self-contained body of water is not absolutely a closed system. The cycle of life in a lake is not entirely inside; more or less regularly there is interchanging between the pond and the land immediately surrounding it; there is always some income and some outgo. According to the conditions of location, the changing conditions of weather and the variations of level of the water table in the soil, there may be more or less regular inflow and outflow of surface water, and more or less subsurface seepage into the lake or leakage outward into the surrounding land. Chemicals leached from the soil are brought in or chemicals in solution in the water may be carried out into the soil or lost in deeply buried sediments. Organic debris from the surface of the land is washed or blown in; grasshoppers, bees, flies, and other insects leap or fall into the water. Midges, mayflies, dragonflies, and other insects, hatched and grown in the water, reach maturity and emerge, some to fly away and deposit eggs in other waters, some to become prey to birds of land and air, and some to fall back and become the food of fishes. Fish-hawks, herons, and mammals of aquatic habit remove from the lake some portion of the community of fish, shellfish, insects, and other small animals or plants, while a part of the wastes of these intruders is left in the lake to resume eventually the form of aquatic plants and animals.

Under some conditions of location and surroundings, these interchanges may effect serious fluctuations in the total content of the life of the lake; if inflow and outflow are inconsiderable, the exchanges are relatively minor. We might be inclined to say, that, practically speaking, a typical pond is virtually a self-contained system, a *closed biotope,* a world within itself, a microcosm. This general idea was well developed many years ago by Professor S. A. Forbes in a paper entitled "The Lake as a Microcosm," a paper in which the conception of the interrelation of organisms within the lake was so clearly and vividly formulated that it was thought worthy of re-publication fifty years after the day of its original appearance—and while the distinguished author was still active in research and in writing!

Nevertheless, in spite of all that can be said for the pond or lake as a self-contained system, we must recognize that there are yet other and more significant interchanges between the water and the outside world. Some interchanges are so absolutely essential that, if the body of water could be effectively isolated from the outside world, nearly all life within would cease within a period of days.

We may think, first, of the interchange of gases between the water and the atmosphere at its surface. The atmosphere serves as a sort of reserve tank into which the water can give up at any time its excess of oxygen, carbon dioxide, or other gases and from which it can draw in times of deficiency. Water itself passes into the atmosphere by evaporation and the water vapor carries with it great stores of excess heat. There are yet more vital links with the world beyond the boundaries of the pond.

The plants and animals within the pond are not inanimate and passive. They are alive and active, always doing something or always in process of change. They are constantly "expending energy," as we say, meaning that they are converting energy from one form into another. In the animal world at least, there is continual "degradation of energy"; this takes place even when there is no obvious movement, because conversion of energy is incidental to every protoplasmic activity. The source of the energy is the sun, and its seizure and storage is effected only by the green plants through photosynthesis in the presence of sunlight. Consequently, for the existence of life, there must stream into the pond or lake a periodic flow of energy from the sun in the form of light, or the short-wave radiation that is utilized, a very small part, in photosynthesis or, in far greater amount, absorbed as heat.

All the processes of life require certain conditions of temperature for their effectuation and the major source of heat for all ponds and lakes is the sun. It might be said that the organic productivity of a body of water and the activity of the plants and animals within it is limited by the amount of heat derived from solar radiation—that the "heat budget" of the lake is a significant factor with respect to its general biological complexion. The heat of the water, attributable directly or indirectly to the sun, is derived partly by conduction from the atmosphere, the surrounding soil and the bottom of the pond in shallow water, but also, in no little part, by direct absorption of radiation coming through the atmosphere to the surface of the water. On the other hand, as we have already noted, there is great loss of heat, as well as of water, through evaporation at the surface—and this, through its part in temperature control, is important to life in the lake.

This is not all the lake owes to the outside world. Heat absorbed at the surface, as well as the oxygen absorbed from the atmosphere or produced in the upper waters, must yet be distributed. Only the shallow shore waters and the superficial layers of the central part of a deep lake could be habitable if heat and oxygen were not conveyed in some way from the upper to the deeper waters. It is only at particular times of the year that convection currents can serve for distribution of heat. Aid from without is needed and this is afforded by the winds that cause surface water to drift from one side of the lake to another and much of it to return at lower levels. Thus the winds promote a more or less general circulation. To a very great extent the life of the deeper water is dependent upon wind-distributed heat and wind-distributed oxygen (Chapter 3). The energy effecting this distribution is a contribution from without the pond.

Finally, as we survey the significant links between the pond and the outside world, we must not overlook the emergent vegetation, the cattails and rushes, as well as the floating-leaved plants, water lilies and some pondweeds, which are in position to absorb carbon dioxide directly from the air and to use it in the manufacture of carbohydrates and other materials for roots, stems and leaves, which, as we shall see, will become eventually the food of aquatic animals.

In at least one respect, then, the lake is anything but a "microcosm"; that is as regards the one-way flow of energy from the sun. Shut out the sun and the greater part of the life in the lake must soon cease and the community be reduced to one of saprophytic organisms such as bacteria and water molds; in time these also would pass away because of exhaustion of their food supply. Accordingly, the concept of the lake as a microcosm must be qualified in a most positive way as regards the relation of the lake to the sun and the atmosphere. Otherwise the concept is more or less valid, with small allowances for various sorts of income and outgo. Since the minor interchanges with surrounding land and atmosphere and the indispensable flow of energy from the sun continue virtually the same from year to year, at least during a short span of years, a particular lake may present a more or less similar aspect at the same season from year to year. In the long run, of course, taking decades or centuries into consideration, lakes undergo notable changes even to the point of complete disappearance. They are marked by youth, maturity, old age, and death.

However constant from year to year may be the general conditions of life within a lake yet, from season to season within the same year, the budgets of income and outgo in temperate climates undergo marked changes. The flow of energy from sun to lake is not the same in January, or even in September or April, as in July. The basic crops of minute green drifting organisms respond to the variations in available radiation and to other conditions within the pond, with marked seasonal fluctuations, which are not always closely predictable. In shallow marginal waters during the warm season a luxuriant growth of submerged and emergent plants absorbs sunlight and builds great quantities of proteins, carbohydrates, and other organic materials; in the fall many of the plants die and in time become divided into minute particles to form an important basic food supply for the lower forms of animal life, and, in decomposition, to draw heavily upon a limited oxygen supply.

Types of Habitats

As we look in a broad way at the habitats or homes of the animals and plants, we find that the lake divides itself into three fairly distinct general regions: first, there is the region that extends out from the margins to the farthermost depth to which sunlight penetrates in amount sufficient to permit the growth of green plants at the bottom; this marginal region we call the *littoral* zone. Farther out and surrounded by the littoral is the central area of always dark bottom which we call *profundal*. In large deep lakes, the profundal occupies the greater part of the total area of bottom. Obviously, the condition of life on littoral and profundal bottoms, respectively, are quite different. Finally, there is the wide expanse and depth of open water above the bottom, the *limnetic* region. This is the greater part of the volume of the lake; it is the home of the swimmers and of the drifters, which, as we shall see, may constitute the bulk of the life of a lake or pond. It must be understood that a small pond may have no real profundal region, but is largely, if not exclusively, littoral or littoral and limnetic.

If we now look particularly at the littoral region, or its shoremost part, and survey the periphery of the lake, we find it is not of the same character all around. Here the shore is marshy, with thickets of cattails growing far out into the water; there it is barren of plants where beaches of sand or gravel are exposed to the free action of waves. The wave-washed sections may be sloping and beach-like or more or less precipitous. Such different portions of the shoreward part of the littoral offer quite distinct habitats for plants and animals.

If we follow the littoral out from the shore, we may encounter a series of more or less clearly differentiated zones. Starting from a marginal zone of plants such as cattails and bulrushes, which has been called the *zone of emergent vegetation,* we pass into a region where the water is too deep for emergent plants to make a start, or to thrive if started, but where there may be abundant floating leaves of some pond weeds (Potamogeton) or water-lilies (Nymphaea), the *zone of floating-leaf plants*. Proceeding outward, we pass over deeper bottom from which not even the larger plants may reach the surface, but where, if the water is clear, there may yet be a more or less dense growth of completely underwater plants such as hornwort (Ceratophyllum), water-weed (Elodea), or stonewort (Chara) occupying the *zone of submersed vegetation*. Often such plants form on the bottom a dense green carpet such as suggests the designation of "submerged meadow." The three vegetational zones described are not always sharply defined, and sometimes are not separately recognizable at all; but they are likely to be observable in large ponds of any locality, whether or not they appear in regular succession or with sharp definition. Each forms a special sort of habitat for animals and microscopic plants; each has its own complex community of organic life and plays a distinctive part in the whole complex system of life in the lake.

Beyond the true littoral zone there is often recognized an intermediate zone of bottom not receiving enough light to support a significant amount of vegetation and yet near enough to the submerged meadows to be tolerably well-oxygenated at all times and to be supplied with enough food to form a suitable home for mussels, snails, clams, and some bottom-loving crustacea. This is the so-called shell-fish zone; the shellfish may, of course, extend outward through all the zones of vegetation.

Beyond the intermediate zone and more remote from the cover of green plants, lies the profundal region proper where green plants cannot grow and where all animal life is dependent for food entirely upon bacteria and other saprophytic plants (the only possible indigenous vegetation) and upon food materials that fall from above or drift outward from shoreward zones. Furthermore, in the absence of green plants, animals of the profundal region must depend for oxygen upon supplies imported from without and so brought in by the very slow process of diffusion, which is virtually insignificant, by convection currents, which in temperate regions are generally effective to the depths only in spring and fall, and by the circulation of the water resulting from winds. Here, of course, we must expect to find a peculiar sort of community composed of bacteria, fungi, and animals that use oxygen most economically and that act as scavengers or feed upon scavengers. In the last analysis, the food supply is organic debris of one sort or another produced elsewhere and overflowing into a region in which no original production can occur. Some of the most interesting of all studies of the lake have to do with the habits and the conditions of living of such animals and with the actual origins of their supplies of food and oxygen; similar studies for the animals of the more shoreward zones are of vital interest, but in the case of profundal animals we have to do with a more complex chain of events.

In some lakes the profundal region becomes one of true stagnation, at least in late summer or in late winter. In the pond, let us remind ourselves, a true profundal region usually does not exist. Something like it may occur where the accumulation of silt is such as to make the bottom too soft, and perhaps too acid, to serve as a basis for most of the rooted aquatics and where decomposition proceeds so continuously and rapidly as to produce a condition approaching stagnation, or virtual deprivation of dissolved oxygen.

Types of Communities Within the Lake

We are here concerned, not with individual organisms or with species, but rather with community life in water. Ordinarily we think of a community as made up of a group of people of both sexes, of all ages and diverse occupations. The biological "community" is much more than that. Even such a home community as is found in any village comprises a good deal more than mere human beings. Our local human community could have no existence without cows, sheep, bees, grasshoppers, corn, wheat, cotton, trees, grass, and hundreds of other living things. An explorer from Mars who might undertake a study of human life on the Earth could not possibly understand the daily doings and the conditions of life of human beings without taking into consideration our relations to these other organisms and to our physical environment with its mountains and plains, its oceans, rivers and lakes, its soils and mineral resources, and its atmosphere.

Within the lake are millions of community members. These represent not one or a dozen, but literally hundreds of different kinds, none of which is inherently more important than another. To particular persons, of course, the different animals or plants have special interests. The angler is concerned with fish, the malacologist with snails and mussels, the algologist with microscopic plants called algae, the protozoologist with microscopic animals. Yet, since none of these kinds of organisms could thrive without many of the others, one can be rated above another in actual importance only by application of an arbitrary and fallacious scale of values. Are the fish or the protozoa or the algae of most importance in the pond? Are the grasses and grains or the cattle more essential to the development of a successful dairy farm? The lake, then, houses a closely woven community of plants and animals of many kinds. The broad community of the lake as a whole subdivides itself naturally into subordinate communities and these into still smaller ones. There are communities of the littoral region; there are those of profundal bottoms and there are limnetic communities.

Within a community, each kind of organism has a part to play; it has a function that generally no other kind can exactly fulfill. Without certain microscopic plants adrift in the water and adjusted to the prevailing physical and chemical conditions, there could be in the open waters no formations of original organic matter, necessary to the growth and multiplication of all the animals including fish. Without a whole series of smaller and larger animals, the substances produced by the plants could never be gotten into forms available for the larger carnivorous fish. Without scavengers, small insect larvae and other detritus-consumers, the materials in the dead bodies of plants and animals would be a long time in coming back into general circulation. Without bacteria and fungi of decomposition, wastes might pile on wastes until the whole world was dead.

The community is then a more or less closely integrated complex of agents with specialized "occupations." Each kind of plant and each kind of animal has its function, or niche, so to speak. The "niche" of an animal or plant may be defined in terms of its contribution to the welfare of the whole community of which it forms a part. It expresses what the species does, if we keep in mind that an organism *does* something, not only when it eats, grows and multiplies, but also when it is eaten. When an animal eats it engages in making its own body and in preparing to produce others like it; when it is eaten it helps to make the body of another animal or to enable the predator to reproduce its kind. Its services of both orders—to its kind, to its enemies and competitors, and to the community as a whole—is what it *does* in the biological sense. That is its "niche."

In this chapter we can take only a very general view of the whole community life and we may get only rough pictures of some of the very important niches occupied by plants and animals of different kinds. First, however, we should distinguish several different modes of living in water. Some aquatic organisms, like all terrestrial organisms, are dependent upon a substratum. In land areas even the birds, although they fly from tree to tree or from Arctic ice to Patagonian plain, must more or less frequently come to rest on a solid substratum. All birds have legs to stand on—and need them. In lakes or oceans all those plants and animals that depend upon some solid footing constitute the *benthos* (from a Greek word meaning bottom). Benthonts may walk or creep on the bottom, on plant stems, logs or rocks, like snails, crayfishes, and insect larvae. They may burrow into the bottom, like worms and mussels. They may be more or less permanently attached and lead sedentary lives, like rooted plants, sponges, some rotifers and protozoa, or, in the sea, like oysters and barnacles. It is one of the notable differences between life in freshwater and life in the sea that the latter has such dense populations of permanently fixed animals—the barnacles, oysters, corals, sea-anemones, sea-lilies (crinoids), ascidians, and many other kinds. Virtually no animal in freshwater is entirely unable to change its position. In another place (Coker, 1949) we have proposed the subdivision of the benthos into *edreobenthos* (stationary benthos), including these that, once they have settled on something solid, remain seated until death, and *herpetobenthos* (crawling benthos), comprising those that creep or are otherwise more or less peripatetic. In freshwater we have virtually no concern with edreobenthonic animals. The freshwater sponges and the moss animalcules (Bryozoa) may seem to be permanently settled with their fixed colonial masses. In a way they are, but even these have a way of setting free parts of their bodies, the gemmules of sponges and the statoblasts of Bryozoa, to continue the life of the mass in other locations.

It is because of the higher density of water, as compared with the atmosphere, that there can be ways of living in water that do not involve putting the feet or the body on the ground. Fish have generally the same two pairs of limbs as do terrestrial animals, but they are not designed for supporting the body. Buoyancy makes the chief difference. The bodies of fish are a little heavier than the volume of water displaced, but only a minimum of effort is required to keep above the bottom; for many species swimbladders contribute to the needed buoyancy. We have in the water, then, two modes of life that are not possible out of water—swimming and merely drifting.

In the *nekton* are included the swimmers, or those animals, chiefly fishes in temperate fresh waters, that are independent of the bottom and have capacities for locomotion which enable them to move against ordinary currents and so to go from place to place at will. Drifters, to be considered in the next paragraph, are independent of the bottom but not of water movements. Bottom-living animals may have strong powers of locomotion and may travel widely, but yet are at rest only on the bottom. It is sometimes difficult to draw a sharp line between the different groups, but the distinctions have real biological significance and practical value. It may be noted, however, that a few fish are benthonic, practically speaking; in the sea, flounders, for example, are highly specialized for life on or in the bottom. It will be remembered, too, that many fishes make their nests on the bottom or attach their eggs to stones or plants. In the sea, on the other hand, most but not all fishes form eggs that float or drift.

Sea turtles are nektonic in habit, although laying eggs upon land. Freshwater turtles and snakes are benthonic or nektonic at different times: they crawl, they swim actively, they float, they come ashore, especially for nesting. In fresh-water, generally,[1] the only true nektonts are the fishes; all other animals, unless it be some freshwater shrimp, are either dependent upon the bottom or are drifters. In the sea, on the other hand, there are such other active swimmers as the squid, some of the larger shrimp, and whales.

It is perhaps difficult for one to believe at first hearing that by far the greater number of the animals on earth neither walk nor creep nor swim with much effectiveness but are, rather, in the class of drifters, or organisms with feeble or no powers of locomotion. Such plants and animals, mostly small in size, constitute the *plankton* and include the greater number of animals in seas, lakes, and ponds. Since the seas cover three-fourths of the earth's surface and plankton animals are found at nearly all depths, and often in immense numbers, it is obvious that animals of the plankton must vastly exceed in numbers of individuals all other animals on earth. We are here concerned, however, with only a small part of the plankton world—that which occurs in lakes and ponds and in the larger rivers.

It may be remarked in passing that the plankton of fresh waters, although often exceedingly abundant, is very different in composition from that of the oceans. The difference is related to the physical differences in density of the medium. In the sea, most of the invertebrate animals have eggs and larvae that drift with the currents until they have reached the stage for transformation into the sessile or creeping forms of the adult. In the lighter fresh waters with less buoyancy effect, such free swimming larvae of the walkers and creepers are generally wanting and, consequently, the diversity of kinds of drifters is much less. In the sea we must distinguish the *meroplankton,* or temporary plankton, often predominant, from the *holoplankton,* which comprises organisms that live their whole lives a plankters. The

1. The exceptions afforded in some waters by some shrimp, fairy shrimp, and medusae will not ordinarily concern the manager of a pond or lake.

PHOTO BY E. W. JENKINS
Courtesy of United States Soil Conservation Service, Fort Worth, Texas

Pl. 15. *Fenced farm pond in pasture with sodded dam, Wetunka, Oklahoma.*

Pl. 16. *String of bass, bream, and catfish, none over eighteen months old, caught from 48-acre fish pond on Dunman Ranch, Coleman, Texas.*

PHOTO BY E. W. JENKINS
Courtesy of United States Soil Conservation Service, Fort Worth, Texas

Pl. 17. *Contentment and hope.*

distinction is of less interest in consideration of fresh waters, since the animal drifters are almost exclusively holoplankters.

It is true that most animals of the plankton have powers of locomotion that may be relatively strong for their sizes; yet the bodies are small and their movements have little effect against currents. Where the waters are fairly still the locomotion may be that of merely "milling around," or whole populations may migrate slowly from one area to another or rise and sink with changes in intensity of light.

Although the larger plankters were probably first discovered by direct observation with the unaided eye and others later by microscopic examination of water dipped from the sea, the real introduction of the plankton to the scientific world came with the use of the straining net, which seems to have begun less than a century and a half ago. As nets of finer and finer mesh were employed, a vast world of microorganisms was brought to view. Generations later, a new method of concentration of minute organisms was devised when, by the use of the centrifuge, there were separated from the water still more minute organisms, chiefly plants, that would pass through the meshes of the finest nets that could be made. Now it has been found that in many, and probably in most waters, the centrifuge-plankton, or *nanno-plankton* (meaning dwarf plankton, which includes bacteria and the smallest algae and protozoans) greatly exceeds in volume the net-plankton.

Drifting organisms occur in all parts of any lake, but densities and compositions of populations may be different in different area and at different depths. Notable changes occur from day to day, according to conditions of sunlight, temperature, precipitation, dissolved nutrients, and the effects of competition and predation. The proper study of plankton is a science in itself. Certain broad statements, made somewhat dogmatically, will be generally applicable: greatest concentrations are neither very close to the surface nor near the bottom; more drifters are at upper levels during the night than in the middle of the day; total quantity of plankton present shows little direct relation to depth and volume of water, but is more commonly proportioned to surface area and to fertility of water; density of population shows notable variation with season—there may be two to five times as much life adrift at times of spring and fall maxima as when summer or winter minima prevail.

In fresh waters there is yet another way of living than walking on the bottom, swimming or merely drifting. The surface tension of water is such that animals of small size may be supported by the surface film if the surface is not too ruffled or broken by waves. Particularly in small ponds and pools, there are bugs (the water striders) and spiders that run on the surface, whirligig beetles that swim while resting on the film, besides spring-tails (Podura), leaf-hoppers, and some spiders. There are flatworms, small snails, and "waterfleas" (the cladoceran, Scapholeberis) that creep or glide on the underside of the film; there are mosquito-wigglers and hydras that suspend themselves from it; there are floating egg-rafts of mosquitos, to say nothing of several kinds of microscopic plants and bacteria and flowering plants (the duck weeds) that may live at the surface. Animals and plants that live in connection with the surface film constitute the *neuston* (from a Greek word meaning boat), and this naturally divides itself into *supraneuston* and *infraneuston,* according as the organisms live above or beneath the film. The neuston does not properly include those Cladocera that in very still water become accidentally caught against the film and are unable by their own efforts to free themselves from it until aided by waves or ripples.

In large lakes another distinctive habitat is on wave-washed shores, where the water is commonly in motion; here there may be communities and kinds of living things closely comparable to those of streams.

Some Interrelations

Let us look now at some of the interrelations. The chain of food relations starts, of course, with the inorganic substances necessary for life. We may assume the presence of such matter in the water; but the exact needs vary with the species, partly as to variety of minerals, and more particularly as to the relative amounts of the various materials required. This brings us to another distinctive feature of fresh waters as contrasted with the seas. Everywhere in all the oceans, all basic chemical substances necessary for life are present, although quantities and proportions vary from place to place. The fresh waters on the other hand show almost infinite diversity in chemical constitution. No two lakes or rivers are precisely alike in their content of chemicals in solution. One may, then, assume a considerable degree of diversity in the suitability of different waters for particular species. For the larger animals, the fishes, for example, the differences are not as noticeable as might be expected—perhaps there are more differences than have been noted. Certainly for the lower organisms the community patterns are extremely diverse, but this is true even for ponds that seem to have identical water supplies; so that it is not safe to assume that the differences are generally explainable on the basis of the chemistry of the water. Thus a half-dozen ponds supplied with water pumped from the Mississippi River at one place had as many distinct patterns of plankton communities. The interrelations of organisms and the relation of organisms to environment are extremely complex; and the conditions of competition, survival, and fecundity for any microorganism are not easily subject to appraisal.

Plants are the *producers,* with the formation of sugar from carbon dioxide and water utilizing the energy of sunlight (photosynthesis); for sugar is basic in the formation of all living substance. The producing plants in lakes may be placed in two categories: the vegetation of the littoral zone, previously described, such as cattails, pondweeds, hornwort, limeworts, filamentous algae, and many others; and the small green or yellow plants of the plankton especially those of smallest size that have been designated as centrifuge plankton or nannoplankton, the dwarf drifters. The last mentioned plants we never see except with the microscope (while algae of the net plankton are often visible to the naked eye), but they occur throughout the lake at all depths to which sufficient sunlight penetrates and often their total bulk amounts to many times that of the drifters taken in the net. They are of vast importance as first links in the living food chain that leads to the production of the largest animals of the lake. The delicate but larger filamentous algae are also part of that first link; they are known to be eaten by protozoa and by larger animals including insect larvae.

What of the larger rooted plants? It has been a matter of comment that some, if not most, of these are not to any great extent directly foraged upon by insects and the larger animals. This is in striking contrast to what occurs on land, where the green grass is being continually cropped by cattle and the leaves of trees are nipped by caterpillars or are browsed upon by other vegetarians. Apparently the larger aquatic plants become forage principally after death, destruction, and comminution to form the great deposits of *detritus* that are a source of food for so many insect larvae, worms, other small animals, and even of some fish. (See next chapter.)

There have indeed been three distinct views as to the basic food supplies of animals. Some have thought that the finely divided remains of the plants of marginal zones deserved first place. Certainly it is important. One writer once assumed that even the larger animals were nourished chiefly by absorption of organic material held in solution in the water. Generally, there is in lakes a great store of this, much more organic material being present in solution than is contained in all the living organisms at one time. The evidence, however, is strongly against the idea of its direct absorption to any great extent by the higher animals. It seems unquestionable that, in waters of great size, the basic food supplies of animals are found in the small plant bodies of the nannoplankton and in detritus. The vegetarian animals of the waters are generally small and they find their food chiefly in most finely divided form.

Since original production can occur only around the margins and in the upper illuminated waters of the great central area of the lake, the animals of the dark profundal region are entirely dependent for food upon what rains down from above or drifts or wanders in from the sides. For lakes of broad extent and great depth the dark region may be under the greater portion of the whole surface. Other things equal, the less dense the popula-

tion of drifters, or the poorer the lake, the greater is the depth
to which light penetrates and, accordingly, the lower is the upper
limit of the region of continued darkness. This is because the
solid bodies of even the smallest plant and animals intercept,
absorb, and scatter the rays of light. Everyone knows that the
sunlight on land is dimmer when the atmosphere is filled with
particles of dust or with minute particles of water. In lake or
ocean the plankton, as well as any particulate inorganic matter,
serves as a "dust cloud" to shade the deeper water.

We are led again to the very necessary distinction between
plankton-rich and plankton-poor lakes, essentially the *oligotrophic* and *eutrophic* lakes, a distinction that is not always simply
made. Richness or poorness of the upper waters greatly affects
the conditions of life in the deeper waters, and somewhat para-
doxically. A lake in a region of barren sand or of archaic rocks
approaches more nearly a "closed" organic system, with relatively
little coming in and little going out. Its total productivity may be
comparatively low, but its deep waters offer a better home than
does that of a plankton-rich lake for a limited population of fishes
and other animals, such as the crustacean *Mysis relicta* that want
cold water in summer, along with a good supply of oxygen. In
a plankton-rich lake, too much organic waste falls to the bottom
to decompose, to deplete the supply of oxygen, to cause "stagnation."

It is appropriate here to mention certain groups of animals
which play a not insignificant part in prolonging the lives of
eutrophic lakes by retarding the process of filling from the bottom. These animals have been termed "sediment-transporters."
The best examples are the slender red tubifex worms and the red
midge larvae, sometimes called bloodworms, two kinds of animals that are not at all related systematically or alike structurally,
but which perform a like function in the lake. Living in tubes,
in the soft bottom, they feed with heads deep down in the silt and
tails waving out in the water. Devouring the buried organic matter, a half inch or two inches beneath the surface of the bottom,
they convert this waste into their own succulent bodies or into
feces which are discharged upon the surface of the bottom to

become available to the aerobic bacteria if only a very little oxygen is present. These animals, which feature in the chapter on "Stream Pollution," live under conditions where the oxygen supply must be very low; in order to make the best possible use of the limited stock of free oxygen, they have in their blood the same pigment that plays such an important part in our own respiration—haemoglobin. Our haemoglobin is in the red corpuscles that float in the nearly colorless liquid of our blood. Both the worms and the insect larvae have the haemoglobin dissolved in the plasma of the blood.

Where one finds abundant red tubifex or red chironomid, it is reasonable to infer that the condition of deposition of organic matter is extreme and the supply of oxygen very limited. Worm and insect are not to be blamed for the condition, but are rather to be regarded as nature's beneficent agents in the alleviation of a condition prejudicial to the duration of life of the lake itself. The indication is that, at least at times, organic sediment has settled on the bottom more rapidly than decomposition could proceed at the surface of contact between bottom and water. That which is buried too deeply becomes unavailable to bacteria that require oxygen for their function in reduction. Without the overturning by worms and larvae it would be subject only to anaerobic decomposition or none. The bed of sediment would thicken more rapidly and the lake would have a shorter life.

CHAPTER 12

Life in the Lake: Plants and Lower Animals

PLANT LIFE

N O NATURAL WATER EXPOSED TO THE ATMOSPHERE IS FREE OF life of some sort.[1] Spores drift in the air and are brought down by gravity or by rains. Rain water is only relatively "pure." It washes from the atmosphere nitrogenous or other nutritive materials: an epiphyte, such as the Spanish moss of southern coastal regions, must live almost exclusively on what it can derive from the atmosphere. Wells and even some underground waters are inhabited by copepods and other organisms.

Waters vary greatly in their content of organisms, both quantitatively and qualitatively. Furthermore, each pond or lake shows marked seasonal changes in the relative numbers of the different species of plants and smaller animals. No two ponds have identical floras and faunas. Even artificial ponds, made as nearly alike as is possible and supplied from the same source of water, may each have at a particular time its characteristic predominating species. We do not know just why this is so. The differences among ponds as to what grows in them is much more pronounced and puzzling than the differences among particular areas of ground. When water areas are compared with land areas, the former seem to have more complex adjustments be-

1. What is said in this chapter and the one following about life in a lake will also apply with minor qualifications to the plants and animals of the more sluggish portions of the larger rivers.

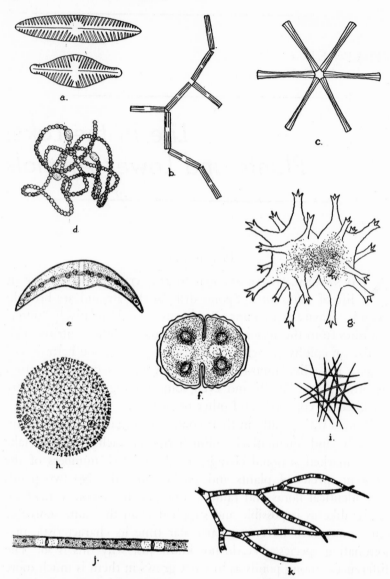

FIGURE 12. Some algae, aquatic plants of microscopic size (all enlarged, (a) through (j) greatly enlarged).

(a) (b) (c) Diatoms: *Navicula, Tabellaria* (in zigzag chain), *Asterionella;* yellow-ish in color, lengths usually measurable in thousandths or ten-thousandths of an inch. (d) A bluegreen alga, *Anabaena.* (e) (f) (g) Desmids, *Closterium, Cosmarium, Micrasterias,* bright green in color, generally less than 1/100″ in length. (h) *Volvox,* thousands of individual zooids, formed in a hollow sphere, with a few reproductive tween the ecological factors, chemical, physical, and biological, which determine the patterns of populations. We do know that chemicals in solution, nitrates, phosphates, and calcium particularly, have something to do, not only with general productivity, but also with the qualitative composition of populations. Prescott (1939, p. 69) has pointed out that, where there is an abundance of carbon dioxide, along with low oxygen content, the algal flora will consist predominantly of filamentous and branched plants. Unicellular and simple colony formers are typical of well aerated water low in carbon dioxide. Certain blue-green algae go with higher nitrogen content.

Certainly, competition among organisms plays a great part in the differentiation of ponds with reference to the communities within them. If a particular plant or animal gets in before or in greater numbers than a competitor, or has other advantages, it has a head start. A long and complex chain of events thus begun may affect the future of the life of the pond for an indeterminate period.

It would be impossible, to say nothing of how tiring it might be in the attempt, to list here every kind of plant and animal that may be a member of the community of life in a lake or pond; nor have we yet more than a fraction of the information needed to appraise accurately the niches of even the leading species. There will be attempted, in this and the following chapter, only a cursory review of some of the categories of organisms, at all levels, that may play significant parts in the general life of the community as a whole. In assuming even such a task one incurs the risk of saying much that is trite to the biologist and of seeming to deal with generalities in a superficial way. Nevertheless, if we are to consider the life in the lake as a complexly interrelated community of all sorts of organisms, it may be neces-

---

bodies within. (i) *Ankistrodesmus,* a minute drifting plant. The slender and very minute bodies (3/1000″ in length or less) of this alga are not easily seen with low power of microscope; but they occur widely in still and running waters, and sometimes in such abundance as to make the water look distinctly green. (j) Small part of unbranched filamentous alga, *Mougeotia.* This or others may cause dense blankets on the surface of a pool. (k) Branching filamentous alga, *Chaetophora,* portion of a colony. (Drawings by W. K. Hubbell. (a) (b) (c) (d) (h) (i) from G. M. Smith; (e) (f) (j) (k) from Ward and Whipple; (g) from Wolle.)

sary to take just such a brief birds-eye view of the whole pattern.

The reader desiring more detail about plants in water may be referred to many special botanical works and particularly to the books on aquatic plants by Fassett and Muenscher and to special articles by Moore, Prescott, Wilson and others. The animals of ponds and streams are treated systematically in many books, of which we need mention here only those by Needham, Morgan, Ward and Whipple, and Pennak.

The plant life of the lake divides itself ecologically, as well as morphologically, into the *rooted aquatics* and the microscopic drifting *algae* and *bacteria* of the plankton and the bottom. A few of the higher plants do not actually root in the soil but may conveniently be considered along with those that are rooted.

Rooted Aquatics

Rooted plants (Figs. 13, 14) play most important parts in the general economy of the water, as is discussed more fully in the chapter on "The Fish Pond." They serve as bases of attachment for sessile protozoa and algae and thus increase the capacity of the lake to support such organisms. They afford shelter or protection for insects, crustacea, and fish, enabling many of these to maintain reserves for breeding, instead of being completely wiped out by depredations of enemies in the open water. So far as they have green parts below the surface, they contribute to the oxygenation of the water and take part in the consumption of carbon dioxide. Those parts that are above water may utilize the carbon dioxide of the atmosphere to make food matter that, sooner or later, becomes part of the food supply of aquatic animals. It has been commented that rooted plants in the living state are not eaten to any great extent by the animals in the water. In the fall, however, many die and decay, to contribute indirectly to the stock of organic detritus which is so important an element of subsistence for insects and even for some fish.

It may be remarked that most aquatic seed plants, although derived originally from land plants, have special adaptations for life in water, including a delicate epidermis, limp stems, and leaves that offer maximum exposure to the eater, being thin and ribbon-like or finely divided. Nutriment can be absorbed from the surrounding water, but nearly all have roots for anchorage and for reception of nutrients from the soil of the bottom. Some have both submerged and exposed leaves, which may be quite different in form. Generally the stems that bear flowers reach to or above the surface of the water. Many have within their stems extensive gas-filled spaces that extend into the roots. Some insect larvae that live under water drill into these air spaces to find oxygen without having to come to the surface.

Undoubtedly, the rooted plants are at times a real nuisance to fishermen and boatmen. Against this must be balanced their useful functions in giving *support, shelter, food,* and *oxygen.* Through their root system they draw from the soil nutriment that by their subsequent decomposition is made available to the minute drifting organisms which could not obtain it directly from the soil.

Familiar representatives of *emergent* plants are some of the grasses, cattails (Typha), bulrushes (Scirpus), grass-like rushes (Juncus), pickerel weed (Pontederia), and wild rice (Zizania). Other plants have expanded floating leaves, which often give altogether too much shade for the algae that might be preferred in the water beneath. Conspicuous among *floating-leaved* plants are water lilies (*Nymphaea*), water shields (Brasenia), water hyacinth (Eichornia), and duck weeds (Lemna and Wolffia). Here also may be mentioned a floating liverwort, *Ricciocarpus natans,* and the water-velvet, *Azolla caroliniana,* which may be red in color.

The *submersed* plants generally have small, narrow or finely divided leaves, with, often, emergent leaves of different form and emergent stems for flowers. In this group we note particularly: milfoil or parrot's feather (Myriophyllum), with many emergent leaves; water-crowfoot (Ranunculus); bladderwort (Utricularia); fanwort (Cabomba); water-weed (Anacharis—also called Elodea or Philotria); and such ribbon-leaved plants as wild celery or tape grass (Vallisneria), bur weed (Sparganium), and some of the arrowheads (Sagittaria). Very common are the pondweeds (Potamogeton) in great variety of forms and habit, some of

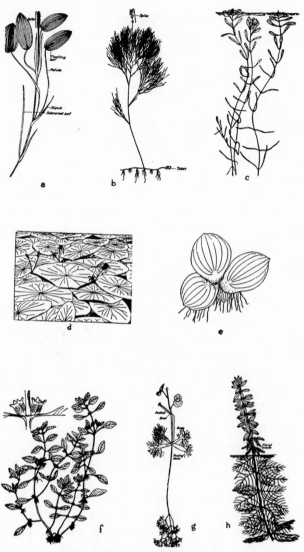

FIGURE 13. Some aquatic plants.

(a) Floating-leaf pondweed, *Potamogeton natans.* (b) Sago pondweed, *P. pecti-natus.* (c) Water starwort, *Callitriche palustris.* (d) Water-shield, *Brasenia Schreberi.* (e) Duckweed, *Lemna polyrhiza.* (f) False loosestrife, *Ludwigia palustris,* var. *americana.* (g) Bladderwort, *Utricularia inflata,* var. *minor,* bladder traps for insects seen in pendant part. (h) Water milfoil, *Myriophyllum heterophyllum.* (All figures from Fassett.)

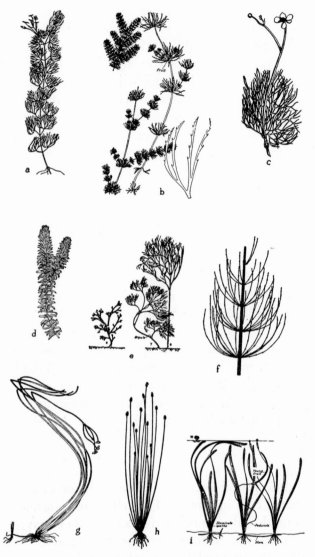

FIGURE 14. More aquatic plants.

(a) Fanwort, *Cabomba caroliniana.* (b) Hornwort, *Ceratophyllum demersum.* (c) Water crowfoot (buttercup), *Ranunculus flabellaris.* (d) Waterweed, *Anacharis canadensis* (Elodea, Philotria). (e) River weed, *Podostemum ceratophyllum.* (f) Horsetail, *Equisetum fluviatale.* (g) Arrowhead, duck potato, *Sagittaria subulata,* var. *gracillima* (from J. G. Smith in Fassett). (h) Spike rush, *Eleocharis obtusa.* (i) Tape grass, wild celery, *Vallisneria americana.* ((b) through (i) from Fassett; (a) from Muenscher.)

which may also have conspicuous floating leaves. The coontail or hornwort (Ceratophyllum) belongs here ecologically, although actually it is not rooted but lives free from the bottom. Here, too, one might consider the stonewort algae, Chara and Nitella: although not botanically differentiated into stem, root, and leaf, they are attached to the bottom where they may form extended masses of dense vegetation with much the same ecological functions as the rooted higher aquatics.

There are also many plants that grow in the wet soils around the pond and may extend out into the water. Notably of this habit are the cattails, previously mentioned, spike-rushes (Eleocharis), smart weeds (Polygonum), false loosestrife (Ludwigia), horse tails (Equisetum), and water purselane (Didiplis). Tops among such amphibious plants are the southern bald cypress and the sour gums (Nyssa), which may not, however, have germinated in the water.

We pass by the overhanging shrubs and trees, such as willows and alders, which drop leaves and insects into the water and may greatly affect the conditions of life in the ponds.

The reader desiring more specific information concerning aquatic plants may be referred particularly to standard reference works, previously cited, in which hundreds of species in more than seventy families are described and illustrated. Means of eliminating undesirable plants are discussed by Martin (1953) and others.

Algae

The algae proper occur as isolated cells or as relatively undifferentiated cells in groups. The cells may be arranged end to end in fine threads, simple or branching; they may remain attached side by side to form more or less expanded thin plates; or they may be grouped in tiny spheres, solid or hollow. They may be free in the water or they may be attached to the bottom or to plants. They may surround themselves with a jelly-like substance. Some have the capacity to move slowly through the water, with or without thread-like organs of locomotion called flagella. It is indeed impossible to draw any sharp line between the flagellate algae and the flagellate protozoa, so that many species are somewhat indifferently classified as plants or as animals.

The single-celled algae are particularly favored by the fish farmer because they usually have no objectionable qualities in respect to fish culture, are capable of high rates of reproduction, and play most important parts in oxygenation of the water and as food for the small microorganisms which in turn become the food of small fishes. Their minute bodies exposed to the water on all sides enable them to avail themselves quickly of dissolved nutrients and thus to initiate the rapid conversion of chemical fertilizers into forms suitable for the sustenance of desirable fishes. The farmer is pleased when, soon after the application of fertilizer to the pond, the water seems to acquire a greenish or yellowish color attributable to a dense population of minute algae; invisible as individuals, they are made apparent to the eye by the tint they impart to the whole mass of water. In city water supplies, however, excessive numbers of small algae are often objectionable.

The brownish diatoms (Figs. 12a, b, c) with microscopic bodies encased in delicately sculptured cells of glassy material are most widely distributed and are nearly everywhere abundant. Frequently, dense populations of diatoms give a brownish or yellowish-brown color to the bottom or other surfaces on which they live. They are also found adrift in the open water. Diatoms are of first importance as "producers" and as basic food supply for small animals, and perhaps even for such larger animals as feed upon mud. There are hundreds of species, boat-shaped, disk-formed, spindle-like, sometimes attached to each other in linear or zigzag chains or forming rings or star-shaped clusters. Apparently they differ markedly in food value; some kinds may be definitely objectionable to small animals.

Bright green desmids (Figs. 12e, f, g), living singly or attached end to end in filaments, and of microscopic dimensions, are also important members of the communities, especially in soft water and where there is a moderate amount of decaying vegetation.

The minute flagellates are of the highest significance, because they may live freely anywhere in the open water and show such quick responses to changes in conditions of chemical fertility. A pond may appear green or may have a green or red scum caused by millions of the tiny flagellate Euglena. Other ponds may be so full of the relatively large spherical colonies of Volvox, up to one millimeter in diameter, as to have a noticeably greenish cast. Again, the pond may have a distinctly yellowish or brownish tint, appearing to be muddy when there have not been rains to make it so; examination of a sample of the water under the microscope may then reveal millions of the bushy, branching colonies of the minute flagellate known as Dinobryon (Fig. 2a), or it may show dense populations of the cluster colonies of Synura (Fig. 2b). The "yellows," including those just mentioned, as well as Uroglena and others, seem to be equally important with the greens, Eudorina, Pandorina, Volvox (Fig. 12h) and others, as fixers of the energy of sunlight in converting inorganic into organic matter. In reasonable numbers they are highly important; when present in excessive numbers, they may still be serviceable to the community in the lake but objectionable to man by imparting the tastes and odors so well and so unfavorably known to officials of municipal water systems. The relations of algae to turbidity, tastes, and odors are discussed in another chapter.

Filamentous green algae, such as Spirogyra, Mougeotia, and others, often form the troublesome blankets on the surface of ponds. When present in too great abundance, they are indeed nuisances, but in moderate quantity they are excellent oxygenators and some of them, Mougeotia for example, may be a choice food for certain insect larvae that in turn are the favored food of some young fish.

Blue-green algae, such as Anabaena (Fig. 12d) and Aphanizomenon, may be present in such great numbers as to discolor the water or to form windrows along the shore. Some can function as nitrogen-fixers. They occur as slender filaments or as balls enclosed in a gelatinous matrix or as solid or hollow spheres. Their presence in quantity is sometimes, but not invariably, suggestive of pollution.

Bacteria and Fungi

Bacteria seem to be present in considerable numbers in almost all lake water, as well as in the bottom sediment. Their part in the lake is little understood, except insofar as they afford food for protozoa and for those higher animals that have a filtering apparatus fine enough to take them, and except also as some are essential agents of decomposition, aerobic or anaerobic, and as others are nitrogen-fixers. No natural water is free or should be free of bacteria, some kinds of which are essential to the completion of the organic cycle within the lake. On the whole, they are just as useful as the somewhat larger organisms that feed upon them. Some are minute enough to pass through the filtering organs of the larger filter-feeders. The public health officials distrust water with a high content of bacteria of the E. *coli* type, not because all of these are agents of human disease, but rather because they suggest at least the possibility of organic pollution that might carry the organisms of disease. The intestinal bacteria of a spring could, however, have come from a salamander as readily as from man or beast.

Fungi, as vegetative colonies or as spores, are nearly everywhere in water, growing weakly or luxuriantly, or awaiting favorable conditions for growth. As agents of decomposition, along with bacteria, they serve a useful purpose in the breakdown of dead organisms, either fully into the inorganic constituents, or partially into minute fragments suitable as food for the many small scavenger animals: but fungi generally require some free oxygen. Fungi are said to be more effective than bacteria in breaking down the hard parts of the bodies of insects and crustacea and the lignin of wood. The yeasts and other fungi concerned in alcoholic fermentations are of little concern here. The sewage fungi, Leptomitus, Achlya, and Saprolegnia, are mentioned particularly in the chapter on "Stream Pollution," but other fungi play lesser parts in all waters with decomposable organic matter. The common "water molds" of the genus Saprolegnia are only too familiar to fish culturists and others concerned with life in water, as they make fuzzy coatings on dead flies or on fish eggs. They even attack live fish, taking advantage of some small abrasion, and often causing death of the victim.

So the variety of plants in the lake is great, and their functions are manifold. No one particular kind of plant is necessary, but the presence of plant life of some sort is essential to the healthy life of a lake or pond. Since so many of the plants are of microscopic size, the quantity of the vegetation in any water is not measurable to the eye.

ANIMAL LIFE

The Principal Phyla

A dozen or more great divisions or phyla of the animal kingdom are represented in freshwater, while some others are restricted to salt and brackish waters.

Let us recall the principal phyla.

1. The *Protozoa* include small animals with bodies of a single cell or of several to many undifferentiated body cells. Some assume fixed positions; some creep or "flow" over solid surfaces; others swim freely in the water by the use of one or a few little whip-like paddles, or of numerous active hair-like cilia; usually they follow, in swimming, a spiral path.

2. The *Porifera,* or sponges, are stationary as adults. They have bodies of many cells of several different types and a supporting skeleton. Thousands of species occur in the sea, but only one family in fresh water.

3. The *Coelenterata* comprise hydroids, jelly fishes, and corals, with or without supporting skeleton and with bodies made of just two layers of cells separated by a greater or lesser mass of non-living substance. A single body cavity serves both as digestive chamber and as passageway for distribution of nutritive material. Nearly all coelentrates are marine; one small group, including Hydra and a few little jelly-fishes, is most important in fresh water.

The *Ctenophora,* or sea-walnuts, which superficially resemble jelly fishes, are all marine and need not concern us here.

4. The *Platyhelminthes,* or flatworms, have no body cavity other than the alimentary passage, which has only one opening to the exterior and may even be absent in parasitic species. Flatworms occur under all sorts of conditions—in fresh water, in the sea, and even on land. Some kinds are parasitic in nearly every type of animal. A single genus of ribbon worms (nemerteans),

now placed in a distinct phylum, occurs along the shores of lakes and streams.

5. The *Nemathelminthes,* or roundworms, with no true body cavity, have an alimentary tract that opens at both ends. They are among the most abundant of all kinds of animals, both as free-living "nemas" and as parasites in almost every kind of animal. Free-living nemas are exceedingly numerous in soils, in fresh water, and in the sea.

The acanthocephs, or hooked worms (*not,* here, the southern "hookworm"), are all parasitic. The tardigrades, or "bear animalcules," minute and secretive, are common in many waters, but usually escape the attention of any but the specialist. These groups will not be discussed further.

Animals of the next three phyla are more complex in structure but are not generally familiar to one who does specialize in zoology or in the study of waters.

6. The wheel animalcules or rotifers, *Rotatoria,* as will be seen, are largely restricted to fresh water, where they are abundant in a diversity of habitats.

7. Moss animalcules, or *Bryozoa,* also called Polyzoa, are mainly marine, but a few kinds are found in fresh waters. Occasionally they are conspicuous in lakes and sometimes they are nuisances.

We are not concerned with the shelled brachiopods, so significant in geology and still occurring in the sea, nor with the arrow-worms (Chaetognaths), most interesting to the oceanographer but absent from fresh waters.

8. The minute *Gastrotricha* are confined to fresh waters. With bodies of microscopic size, up to 1/2 mm. (1/50 inch) in length, they are often mistaken for protozoans. They occur widely, and sometimes abundantly, among debris and algae upon which they feed. Too little is known about the gastrotrichs to justify special attention in this chapter.

The remaining phyla embrace animals that are more generally familiar to the casual observer.

9. The segmented worms, *Annelida,* comprise earth worms, sandworms, naids, and leeches. Most worms are marine, but

freshwater representatives of the phylum will merit special consideration in later paragraphs.

10. The jointed-legged arthropods include the most abundant and most significant macroscopic animals of fresh water. The crustacea (notably copepods, ostracods, and cladocera) are usually dominant, at least among drifters, in lakes and ponds; insects are predominant in streams but also have high significance in still waters.

11. The mollusca, as snails, mussels, and clams, play a great part in the economy of both running and still waters. Other divisions of the mollusks are strictly marine.

Echinoderms, embracing star fishes, sea urchins, and crinoids, or sea lilies, all live in saline water.

12. The *Chordata* naturally divide themselves into *protocordates,* precursors of the vertebrates, and the vertebrates proper. Since all of the former are marine, we are relieved from further consideration of them. The higher chordates, or vertebrates, are of much concern to us, as including the lampreys or cyclostomes, the elasmobranchs (sharks and their relatives, only a few of which occur in certain fresh waters), the true fishes, the amphibians (frogs and salamanders), the reptiles (turtles, snakes, and crocodiles), the birds, and the mammals.

Single-celled Animals

The phylum *Protozoa* comprises animals of microscopic size, with bodies composed of a single cell or of a limited number of undifferentiated cells—that is to say, cells united to form multicellular bodies but all alike, except, sometimes, for specialized reproductive cells. Five subdivisions are recognized. (a) The *Flagellates* (Figs. 2, 15b) have one or a few semi-permanent whiplash-like appendages known as flagella; there is no clear line of separation between flagellate algae and flagellate protozoa. (b) The *Rhizopoda* (root-like feet) of which amoebas are best-known examples (Figs. 15a, d), have no paddles or whips for locomotion; the substance of the body merely flows out in the direction of movement, forming temporary "feet" or *pseudopodia* (meaning "false feet"). (c) The *Ciliata* (Fig. 15c) have innumerable small

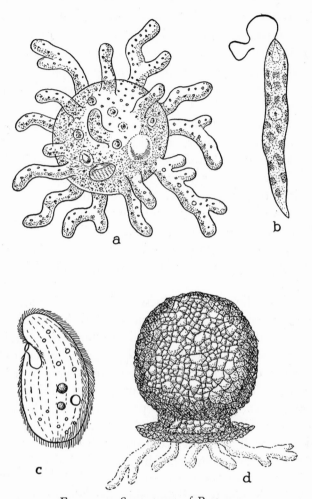

FIGURE 15. Some types of Protozoa.

(a) A Rhizopod (root-footed), *Amoeba.* (b) A flagellate, *Euglena* (generally green in color, and equally well called an alga). (c) A ciliate, *Colpoda.* (d) A Rhizopod, an amoeboid Protozoan with greater part of body enclosed in a "house" made of sand grains or other material, *Difflugia.* (Drawings, except (b), by W. K. Hubbell; (a) (d) after Leidy; (b) after G. M. Smith; (c) after Ward and Whipple.)

active hair-like projections from the body, known as *cilia* and used as paddles in locomotion. In some the cilia cover the whole surface of the body; in others they are restricted to particular zones of the body. (d) There are still others, a smaller number, which have cilia and swim only in the young stages; later they attach and develop suctorial tentacles;—these are the *Tentaculifera* or *Suctoria*. (e) In the last division are the *Sporozoa,* which are parasitic in or on aquatic or terrestrial animals. The non-aquatic malarial germ is the best known example of this group, but there are others that live as internal or external parasites of aquatic animals, such as daphnias and copepods.

The limited space that is given to the Protozoa here is in ŋo way proportionate to their ecological significance. Probably the most numerous animals and the greatest number of animal species in a pond are these generally invisible but active agents in the "conversion" of bacteria, algae, and dissolved nutrients into forms of "meat" available to small carnivorous animals. Not all Protozoa are grazers or scavengers. Some are distinctly carnivorous, feeding upon other protozoa and even upon multicellular animals. Large unicellular amoebae may devour small multicellular rotifers.

Notwithstanding the smallness of individual bodies, certain protozoa may occasionally be conspicuous to the observer on the bank of a pond. Colonies of the ciliate Ophridium, a relative of the better known Vorticella, may be seen as green masses of jelly, the size of a marble, or rarely even as large as a baseball, conspicuous at the surface of the pond, or attached to emergent leaves of plants. A "show" of protozoa is not the rule; yet, whether we see signs of them or not, almost everywhere in ponds and lakes, as well as in the scum on the bottom in streams, are innumerable protozoa in great diversity of kinds. Some swarm in the silt at the bottom and on the stems of plants; some attach to the bodies of plants or living animals; others swim freely in the water.

In the paragraphs on algae we have already referred to the highly important green and yellow flagellates. There are other flagellates that have no chlorophyll and apparently no synthetic capacity; they feed upon bacteria or dissolved organic nutrients. Undoubtedly, they play important if undistinguished parts in the organic cycle, serving along with algae as food for next larger organisms in the food chain.

The rhizopods, although well represented in the bottom sediment everywhere and often in floating scum, play a relatively small part in the life of the open water. The shell-bearing Difflugia and some of the Heliozoa, little ball-like masses of protoplasm with many slender ray-like projections, or pseudopods, may sometimes be common in the plankton, or drifting community.

Neither are the ciliates typical for open-water habitats; but they are almost universally distributed in great variety in ponds and in the sediments of ponds, lakes, and streams. Where there is much organic pollution, ciliates may occur in extreme abundance. There are colonies of ciliates that catch the eye. Sometimes copepods or other things appear fuzzy, as if they were covered with mould, when the "fuzz" represents only large colonies of stalked vorticellid ciliate protozoa. More obvious yet are the great green masses of another vorticellid, Ophridium, previously mentioned.

Sponges (*Porifera*)

Sponges (Fig. 16b) are associated chiefly with the seas, but a few species live in streams, ponds and lakes. They are seen as irregular gray-green or reddish brown masses, forming incrustations or more or less erect bodies on stones, logs, or the surfaces of dams. They may be an inch, or more or less, in diameter or in height. The greenish color is due to symbiotic algae living within the masses, the rusty color to the gemmules mentioned below. Their glassy skeletons of fine spicules make them harsh to the touch.

The name, Porifera, meaning pore-bearers, derives from the fact that over all the free surface of the colonial mass there are innumerable small openings through which, by the activity of internal flagellated cells, water is made to stream into feeding chambers; the current passes out again through a few larger openings. Obviously sponges are not to be sought in shallow muddy ponds where they might easily be suffocated by falling silt. It is said that they do sometimes occur in such waters in protected place, as on the lower sides of floating timbers. Freshwater sponges lack the connected framework skeleton of most marine sponges; rather, the body gains support and protection from in-

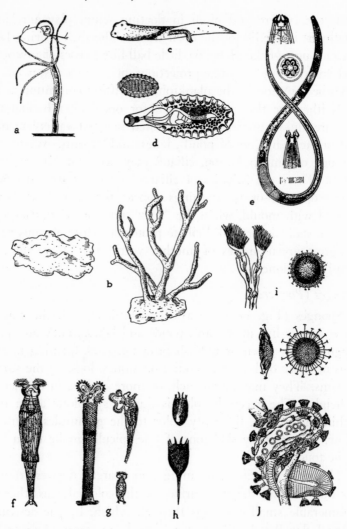

FIGURE 16. Some types of lower multicellular animals of the water (all magnified).

(a) Hydra in process of capturing with poison or adhesive darts a Daphnia to be taken whole into the digestive cavity through the highly distensible mouth seen within the circlet of tentacles. (b) Freshwater sponges, encrusting type of running water and branching type of still water (from Carpenter). (c) A flatworm with proboscis protruded from lower surface. (d) A parasitic flatworm, *Cotylaspis insignis*, which is found in many freshwater mussels (from Ward and Whipple). (e) A free-living nematode, or roundworm, *Teratocephalus* (from Ward and Whipple). (f) A common creeping rotifer, *Philodina*. (g) A rotifer, *Melicerta*, that builds tubes attached to rocks of the faces of dams or on rocks in running water; an individual removed from its tube and a small male. (h) Body housing of a free-swimming rotifer, *Keratella* (*Anu-*

numerable separate minute silicious spicules. Sponges occur chiefly in fairly soft, clean, and clear waters. Like the marine sponges, it may be remarked, they are somewhat malodorous even when in best living condition.

On an earlier page mention was made of the sponges as one of the few animals in fresh water that seem to live permanently sessile lives (after the larval state). The colony itself never moves from its place of attachment. Within the mass, however, there will usually be found many little protected "internal buds" or *gemmules,* each of which is a mass of cells in a tough resistant case. When separated from the body, as by the disintegration of the active portion of the mass, a gemmule may drift to another place to sprout and begin the development of a new colony.

The spicules of freshwater sponges seem to protect them from carnivorous animals. Their ecological significance may be chiefly in the part they play as competitors of other animals in the consumption of minute particles of food. Nevertheless, freshwater sponges, owing to their general inedibility, offer effective protection to certain kinds of animals that have become adapted to life within the sponge; such are the larvae of the sponge-flies, Climacia and Sisyra.[2]

Polyps and Jellyfish (Coelenterata)

The members of this phylum (hydroids, sea anemones, corals, Portugese man-of-war) are chiefly in salt water. In fresh water the group is represented mainly by the polyp Hydra (Fig. 16a), with slender sack-like body and circlet of long flexible tentacles, each armed with numbers of poison darts with which it paralyzes or seizes its small prey. Generally attached to plants, sticks, stones, or other solid objects, they may also hang head downward

2. I have also found a Leptocerid caddisfly larva, which lives in a papery case, completely overgrown by and imbedded in masses of sponge growing on stones in the Allegheny River of New York.

___

raea), which may have different forms in different generations. (Rotifers from Ward and Whipple.) (i) A moss-animalcule, or bryozoan, *Plumatella,* small part of a branching colony found in streams and a statoblast, or internal bud, greatly magnified (from Carpenter). (j) A bryozoan of still or slowly flowing water, *Cristatella,* many individuals joined in a gelatinous mass and capable of slow creeping movement; statoblasts are seen within the mass and, much more highly magnified, outside, in face and edge views. The statoblasts serve as "internal buds," and when escaped may lodge elsewhere and start new colonies (from Ward and Whipple).

from the surface film or even drift in the open water. When body and tentacles are extended, the delicate slender whole may be several inches in length. Contracted, the hydra appears as a formless lump the size of a match head or smaller. Never conspicuous, hydras are significant as predators on crustacea and other small animals of the plankton. Large hydra may even capture and engulf larval fish—victims that may be much bulkier than the captor. When the little fish has been taken into the highly distensible digestive chamber, the body of the hydra is stretched so thin as to be hardly observable; in an early stage of digestion the fish seems merely to be coated with a thin film; the film is the hydra.

Hydra feeds voraciously, growing rapidly and reproducing by successive lateral buds, which develop mouth and tentacles before separating from the parent Hydra. Hydra itself seems to have but few enemies, but it is preyed upon by turbellarian flatworms of the phylum to be mentioned next. It is said to be eaten also by large copepods. There are several species distinguished in part by color—brown, gray, or bright green; the green color is due to algae that live symbiotically in the inner of the two thin layers of cells that form the body wall.

In some localities one may find Coelenterates of other genera, less readily observable, but quite likely more widely distributed than the records indicate. One of these, called Craspedacusta, produces free-swimming jellyfishes, or medusae, a half-inch or so in diameter. Since they are lively and likely to attract attention when seen, it is now hardly explicable that freshwater jellyfishes were entirely unknown until fairly recently. For a long time there were only three or four records of their occurrence in America. Then records came more and more frequently until freshwater jellyfish have been reported from more than half the states of the Union. The conditions governing their occurrence are not now known.

The great division Platyhelminthes (meaning "flatworms") comprises the tapeworm, flukes, and many other parasites, and includes also the simple flatworms of streams and lakes, Planaria and others, which creep slowly over the bottom, on debris or beneath the surface film of water. With the use of protrusible probosces (Fig. 16c) some kinds of flatworms consume all sorts of small material, including diatoms, filamentous algae, copepods, young fresh-water mussels, and hydras. Undoubtedly they play a great part in controlling the abundance of certain kinds of animals free in the water and on the bottom and in maintaining a normal balance of life within the pond. Mostly the free aquatic flatworms are small, less than half an inch in length, but much longer ones are known—even up to a length of about six inches. Rhabdocoel flatworms of microscopic size are easily mistaken by the unwary for protozoans. As everyone knows, parasitic tapeworms may lengthen in colony chains.

Any adequate account of flatworms that are parasitic in fish, mollusks, crustacea, and other freshwater animals would require chapters. Let us mention only two that are of particular human interest. There is the famous sheep liver-fluke whose eggs, when dropped in the pasture with feces from the host and carried into the water, develop into free-swimming larvae called *miracidia.* A miracidium that encounters a snail of the right species bores its way into the body of the snail, where it changes into another form and goes through several generations by asexual reproduction. In time, another kind of larva, called *cercaria,* emerges from the snail to lead a brief free-swimming life. Soon the cercarian larva settles down on a leaf or blade of grass and forms a protective cyst. When the grass bearing cysts is eaten by sheep, juvenile flukes escape from the cysts in the stomach or intestine and invade the bile duct to develop into flukes of another generation.

There is also the broad-headed tapeworm, introduced comparatively recently from northern Europe into the region of the Great Lakes. When eggs from these tapeworms in the alimentary tract of man, dog, cat, fox, or other carnivore pass with sewage, or otherwise, into the water, they develop into swimming larvae called *coracidia.* These may be devoured along with other small organisms by copepods of certain species. Instead of being digested by the copepod they invade the tissues of the small crustacean and transform into another larval stage known as the *pro-*

cercoid. If infected copepods are taken into the stomach of a fish and digested, the resistant procercoid penetrates the wall of the digestive tract to live in the flesh of the fish. It is now a *pleurocercoid.* When man, dog, or other mammal eats *uncooked* fish, the pleurocercoid, if present in the fish, may be taken into the alimentary tract of the new host to develop into the sexually mature tapeworm. Until this parasite came into America not many years ago, there were in this country no known parasites common to fish and man. Although it occurs as yet chiefly in the region of the Great Lakes, there has been a recent record from Florida.[3] The parasite may well be spreading.

Roundworms

Roundworms of the phylum Nemathelminthes (Fig. 16e) are far more numerous than the flatworms, whether one considers individuals or species. They are abundantly represented in the lists of parasites of crustacea, worms, fishes, frogs, turtles, and other animals. There are also a vast number of kinds of small non-parasitic free-living nematodes in the sediment that covers the bottom or encases plant stems and other solid objects. Little is yet known of the significance of "nemas" in ponds and streams. Doubtless they exert a great influence there, just as they are highly significant in agricultural soils, where some kinds are beneficial and others harmful. Generally the free-living roundworms are extremely slender and much less than half an inch in length. Only their lively wriggling movement could catch the eye. Parasitic roundworms may be very much longer.

Occasionally one observes, even from a little distance, the long slender "horsehair worm," Gordius or a related kind, moving through the water with wavy motion. It may be as much as a yard in length. The adults live in water, but intermediate stages are parasitic in grasshoppers or other invertebrate animals. These "worms" are now placed in a distinct phylum.

There are also parasitic hook-headed worms (Acanthocephalids) of various species.

3. Letter of Dr. Earnest Carroll Faust.

Wheel-worms or Rotifers

With the rotifers (*Rotatoria*) we have come to one of the most prominent of the types of animals that make up the plankters or drifters (Figs. 16f, g, h). Rotifers occur in almost all sorts of aquatic situations. Some live in attached houses, permitting residence in very swift waters; others creep about in the bottom silt or wander over plants and debris. Still others regularly live adrift in the open water, either as free individuals or as swimming colonies of similar units attached to one another but capable of separating. They are among the most widely distributed and abundant of freshwater animals.

Perhaps the smallest of all multicellular animals, rotifers have well-specialized organs; but the number of cells of the whole body is so limited that in some cases they have been subject to actual count. Because of their small size rotifer are a source of food for a relatively large one-celled animal, the protozoan *Amoeba proteus*. I have found several rotifers in food vacuoles within the body of a single amoeba.

There are rotifers of stagnant swamps, rotifers of clear lake water, rotifers of temperate and of tropical regions; but it is a remarkable fact, according to Jennings, that the same species of rotifer may be found in various parts of the world where similar water conditions are found; he says, "two bodies of water half a mile apart, presenting entirely different conditions, are likely to vary more in their rotifer fauna than two bodies of water 5000 miles apart that present similar conditions."

Rotifers feed generally upon diatoms, protozoa, bacteria, and other minute organisms, which are continually whirled into their mouths by the action of the ciliated disks or coronas. Only a few species are predatory. Accordingly, they are one of the most significant of the converters of small particles of food into forms large enough to be available to higher animals. Small as they are, they are so prolific in reproduction as to constitute one of the basic food supplies for small animals in the open water and elsewhere.

Moss Animalcules

The Bryozoa that form moss-like branching colonies (Plumatella [Fig. 16i] and Fredericella) are inhabitants of streams and ponds. Those with copious housing of a jelly-like material (Pectinatella) may thrive in ponds, reservoirs, and lakes and sometimes cause a bad odor and taste. The colonies may even invade the outlet-pipes of reservoirs to form soft but effective plugs. Colonies with their gelatinous housing make masses of any size up to 10 or 12 inches in diameter. Cristatella makes small circular or long worm-like gelatinous rugs that have the notable capacity to creep slowly over submerged branches of trees or on the undersides of lily-pads.

Segmented (Annulate) Worms

The annulates (*Annelida*) are represented largely by the freshwater oligochaetes and leeches. The name oligochaete, meaning few-bristled, refers to the small number of bristles, or setae, *in a tuft,* of which there are generally four on each segment. Much the greater number of species of true worms are polychaetes (with many bristles per tuft), but nearly all of these are marine. Common earthworms are the most familiar of the oligochaetes, and some of these wander out into the water or live regularly in the bottom mud or among the rocks.

The more typical freshwater oligochaetes are small, often translucent and sometimes brightly colored. There are species characteristic of marshy areas or tributary waters. Such are the beautifully pink and orange speckled Aeolosoma, the bristly Chaetogaster, the delicate and highly translucent Nais, Dero, and others. Since these reproduce chiefly by division of the body, "they may multiply with such rapidity that they can extensively populate large masses of moribund algae in a very short time, and their activity accounts in part for the speedy disappearance of such masses in the autumn." Typically, they feed upon decaying vegetable matter, but Dr. Frank Smith tells of one common Naid species (*Chaetogaster diaphanus*) that feeds by preference upon a small Cladoceran (*Chydorus sphaericus*), which they catch and devour in large numbers (Ward and Whipple, p. 636).

The pale red Tubifex worms, are of especial interest because of their ability to live in foul bottoms where the decomposition of organic matter is proceeding rapidly and where, in consequence, the oxygen supply is greatly depleted. The red color is caused by hemoglobin in the plasma of the blood, which enables them to use the limited supplies of oxygen to the best advantage. Where bottom conditions are particularly foul they often occur in such great numbers as to make distinct reddish patches a few inches or sometimes several feet in diameter. These very slender worms may be a couple of inches in length with an inch or more of the body actively waving in the water to absorb oxygen while the rest of the body extends deeply into the mud.

Tubifex in some ponds, like earthworms in meadows, seems to render an important service to the community life in that they effect a turnover of the accumulated layers of organic detritus on the bottom of the pond. We have had to mention these worms in the chapter on "The Lake or Pond as a Place of Life," as well as in the chapter on "Stream Pollution." At times the income of dead organic matter may exceed the ordinary rates of consumption and decomposition; so that the bottom sediment is built up layer after layer, and put out of reach of the creeping and swimming animals. With heads an inch or more down in the humus at the bottom, Tubifex (Fig. 11) feed on the buried organic matter, passing into their bodies a stream of material much of which is deposited on the surface; so they effect a continuous overturn of that stratum of the bottom through which they may extend. Tubifex in turn is consumed by such small animals as wander over the bottom and are successful in seizing the worm or a part of it before it can retract within its tube. Thus they save from permanent loss much of the seasonal excess of organic deposition that was temporarily buried, and bring it back into circulation in the organic cycle of the pond.

Discodrilid worms, halfway between oligochaetes and leeches, and, like the latter in being without setae, may frequently be found, wandering in numbers over the body and limbs of crayfishes. Whether or not they are true parasites, they enjoy free transportation and opportunities for feeding from the same table as the host.

Leeches are flattened annulates without bristles, or setae, and with an external segmentation that does not conform closely with the interal plan. They are found swimming, creeping, hiding under rocks, in the mud or among plants, or attached to the bodies of fishes or other animals—or to human bathers and waders. They occur in both running and still waters, but more abundantly in the latter. "In the small lakes of our northern borders they fairly swarm" (Moore, 1918). *Macrobdella decora,* often used by physicians as a substitute for the European "medicinal" leech, can be a genuine nuisance to bathers in northern lakes, as can another species, *Philobdella gracile,* in waters of the Gulf States. Leeches have "negative values," not only as pests to man, but also as either temporary or nearly permanent parasites on fishes, turtles, frogs, and salamanders. Different species have diverse feeding habits and the same species may shift from one diet to another as they feed upon snails, worms, and insect larvae —and even upon other leeches. Some will leave the pond in search for earthworms, and one variety, at least, is at home in the soils of gardens far removed from water. In blood-sucking the leeches with jaws make a painless incision and secrete from salivary glands an anticoagulant for the blood. They can ingest a relatively large supply of blood, and, by adding a preservative secretion to the solids filtered from the liquid blood, make the meal last for a year or more (Moore, 1918).

Snails, Mussels, and Clams

Two classes of the *Mollusca,* with which we are concerned in fresh waters, are the gastropods (stomach-foots), or snails, and the pelecypods (hatchet-foots), or mussels and clams. The many kinds of snails fall into two distinct groups, the lung snails and the gill snails. The gill snails (Fig. 18) are the most truly aquatic, being dependent upon the dissolved oxygen in the water, and therefore unable either to maintain life out of water or, one might think, to endure very bad conditions within the water. Strangely enough, however, certain gill snails are reported as characteristic of heavily polluted water, as mentioned in the chapter on "Stream Pollution." The foot carries a hard disk by means of which the shell is tightly closed when the animal retracts its body in order to prevent drying out while the snail is temporarily out of the water. The lung snails (Fig. 17) have no such disk; they emerge from the water at will. Most of them, in fact, must have access to the atmosphere; they are frequently seen on plants or rocks above water; often, too, they glide along on the underside of the surface film. Since they do not necessarily breathe under water, some kinds may occur in enormous numbers in water that is quite foul. Among the lung snails are Lymnaea, Helisoma, Physa (with left-turned shell) and Ancylus (with a small "cap-shell" which has no obvious spiral turn). The eggs of aquatic snails are usually deposited in small masses of jelly: but some kinds are viviparous.

Two distinct types of bivalved mollusks are represented in lakes and ponds. Freshwater mussels of many species are found and some are quite large (Figs. 15a, b). With hatchet-like foot they plow into the bottom leaving only the hinder end of the shell exposed. Having there two siphonal openings, they keep, while feeding, a stream of water passing in through one opening and out through the other. Inside, the water is filtered through the basket-like gills. Oxygen is absorbed and carbon dioxide given off. At the same time the minute plants and animals are filtered out to be rolled into a ribbon of mucus and passed on into the

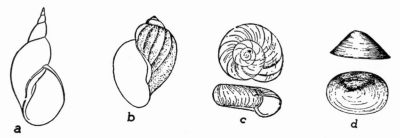

FIGURE 17. Pulmonate aquatic snails (air-breathers).

(a) *Lymnaea stagnalis.* (b) *Physa costata.* Note that this snail is "sinistral," its turns counter-clockwise as contrasted with the clockwise turns of the "dextral" *Lymnea.* (c) *"Planorbis glabratus,"* presumably now called *Helisoma duryi* (Weatherby). (d) *Ancylus newberryi,* cap shell. A spiral is not apparent. (All figures from Walker.)

mouth. The young develop within "marsupial pouches" (modified portions of the gills) and emerge from the shell of the
mother in the form of a *glochidium,* which is of microscopic size
and quite unlike the parent form. The glochidia generally attach to the gills or fins of fish where they become completely
encased by the tissues of the fish. Particular species of mussel
require particular kinds of fish. During a period of parasitism,
lasting several weeks, they undergo metamorphosis into the general form of the adult. The young mussel then breaks out of the
cyst and falls to the bottom to begin its free life. It is now subject to the depredations of flatworms and other enemies. If it
successfully passes through the juvenile stage to develop a fairly
hard shell, it is thereafter relatively safe, except from parasites

a   b   c   d

FIGURE 18. Gilled aquatic snails.

(a) *Campeloma subsolida.* (b) Operculum of a *Campeloma.* (c) *Pleurocera acuta.*
(d) *Goniobasis virginica,* a common snail of brooks. ((a) (d) after Ward and Whipple; (b) (c) from Walker.)

and a few strong-jawed predators, such as muskrats, raccoons,
and drum fish. The filtering action of freshwater mussels is well-
demonstrated by placing one in an aquarium with water slightly
cloudy with bacteria or other small organisms; the water may
soon become clear. There are one or two species of mussel that
can complete the life history without parasitism (Coker et al.,
1921).

Fresh-water mussels of species without heavy shells occur in
fairly soft waters. Those with heavy shells and most brightly
pearly nacre are particularly abundant in calcareous waters of the
Mississippi and Great lakes drainages. Their shells, as object of
fishery, support the fresh-water pearl button industry (Coker,

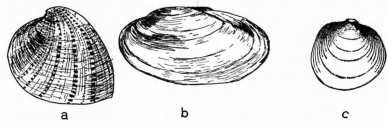

Figure 19. Some bivalve mussels.
(a) Butterfly mussel, *Plagiola*. (b) Yellow sand-shell, *Anodontoides*. (Drawings by W. K. Hubbell after Coker.) (c) Peashell, *Musculium* (from Ward and Whipple).

1919). Frequently they yield pearls of high value. (Kunz, 1898).

There are certain curious phenomena about the parasitism of mussels on fish. As previously mentioned, and as is the case with most parasites, particular kinds of mussels have special hosts. There are also parasitic copepods, often quite different, it may be said, from the free-living copepods discussed on an earlier page. A specialist in parasitic copepods, the late Professor C. B. Wilson, when working alongside specialists in mussel parasitism, observed that the mussels in parasitism seemed to give the fish host protection against the copepods—and perhaps vice versa. It might be said, then, that the fish, while helping the mussel along the path of life, actually derives in partial compensation some therapeutic advantage from its parasite. An extreme case was that of the sheepshead fish, which was actually always loaded with glochidia of the butterfly mussel,[4] but always in his experience free from parasitic copepods. Now it happens that the sheepshead feeds heavily upon mussels, the shell of which it crushes with powerful pharyngeal jaws. The sheepshead is thus easily infected with the glochidia of the butterfly mussels. In nursing, involuntarily but inevitably, the glochidia of the prey, this fish is, in a sense, participating in growing its own food. (Coker et al., 1921, p. 156).

Peashells or fingernail clams (Fig. 15c) feed in the same way as do mussels but are very different from mussels in structure and life history. Their nearest relatives are in the sea or in brackish

4. The sheepshead, or drum, *Aplodinotus grunniens;* the butterfly mussel, *Plagiola securis.*

waters. They are always small, fingernail size or smaller. In broad pouches within the shell, the young develop into the form of the adult; when liberated, they need no period of parasitism. The young have a tuft of thread (a *byssus*) for attachment. They burrow in the bottom or attach themselves to rocks or debris. The inside of the shell left from a dead mussel seems to be a favorite shelter. Mussel fishermen often mistake them for young mussels and assume erroneously that the young have consumed the parent! Peashells seem to have much lower oxygen requirements than mussels, for they are found in many situations where the conditions would be intolerable for mussels.

CHAPTER 13

Life in the Lake:
Jointed-Leg Animals
and Vertebrates

THE ARTHROPODA

W E COME NOW TO A DIVISION OF THE ANIMAL KINGDOM THAT includes more than three-fourths of all the kinds of animals in the world. The phylum of arthropods (jointed legs) embraces all animals with externally jointed limbs and with a continuous and firm body covering, or true exoskeleton. A group so large, and, through crustacea and insects, so prominent in fresh waters must be considered by classes and even by subclasses or orders.

The Crustacea

Among the arthropods it is the Crustacea that are primarily adapted to life in water. The most primitive types are grouped in the subclass Branchiopoda, comprising the phyllopods (leaf-like feet), or fairy-shrimp, and the Cladocera, some of which are well known to amateur aquarists as "daphnes." The aptly named "fairy-shrimp" (Fig. 20), a quarter of an inch to an inch or more in length, are most graceful in form, translucent, and often tinted with delicate brilliance. They are frequenters, primarily, of temporary waters, such as woodland pools and gravel pits, in which they tide over the dry periods as resistant "resting eggs." I have known clam-shaped Estheria to occur in enormous numbers in a

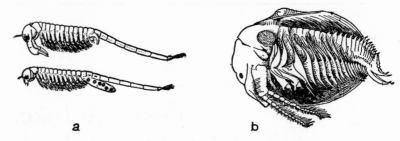

FIGURE 20. Water-fairies of contrasting forms.

(a) *Branchinecta,* with naked bodies. (b) *Estheria,* in bivalve shell like that of a cladoceran. The translucency and delicate tinting justifying the common name is entirely lost in a line drawing. (Both from Ward and Whipple.)

bathing pool, artificially formed below hillside springs. Although this was not a likely place for them, the water-fairies, a quarter to three-eighths of an inch in length, were present in such enormous numbers that bathers were deterred from using the pond. Sand from a gravel pit, a more likely habitat for fairy-shrimp, had recently been dumped into the pond in great quantity; it is possible that the resting eggs had been introduced along with the sand.

Cladocera, on the other hand, are always present in ponds and lakes and often in great diversity of species, only a few of which are strictly "Daphnias." Except for the larger Leptodora, which may be three-quarters of an inch in length, the Cladocera (Fig. 21) are small with lengths measurable in millimeters or fractions of a millimeter. There are those that creep in the silt on the bottom, falling prey to oligochaete worms and, doubtless, to most bottom feeding animals. There are others, such as Simocephalus, Bosmina, and Moina, to be found more abundantly among the cattails and in other weedy places. One kind, at least (Scapholeberis), commonly runs upside down on the under side of the surface film. A few species, such as Daphnia proper, Ceriodaphnia, Acroperus, Holopedium with its gelatinous cases, and Diaphanosoma, are most likely to be found swimming freely in open waters. The aberrant Polyphemus and the rapacious, naked-bodied Leptodora, quite different in appearance and habit from the ordinary run of Cladocera, have been thought to be northern

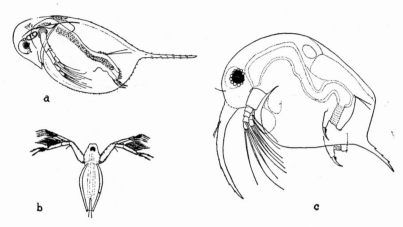

FIGURE 21. Cladocerans.
(a) *Daphnia.* (b) *Diaphanosoma* of open water. (c) *Bosmina* (more enlarged). The post abdomen of hinder extremity of the body proper is shown retracted with solid lines, extended with dotted lines.

in distribution, but they occur more widely than has been assumed; they are known from ponds in North Carolina. Leptodora is characteristically limnetic and, unlike most Cladocera, is decidedly predatory.

The feeding of cladocerans generally is by filtration, and this has much signifiance in the turnover of food in the pond. Portions of their limbs pull water toward the bodies in almost continuous stream. A part of the current thus produced is turned forward through a "filtration chamber" between the body above and the limbs below. The stream of water continues outward through fine-meshed filters formed by setae with feather-like barbs. The fine material left in the chamber by the filter is then pushed by specialized parts of appendages into the mouth. The meshes of the filter of a particular limnetic cladoceran, as measured by one of my students, had a diameter of scarcely more than one-thousandth of a millimeter ($1/25,000$ of an inch). The screen would hold back protozoa or algae, however small, and most of the bacteria. I have watched a limnetic Daphnia feeding continuously in a culture of small protozoans (Chilomonas), when occasionally a large protozoan, such as Paramoecium, would get into the chamber. Apparently, it was too large for

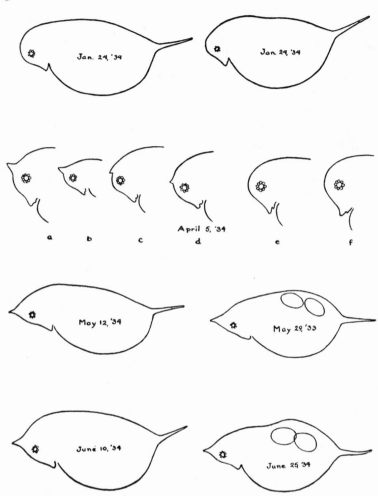

FIGURE 22. Seasonal cycle of forms in a species of *Daphnia* of a reservoir. Winter generations at top; summer generations at bottom.

manipulation as food: the chamber would be opened, the Paramoecium pushed out and the briefly interrupted filtering process resumed. Cladocera must have a distinct effect in clarifying water clouded with algae and protozoa.

Some Cladocera are remarkable in that they pass through a cycle of forms from generation to generation, so that winter and summer forms are so different that, without knowledge of the

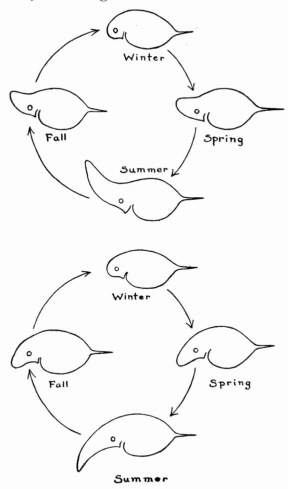

FIGURE 23. More extreme cyclomorphosis in different races of *Daphnia* from large lakes, somewhat conventionalized. The winter generations in these two races from different lakes are indistinguishable; individuals of the summer generations were once considered of different genera from those of winter.

sequence of forms, one would not know they were of the same species (Fig. 22). It is not the change in an individual that is notable: it is the change from generation to generation. "Great-grandchildren," so to speak, are strikingly unlike the great-grand-mother in appearance, but their own great-grandchildren of the next summer may be good replicas of the maternal ancestor of the preceding summer. The principal change is in the forms of the head, which develops in the warm season prolongations, often quite bizarre, that are called "helmets," but which are only continuations of the head, forward, upward, or downward, according to the race. Some rotifers and diatoms also manifest their own versions of this "cyclomorphosis."

Cladocera can multiply with great rapidity because, ordinarily, only one parent is needed and frequent batches of many eggs are extruded. On the other hand, crowding or some other condition leads to the development of males and of a very small number of eggs of a different sort that require fertilization. The fertilized egg may undergo a long period of rest to tide the race over a time of unfavorable conditions. (Cyclomorphosis in Cladocera is discussed by Coker, 1939, and Brooks, 1946; the conditions governing sexual reproduction by Berg, 1931, and Banta, 1939.)

Undoubtedly, the Cladocera, as a whole, and the copepods to be mentioned next, are the chief consumers of the more minute forms of plant and animal life in almost any body of standing water and they constitute the main food supply of the next larger animals, including young fishes. Occasionally they are rivaled in numbers in the plankton by the rotifers previously discussed. All larval fishes, whatever may be the habit of the adult, feed upon Entomostraca; this is a name that is applied rather loosely to the Cladocera, copepods, and ostracods, small crustaceans just visible to the naked eye, or a little larger, up to half a centimeter, rarely more, in length.

With the free-living copepods we come to an order of small animals that outranks all others for virtual universality of distribution in water. Individually they are small: a copepod two or three millimeters (about 1/10 of an inch) in length is large for the order. Collectively they are highly important. Those of fresh water are of three distinct types, which may roughly be distinguished as the "water-treaders," the "leapers," and the "creepers."

The *calanoids,* water-treaders, include copepods with first antennae of more than twenty segments and about as long as the

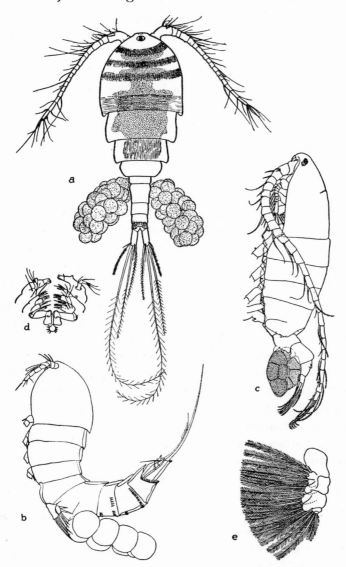

FIGURE 24. Copepods.

(a) Cyclopoid copepod, *C. ater*, with two egg sacs, antenna about length of trunk of body. (b) Harpacticoid, *Moraria virginiana* (drawing by Marjorie Carter), with single egg sac, antenna about length of first segment of body. (c) Calanoid, *Diaptomus birgei*, with single egg sac, antenna about length of whole body. (d) Scraping mouthparts of harpacticoid (mandibles, first and second maxilla and maxilliped). (e) Filter comb on second maxilla of calanoid, used for straining microscopic food from the water.

body (Fig. 24c). They are almost entirely limnetic in habit; that is to say, they keep in open water and, therefore, are to be found most commonly in lakes and the larger ponds. They almost never rest on the bottom or lodge on vegetation. Rather, they continually tread water by extremely rapid strokes of their second antennae. In doing so they maintain a favored level while free in the water and, at the same time, draw a stream through the exceedingly fine-meshed setal combs on one pair of their mouthparts. Thus they filter out bacteria and the other extremely small organisms that form their chief source of food. As inveterate filterers, they serve a significant function in keeping the open water pure and clear. Their feeding habit is similar in a general way to that of the Cladocera (except Leptodora). We may say, in fact, that Cladocera in the weedy parts of a pond, calanoid copepods and Cladocera in the open waters, and the mussels and clams in the bottom are the macroscopic animals that do most to filter the water, keeping it relatively clear, and to convert bacteria and the most minute plants and animals into forms of organic matter available as food for the larger animals.

The filtering mechanism of calanoid copepods has been carefully studied by several investigators. (See particularly: Storch and Pfisterer, 1925; Cannon, 1928; Storch, 1929.) It offers features of unusual interest. As might be supposed, there is some disagreement as to details, but the essential features of the remarkable mechanism seem clearly established. The second antenna and parts of two other small appendages, serving as peculiarly swift-acting paddles (see below), pull water toward the body. This "locomotory stream," or "swimming vortex," formed by treading water, as it were, keeps the animal from sinking of its own weight or moves it forward, according to vigor of action. Whatever minute articles of food are adrift in the water pass with the stream alongside and beneath the body; but feeding is not yet accounted for. The "filter chamber" is in the middle just below, enclosed by the body above, an "upper lip" in front, a loose meshwork below made by the long barbed setae of the thoracic legs pointed forward, and, on each side, by a wide fan-shaped comb of finely barbed setae on the second maxilla (Fig. 24e), the second pair of limbs behind the mandibles, which are alongside the mouth. The outside swirls previously mentioned have a secondary "aspiration" effect to "suck" water out from the filter chamber through the filter combs. To keep the aspiration stream or suction current going, water must flow into the filter chamber from below and behind as the "food stream." As food left behind accumulates in the chamber, it is pushed forward by an inner lobe of the first maxilla toward the mouth. Presumably the mandibles act to crush the foods, if necessary.

The liveliness of the little paddles used to make the primary streams may be grasped from the fact that Storch, employing the best moving picture apparatus of the time, estimates a rate of 3,000 strokes per minute, while Cannon, with the more accurate stroboscope, arrived at a frequency of about 1,000, or 17 beats per second. Some space has been given to the feeding mechanism of calanoid copepods, not only because of the special interest of so elaborate, so lively, and so efficient a bit of living machinery, but also because, without some understanding of the feeding operations of at least one of the filterers, we can have little grasp of how the most minute drifting organisms are winnowed out of the water and made into items of food visible to the smaller predators. Copepods and cladocerans are only some of the filterers that play so great a part in the economy of a pond or lake. They are all significant "converters," agents for clarification and helpers in purification.

The *cyclopoids* (Fig. 24a), including copepods with first antennae of moderate length, about as long as the broad anterior part of the body, and differing otherwise from the calanoids, show more diversity in habitats and modes of living. Typically darting here and there through the water, they seize and devour almost any form of organic matter of available size. Some feed upon Cladocera and even, on occasion, upon their own kind and young. Some species, at least, seem to have no difficulty in feeding on minute organisms. Although cyclopoids are primarily inhabitants of the weedy zones, a few species creep amidst debris on the bottom, and a small number, like *Mesocyclops leuckarti,*

M. edax and *Tropocyclops prasinus,* are primarily limnetic in habit.

Harpacticoid copepods (Figs. 24b, d), with very short first antennae, represented by Canthocamptus, Attheyella, and other genera, are characteristic inhabitants of spring-runs. A few of them may be found along shore in bottom silt and debris, where they crawl (or occasionally swim) to scrape the organic film where they find it. Still others live in the films of water deep in the sand beaches. Ordinarily, they are relatively insignificant members of the community of ponds and lakes, although instances occur when harpacticoids are numerous in the plankton of open water.

Contrary to what is said in some of the books, in none of the copepods do the first antennae serve as organs of propulsion. Rather, they are balancing or suspensory in function; in many males they are used for clasping the mate. Active swimming is effected by limbs of the thorax, the "swimming feet."

So, among copepods, the treaders of water, the leapers, and the crawlers—or, in feeding habit, the "filterers," the "seizers" and the "scrapers,"—fill fairly distinct niches in the complex of pond life. Taken together they cover a wide field and play a chief part in the complex organic community life of most quiet waters. No other single order of the animal kingdom is so widely distributed and so significant in conversion of algae, bacteria, and protozoans into food for the next larger animals.[1]

A small degree of cyclomorphosis is known for some copepods (Coker, 1933, 1934a; Yeatman, 1952), and copepods of the same brood may be much larger and better equipped with spines if reared in cold water than if developed in warm water.

Ostracods, of the same order of size as cladocerans and copepods, have bodies embraced in clam-like shells. They are chiefly

1. The ascription of differential habits of movement and feeding to the several major groups of fresh-water free-living copepods (calanoids, cyclopoids, and harpacticoids), as "water-treaders," "leapers," and "creepers" or as "filterers," "seizers," and "scrapers," although generally valid, must not be supposed to require no qualification. Copepods of all three groups can swim vigorously, using their thoracic "swimming feet"; calanoids are known to take prey of substantial size on occasion (see Lowndes, 1935); cyclopoids must be capable of filtering, since some can be reared in culture media provided with only extremely minute organisms as food; others live habitually in the open waters of lakes, where there are no possibilities of lodgement. Flat generalizations about living animals often have pitfalls for the unwary.

creepers on the bottom, inhabitants of shallow, weedy, and swampy ponds. Some kinds are able to rise to the surface to feed by scraping roots and leaves of floating duckweed and then to fall to the bottom. Thus they may be caught in plankton nets as "adventitious plankters." (Good accounts of ostracods are given by Sharpe, 1918; Hoff, 1942; and Pennak, 1953.) They are best collected, according to Sharpe, by dragging a cone-net through submerged plants or by stirring up the bottom ooze and drawing the weighted net to and fro over the bottom; he recognizes groups that swim, others that creep on the plants or on the bottom, and still others that burrow in the ooze.

Of higher Crustacea (Malacostraca), the Amphipods (scuds), Isopods (sowbugs), freshwater shrimps, and crayfishes are chiefly to be considered, although mention should be made of *Mysis relicta* (an assumed relic of sea fauna—now called *Mysis oculata relicta*). The dainty translucent "relict shrimp," or "opossum shrimp," half an inch to an inch or more in length, is found in the cool depths of the Great Lakes and other deep lakes of the northern states and Canada, as well as in lakes of Great Britain, northern Europe, and Siberia. Where Mysis occurs it may be a chief article of food for fishes. Its nearest relative is found in northern sea waters. A less closely related species of the same subfamily is found in lakes and rivers west of the Rocky Mountains. Another is reported from Louisiana (Banner, 1953).

The isopod, Asellus, less than an inch long, occurs very commonly in small ponds where it lives among decaying vegetable matter. Of Amphipods, Gammarus, Hyalella, and Eucrangonyx may all be found in smaller ponds. *Hyalella knickerbockeri,* half an inch or so in length, is extremely widely distributed in America, occurring in rivers, ponds, and lakes from coast to coast and from the very low lands to the high lakes of the Rocky Mountains and the Andes. The genus Gammarus probably comprises the species of amphipod that are most likely to be encountered everywhere in lakes and smaller bodies of water. The deep waters of Lakes Superior and Michigan have many Pontoporeia, a larger amphipod whose closer relatives are all marine.

The true freshwater shrimps, Palaemonetes and Macrobrachium, are of rather restricted distribution in southern waters. The former, an inch or more in length, has a body of extreme transparency. Some of the latter are large enough to be an esteemed article of food along the lower Mississippi River. The largest Crustacea occurring in ponds are the crayfish, of which there are a great many species in the eastern genera, Cambarus and others, besides those in the western (and European) genus Astacus. Their size and activity make them most significant as scavengers and predators in the animal community and as articles of food for the larger fishes. The burrowers and "chimney builders" may play havoc with earthen dams around ponds.

Spiders and Mites

Of the segmented animals with externally jointed limbs only the Crustacea are primarily adapted for life in the water. Some of the smallest may effect interchange of gases with the surrounding water through the surface of the body generally, but the larger crustacea and some of the smaller are provided with gills. Most other arthropods are primarily adapted for life on land, having an air-vascular system which conveys atmospheric gases from spiracular openings on the outside to all parts of the body. This is the *tracheal system* with elaborately branching tracheal tubes. Nevertheless, some spiders enter water; water-mites and a great many insects have secondary adaptations for life in water.

The arachnids are better represented in the sea than in fresh water. We need mention here only the few spiders that invade fresh waters and the abundant water-mites. Spiders are often seen running on the surface whence they may dive into the water in search of aquatic prey. They need never be confused with the "water-striders," which are insects.

If a fish passes below it, [the spider] makes a sudden dive, its whole body going under water. Its long legs are wrapped round the fish, which is bitten and dragged ashore. The spider then eats the fish with unusual speed, leaving nothing except the backbone! It has also been seen to eat tadpoles of the toad *Bufo carens* and adults of the small frog, *Rhappia marmorata* (Savory, 1928).

Savory, as quoted, was referring to a foreign species, but he

PHOTO BY JACK DERMID
Courtesy of North Carolina Wildlife Resources Commission

Pl. 18. *The farm pond affords a place for swimming.*

Pl. 19. *Largemouth black bass.*

PHOTO BY JACK DERMID
Courtesy of North Carolina Wildlife Resources Commission

Pl. 20 and Pl. 21. *Forage and pan fish:* (above) *southeastern blue gill, or bream;* (below) *robin.*

adds that "McCook's great work on American spiders gives instances of the capture of fish, mice and snakes . . . some . . . much larger and stronger than the victorious spiders." There is a European spider that lives at the bottom of ponds breathing air it carries down with it. It even builds an "aerial" nest under water. The secret of the paradox is that the spider spins a web among the plants, then caches under the ballooning web an adequate quantity of transported air. In this homemade air space the eggs hatch and the young enter upon life, while the mother spider may use it as a winter retreat (Comstock, 1948, pp. 597, 598).

Water mites (Fig. 10), closely akin to spiders, but without divisions of the body into the two regions characteristic of the latter, are more definitely aquatic. They vary in size from less than 1 to 8 mm. (about 1/3 of an inch), and are often conspicuous in shallow or weedy water for their bright colors in red or green, perhaps with splotches of brown and black. They may be seen running, with the four pairs of legs typical of spiders and mites, resting on the bottom, or on plants, or, sometimes, swimming through the water. They feed by sucking the juices from prey of diverse kinds, including crustacea and aquatic insect larvae. A few species are parasitic in freshwater mussels, sponges, and colonial protozoans. They also form a part of the food supply of fish (Wolcott, 1918; Pennak, 1953).

Insects

Insects play a great part in the community life of fresh waters, being most prominent in the bottom fauna. Because insects have the tracheal system for distribution of free gas through fine tubules running throughout the body, the blood of terrestrial insects serves chiefly for conveyance of nutritive matter and is usually not very liquid. Many aquatic larvae of insects, as well as aquatic adults have to come to the surface periodically for replenishment of the tracheal airs. . Others have external tracheal gills provided with a branching complex of tracheal tubes rather than the elaborate net of fine blood capillaries characteristic of gills of vertebrates and crabs. Tracheal gills absorb free-oxygen from the surrounding water. Nevertheless, a few insect larvae of the water have developed "blood-gills," through which the blood stream is oxygenated, although tracheal vessels may function also.

No insect has to spend its entire time in water. Eggs and larval and pupal stages of some are fully aquatic—only the adults are aerial (mayflies, stoneflies, mosquitos). Some deposit eggs above the water: the hatched young drop into the water to complete there the larval development (horseflies, dobsonflies). Some, as advanced larvae, crawl out to pupate on land (dobsonflies, some dragonflies) and emerge in the air. Still others remain in water as adults (most of the aquatic bugs and beetles); but even those of most extreme aquatic habit retain the capacity to fly or walk outside of water and thus to pass from pond to pond.

For insects of ponds and lakes, we are concerned chiefly with those of seven orders: mayflies, caddisflies, dragonflies and damselflies, two-winged flies (flies, gnats, mosquitoes and midges), moths, true bugs (Hemiptera), and beetles. We pass over the spring tails, the spongilla flies, whose larvae are housed in masses of freshwater sponges, and the few wasplike insects of fresh waters. Some moth larvae will be mentioned.

Of the order *Megaloptera*, which includes the helgrammite or dobsonfly larva (Corydalus) and the fishfly larva (Chauliodes) of streams, only the larvae of the alderfly (Sialis) is common in ponds and lakes. They are generally found in sand or mud along the margins, but sometimes in deeper water. They prey on insect larvae and other small animals. The stoneflies (Plecoptera), prominent in swift streams, are not so common in still or sluggish waters.[2]

Mayfly nymphs may be abundant in net collections taken in the weeds. They are of the order *Ephemeroptera,* a name related to the word "ephemeral," and derived from the fact that, in the stages of life when they have wings, they are short-lived in the

2. For one concerned with aquatic life, particularly the aquatic insects, the handiest guide is Dr. Anne Haven Morgan's *Field Book of Ponds and Streams.* A charming old book, *The Natural History of Aquatic Insects,* by Professor L. C. Miall, originally published in 1895, reprinted in 1934, is always to be recommended to those who want to know how the insects live. Various books on particular groups are cited in the following pages. Robert W. Pennak's *Fresh-water Invertebrates of the United States* is an invaluable comprehensive work, as is Ward and Whipple's *Fresh-water Biology.* Needham and Needham's *A Guide to the Study of Fresh-water Biology* is useful for the keys and illustrations.

extreme, often living as flying insects only a day or two, or for a few hours, just long enough to molt once more, to mate, and to deposit eggs in the water. The young that hatches from the egg is called a nymph;[3] it requires a year, or sometimes two years, to complete its development with many molts. There is no pupal stage. In the last aquatic stage the nymph finally rises to the surface, its outer integument breaks open, and the notably delicate winged insect flies away. Mayflies differ from all other insects in undergoing a final molt with change of form *after* they begin to fly. Thus there is a winged "subimago" and an "imago," or true adult. Having so brief a time to live the winged mayflies require no food and do not even have mouthparts; the alimentary canal may be filled with air for buoyancy; their one function or occupation out of water is to start a new generation in the water. (See Needham, Traver, and Hsu, 1935.) (Figs. 6e, f; Pl. 12.)

Mayfly nymphs are readily identified as such if we note the three, or in some species only two, long slender tail appendages provided with hairs and sometimes distinctly plumose, and if we observe also the vibrating "gills" borne on the hinder segments of the body. With mouthparts adapted for raking and scraping they feed upon detritus or upon the small plants and animals

3. If an insect during free life undergoes radical change in form, or "complete metamorphosis," as in the caterpillar-butterfly sequence, an immature state after the egg is called a larva. When there is only gradual and progressive change, or "incomplete metamorphosis," as with grasshoppers, the young are called *nymphs*.

In the former a quiescent pupal stage intervenes between larva and adult. Among aquatic insects, fishflies, caddisflies, beetles, gnats and their relatives, moths, and wasps have complete metamorphosis: the life cycle includes egg, larva, pupa, and adult.

In insects with incomplete or gradual metamorphosis, the young, or nymphs, resemble the adult except in size, and in the absence of wings, which often begin to develop in wing pads on comparatively young nymphs. There is no pupal stage. Stoneflies, mayflies, dragonflies and water-bugs are aquatic insects with gradual development; the life cycle is made up of egg, nymphs, and adult or imago (with a subimago for mayflies). The successive stages of nymphs or larvae are called *instars*.

The springtails (Collembola) undergo no metamorphosis: the young that emerges from the egg differs from the adult only in size.

Aquatic nymphs of stoneflies, mayflies, dragonflies and damselflies have *tracheal gills* for absorbing gaseous oxygen dissolved in the surrounding water. These are lost at the last molt, since they are not required by the aerial imagoes. Dipteran larvae may have *blood gills*, which are not found in the adult.

Aquatic nymphs, and perhaps some larvae proper, are often called "naiads," an undesirable appelation, since naids are small aquatic earthworms.

that live on plant stems and debris. They, in turn, are food for fishes and other animals large enough to eat them. Since, and even before, the classical description of the emergence of the mayflies by Reamur a little more than two hundred years ago, it has been known that almost the whole population of some kinds may emerge in mass, mate, and die on a single day. Then they form above the water actual clouds of dancing and mating flies that soon perish and fall upon the water to become the prey of fish. The day of emergence of mayflies is, indeed, a great feast day for the fish that capture in great quantities both the nymphs and the falling imagoes. With some species the emergence after a year or two in the water covers several days—or emergence may be spread out over a considerable period.

Caddisflies, of the order *Trichoptera* (meaning hairy-wings) have also a long life in the water and a short life in the air. Often, too, they emerge in mass, when they are conspicuous as clouds of flying insects, floating islands of dead bodies or windrows of corpses on the beaches. Unlike the mayflies, they have true larvae and a pupal stage from which they emerge, after complete change of form, as the flying adult. These are moth-like in appearance; close examination reveals that the wings are not covered with scales but are equipped, instead, with rows of hairs. Unlike the mayflies, the larvae live mostly in cases of some sort. These may be woven tubes which sometimes are branching cylinders submerged, except for an open end, in the fine silt of the bottom. More often they are cylindrical houses made of formed material, strengthened with sand grains, fine gravel, bits of leaves nicely cut out for this use, seeds, sticks or other debris (Fig. 26).

Although caddises are most frequently observed in swift streams, there are species that live exclusively in still waters. Characteristic of ponds and lakes are Limnophilus, with rough, bur-like tubes armed with many cross-sticks and other vegetable matter, Phryganea, on submerged plants, with houses of narrow strips of leaves put together in spiral form around a cylinder, Triaenodes, with elongate cases having the form of a cornucopia decorated with fragments of leaves, and a very few others. Under favorable conditions some of these may occur in great abundance.

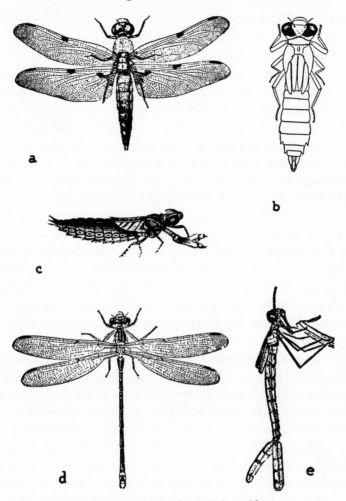

FIGURE 25. Dragonfly and damselfly.

(a) Dragonfly (from Furneaux). (b) Dragonfly nymph (from Needham and Heywood). (c) Nymph of dragonfly with "mask" (labium) extended (from Furneaux). (d) Damselfly (from Needham and Heywood). (e) Damselfly nymph (from Ward and Whipple).

Caddises vary widely in feeding habits; a few are distinct predators, killing and devouring other larvae. Others seem to feed chiefly upon detritus and organic scrapings. Although protected to some extent by their cases, they may be devoured, case and all, by fish. Indeed, some species are known to anglers as "stick-bait." The best comprehensive American works on caddis-flies are those of Betten (1934) and Ross (1944), both being useful outside of the states for which they were especially written.

Among the largest of insect larvae in a pond are the nymphs of the dragonflies and damselflies, the familiar "mosquito-hawks" or "snake doctors" of the order Odonata. The still waters of ponds and lakes are pre-eminently their homes; and no insect is more conspicuous around the pond than the active and generally useful "mosquito-hawks," which play a part in controlling the numbers of mosquitoes and other small insects in the air, while the predatory young do much to regulate the abundance of small animals in the water. Simple distinguishing features of adult damselflies, it may be remarked, are to be found in the slender body that widens behind, the very short wide head that makes the cross for the T-form of the whole body, and the habit of turning the wings upward and backward when at rest. Dragon-flies have stouter bodies, tapering behind, and generally the wings are spread horizontally when at rest. (See Needham and Hey-wood, 1929.)

The largest nymphs may be nearly two inches in length. The slender bodies of damselfly nymphs have three generally flattened appendages behind, which serve both as tracheal gills and as sculling blades in locomotion. They may be mistaken for mayfly nymphs unless one notes the absence of gills on the back or sides of the abdomen. In contrast, the caudal appendages of dragonfly nymphs are inconspicuous; the abdomen is wide and thick and is largely occupied by a respiratory chamber. Water is "inhaled" and "exhaled" through an opening at the rear end. If the water is expelled with force, the effect is that of jet-propulsion and the nymph is driven forward sometimes with considerable rapidity. When nymphs are kept in a shallow dish in the laboratory, they may squirt water a distance of several feet.

Both dragonfly and damselfly nymphs may be distinguished from all other insect nymphs and larvae by the remarkable plate-like mask on the underside of the head. This serves several distinct functions. When folded against the body, it is a screen that conceals the jaws from unsuspecting prey; when unfolded and thrust forward, it is used as an arm for seizing prey; and, finally, when folded back, it may act as a plate to hold the food while it is being eaten. This structure is the highly modified labium, or so-called "lower lip," characteristic of all insects, but in this order highly specialized in form and function (Fig. 25e).

Damselfly nymphs are chiefly climbers. Nymphs of dragonflies show greater diversity in habits and form. There are climbers that wander over plant stems, there are creepers on the bottom, and there are burrowers that live in the sand or mud; as the burrowers wander about, they may leave furrow-like trails that are readily observable in the shallow waters near the shores. Adult dragonflies and damselflies affect the life of the pond as they feed upon mosquitoes, midges, and other insects which have emerged from the water and might otherwise deposit eggs in it.

The nymphs are definitely predators, even sometimes upon young fish. "Some of their food, such as chironomid larvae, mayfly larvae, entomostraca, etc., is the same as that of young fish, but they also eat the larvae or adults of many animals that are directly harmful to small fishes, such as diving beetles, water boatman, crayfish, and Cypris" (Wilson, 1920, p. 246). They, in

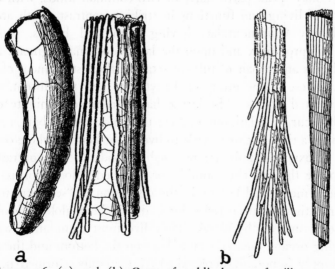

a b

FIGURE 26. (a) and (b) Cases of caddis larvae of still water, *Limnophilus* and *Phryganea* (from Lloyd).

turn, are eaten by larger fish. Someone has spoken of the "constant war" between dragonfly nymphs and the black bass. Wilson, after careful studies, concluded that they were much less harmful in the pond than they were useful in the destruction of enemies of fish and in serving as food for fish.

The order of two-winged flies, the *Diptera,* is of especial interest in this review for several reasons, but primarily because it includes the midge larvae, those least conspicuous but most numerous and important of all aquatic insects. Among organisms of the bottom, midge larvae seem to play a paramount role in converting organic detritus and microscopic organisms into the form of their own bodies and they afford one of the chief foods of fishes. Professor S. A. Forbes, after extensive studies of the food of fishes, said: "Among aquatic insects, minute, slender dipterous larvae, belonging mostly to Chironomus, Corethra and allied genera, are of remarkable importance, making, in fact, nearly one-tenth of the food of all fishes studied." There are many kinds of midge larvae, living in mud on the bottom, in delicate tubes on submerged sticks and other debris, on plant stems, beneath lily pads, and elsewhere.

We may speak particularly of two common kinds, with conditions of living and functions in striking contrast. Both are of the family Chironomidae, having cylindrical bodies, prolegs upon the prothorax and upon the last abdonomal segment, anal blood gills and a pair of tufts of setae on the last segment of the body. Those of the group of Tanytarsus have translucent, delicately tinted bodies. The larvae hatch from very minute eggs which occur in gelatinous masses; they may swim about in the water for a time but soon settle to live in the bottom where conditions of oxygen-supply are reasonably good. In the contrasting group are the red chironomids, or so-called "blood-worms." It has been mentioned before, in the discussion of "sediment-transporters," that the deep red color is due to hemaglobin dissolved in the plasma of the blood. They live most abundantly where decaying organic matter accumulates on the bottom and the oxygen supply is notably depleted. Living in tubes formed in the bottom ooze, they play essentially the same part in the turnover of the accumulated sediment as the tubificid worms previously mentioned. (See also chapter on "Stream Pollution.") It has been said that the presence of red chironomids in numbers is a certain indication of deficiency of oxygen, while the presence of Tanytarsus in quantity is as good a sign of moderate or high content of dissolved oxygen. These two types of midge larvae, may, therefore, be regarded a "indicators" of physical conditions in the bottoms of lakes.

Another midge larva of some ecological interest is a species of Orthocladius, whose larva lives in the masses of algae that sometimes appear as a blanket on the surface of a pond. Dr. Emmeline Moore (1919) found that this larva in ponds at Fairport, Iowa, fed by preference upon a particular kind of filamentous alga (Mougeotia), which it sought out among other algae, and that the midge larva formed the chief food of young largemouth black bass. Thus she established a definite food chain from plant to fish: Mougeotia-Orthocladius-black bass.

Other Dipteran larvae, often most conspicuous in small ponds, are those of mosquitoes (Culicidae), which constitute an important element of the food supply of small fishes. Their presence in numbers is commonly limited to zones of vegetation where there is adequate protection from enemies, including the small fishes, beetles, and bugs. Top minnows are often relied upon to control the breeding of mosquitoes in pools and small ponds. The minnows may be quite ineffective if there is much vegetation. Apparently, the wigglers deliberately use plants as screens against the enemy.

A most interesting Dipteran of the pond is the half-inch "phantom larva," generally known as Corethra, but now technically called Chaoborus. Their bodies are of glassy transparency except for the two pairs of small air sacs which appear as paired dark specks near each end of the body. They are unique among insects in being strictly pelagic or limnetic: as the only insects that do not have to visit the surface for breathing, or to sit, cling, climb, or burrow, they are as free in the water as are copepods and Cladocera. Corethra larvae are predacious, seizing Entomostracans and rotifers with their antennae and devouring them.

Because of the air-sacs within the body some species of Corethra are able to live during most of the daylight period in the depths of lakes where oxygen is almost entirely wanting and where, therefore, they are safe from most of their enemies. At night they rise to higher levels as practically invisible phantoms to seek their prey and renew their supplies of oxygen.

In the decaying leaves along shore, especially in smaller ponds, one may sometimes find the slender-bodied larvae of the phantom cranefly, with its needle-like breathing tube extended to the surface of the water, or the larvae of the dronefly, or rat-tailed maggot, with its long telescopic air tube (Fig. 11); or one finds the stiff spindle-shaped larvae of a soldier fly thrusting the small hinder end of its body through the surface film to draw air into the spiracles. These, particularly the rat-tailed maggot, seem most at home—at least they are safest from competitors and enemies—in foul water.

Only brief mention need be made of the *Lepidoptera*, the order of butterflies and moths. We do not generally associate moths with water; but there are aquatic caterpillars. The lily-leaf caterpillars, which live beneath the water in little cases made of two pieces cut from a lily pad, sometimes work noticeable damage to the water lilies. Other species use the leaves of pond-weed (Potamogeton), of Nuphar (the spatterdock or yellow water lily), or of the tape grass (Vallisneria). A particularly pernicious aquatic caterpillar is the "rice caseworm" of Eastern Asia, Japan, and the Dutch East Indies. The flying insect that emerges from the pupa of the lily-leaf caterpillar is a small moth, which may travel on the surface film, partly running, partly flying—at least, with wings fluttering, its legs give support on the surfaced film (Berg, C. O., 1950).

The insects dealt with so far live in water only as nymphs or larvae, the winged adults being aerial in habit. The aquatic representatives of the next two orders may live in or on the water at all times, although many retain wings and may emerge on occasion to crawl about or to fly from one pond to another. Some live in streams, but they are mostly in pools, ponds, and lakes.

Technically, only insects of the order *Hemiptera* are properly called "bugs." For this group any of the standard reference books is useful; but Hungerford's volume of 1919 is the best special work, not to mention his later papers. Most familiar of aquatic bugs are the water striders. Running over the surface, and occasionally diving beneath it, are the larger water striders of the family Gerridae, with long slender bodies and the smaller ones of the family Veliidae with shorter and stouter bodies, the "broad-shouldered water-striders," certain kinds of which are mentioned in the chapter on "The Upland Stream." Water striders prey in part upon insects that rise to the surface and upon those that fall from the overhanging bushes (Fig. 27).

Within the water, but occasionally rising to the surface for new supplies of oxygen, are the "back swimmers" (Notonectidae) and "water boatmen" (Corixidae) often to be found in great numbers. The back swimmers have backs formed like the bottom of a boat and navigate upside down; they hang head-downward from the surface or dive swiftly, using their long hind legs as oars. On the underside of the body, actually the upper side as they swim, they carry a silvery film of air for breathing while they are submerged. The buoyancy of this film of gas causes the inversion of the body. Under water they either swim actively or cling by their front feet to a stick or a plant stem. Equipped, as are all Hemiptera, with puncturing and sucking beak, they attack and suck the juices from tadpoles, smaller fish, and other insects. When held in the hand, one may inflict a severe sting with the beak, as, doubtless, it does to its natural prey. Back swimmers are very destructive to young fish and other small animals.

Water boatmen, on the other hand, always swim with backs up, employing, like back swimmers, their oar-like hind limbs. Their bodies are "wrapped in a glistening blanket of air"; consequently, to remain submerged they must cling to something, which they do by the use of the middle legs. They are said to prey on mosquito larvae; yet water boatmen, unlike other Hemiptera, are not notably predacious but feed to a considerable extent upon vegetable matter, including diatoms and filamentous algae of the bottom.

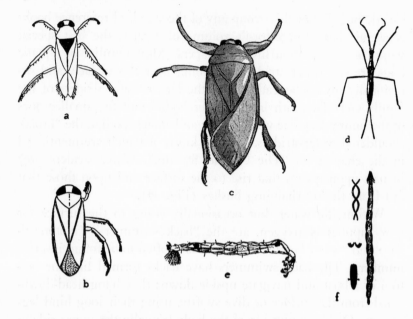

FIGURE 27. Some true "bugs" and gnats.

(a) Back swimmer, *Notonecta* (from Imms). (b) Water boatman, *Corixa* (from Imms). (c) Giant water bug, electric light bug, *Lethocercus*. (Drawing by W. K. Hubbell, after Essig.) (d) Water scorpion, *Ranatra* (from Comstock). (e) Phantom larva, *Chaoborus* (*Corethra*), of a midge. (f) Larva of a small gnat, "No-see-um," *Ceratopogon* (from Miall).

The "water scorpion" (Ranatra), which may be nearly two inches long, resembles in external form the "walking-stick" of the land (an orthopteran, or relative of the grasshoppers and crickets, a group rarely represented in water). At the end of the body they have a long air-tube, through which they draw from the atmosphere while the head and raptorial forelimbs hang two or three inches beneath the surface; they are extremely predacious. A smaller "water scorpion" (Nepa), less than an inch long, crawls in debris about the shores.

The largest Hemipterans of the pond are the giant water bugs of the family Belostomatidae, wide, flat-bodied, predacious insects. Middle and hind legs, flattened and fringed, give power for propulsion; forelimbs serve as strong arms for seizing prey; the long sharp proboscis inflicts a severe wound and sucks out juices from the victim. The bugs have short air-breathing organs at the end of the abdomen. Largest of these are the "electric-light bugs" (Lethocerus), two inches or more in length, and very destructive to fish. It has been observed to catch a young pickerel three and five-eighths inches long (Hungerford, 1919, p. 149).

Only two other groups of water bugs can be mentioned. The "water measurers" (Hydrometra), half an inch or less in length, are semi-aquatic in habit; they wander amidst the cattails and floating algae, spearing mosquito larvae and other prey beneath the surface. Little "creeping water bugs," (as Pelocoris of the family Naucoridae) creep about in dense vegetation. Of all the water bugs only the water boatmen are lacking in rapacity, and most of them, when handled, can inflict a painful puncture.

Back swimmers, water scorpions, and giant water bugs undoubtedly play a very great part in controlling the abundance of other insects and larger animals of the pond, for they attack and destroy animals very much larger than themselves; they are all the more destructive because they do not devour the bodies but only suck the juices. As with the true bugs, so it is with the beetles (*Coleoptera*), that ponds and lakes, rather than swift streams, harbor the greatest number of aquatic species and of individuals. Milling about over the surface are bevies of the familiar "whirligig beetles," "sweet bugs," or "apple bugs" (Gyrinidae). They seem to have four eyes, two that look upward into the air and two that look downward into the water. Actually, there is only a single pair of eyes located on the sides of the head; but the sharp flanged margins of the head before and behind the eye extend across it to make a continuous flange. The part of the flange that bridges the eye so separates the upper facets of the eye from the lower that there seem to be distinct upper and lower eyes. Occasionally these habitants of the surface film dive beneath the surface, for they are predatory. The larvae are less readily seen as they crawl like caddisflies through the debris at the bottom, preying upon young mayflies and other small aquatic insects. The Halipids, or "crawling water beetles," are all very small, one-fifth of an inch in length or less, but they are numerous and widely distributed in the debris and vegetation of most ponds. In both larval and adult states they are said to feed almost exclusively upon filamentous algae and the plants Chara and Nitella.

Generally the most conspicuous, as well as the most rapacious of water beetles, are those of the family Dytiscidae which well merit the common name of "predacious diving beetles." Some of them, Dytiscus and Cybister for example, are among the largest of aquatic insects—an inch to an inch and a half in length. There are many species and great diversity of sizes; but even the smallest kinds, hardly more than microscopic in size, seem to be highly predatory. When at the surface "diving beetles" hang head-downward, lifting their wing covers to draw in air. In the chambers beneath the covers, invisible from the outside, they carry a supply of air that enables them to stay under water for a considerable length of time. The larvae, known as "water tigers," are as rapacious as the adults. When at rest they also hang head-downward from the surface, for they breathe air directly from the atmosphere through a pair of spiracles at the tip of the abdomen. Beneath the water, they crawl about seeking tadpoles, snails, small fish, and other objects of prey (Fig. 28).

As an exaggerated picture of the normal warfare beneath the surface of the pond, there may be cited a chance observation in our laboratory: a single larva of Cybister about three inches in length was left one evening in an aquarium with two or three

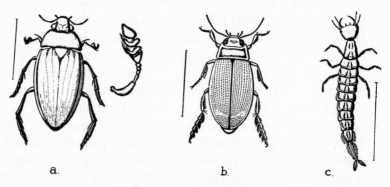

a.   b.   c.

FIGURE 28. Some beetles.

(a) Water-scavenger beetle, *Hydrophilus,* the clubbed antenna is folded in and not seen in the figure of the whole animal but is shown, enlarged, at right. (b) Predaceous diving beetle, *Dytiscus.* (c) Water tiger, larva of predaceous diving beetle (from Miall).

dozen back swimmers; at once water tiger attacked back swimmers and back swimmers fought tiger. By morning the water tiger had killed all the back swimmers but three, and the back swimmers had killed the water tiger.

Almost as abundant and sometimes nearly as large as the diving beetles are the hydrophilids or "water scavenger beetles," which, in the adult state, feed chiefly on algae and, therefore, are of very different biological significance as compared with the dytiscids. Scavenger beetles may be distinguished from diving beetles by their habit of hanging from the surface with the head up, by the possession of short clubbed antennae and, commonly, by the silvery sheen of the undersides of the body. At the surface air is raked in by the antennae and then carried as a shining film of gas beneath the body. Although adult hydrophilids, in contrast to dytiscids, are typically vegetarian, yet the larvae are carnivorous and perhaps equally as destructive as those of dytiscids. One of the most common hydrophilids is Tropisternus, a shiny black beetle half an inch or less in length.

The larvae of a few Chrysomelid or leaf-eating beetles, Donacia and Galerucella, live on underground stems of water lilies, pondweeds, and other aquatic plants. The presence of these is evidenced in season by the round holes cut through the leaves of lily pads. Through such holes the female, which walks on the lily pads or flies in the air, thrusts its ovipositor to place a double row of eggs in a gluey mass surrounding the hole in the leaf. The eggs are in the water and the larvae, when hatched, fall to the bottom to live on the underground stems, feeding upon plant tissues and drawing oxygen from the "air-spaces" that are found within the plants even at a depth of several feet below the surface of the water.

Of course, destruction and scavengering in the pond are not the sole community functions of beetles and bugs; they form part of the food supply of fish, turtles, and ducks—and of other beetles and bugs, too, as shown, particularly, by Wilson (1923).

VERTEBRATES

Consideration of the animal kingdom by its great divisions is concluded with mention of the *Chordata*, which for fresh waters embraces only the vertebrates. We think now of fishes of many kinds, of frogs and salamanders, of turtles and snakes, of birds and mammals. Among birds, we are concerned not only with those called aquatic, which swim and dive or wade, but also with the kingfishers and those more strictly terrestrial in habit which feed in part upon insects that emerge from the stream—"a phoebe nest under every bridge," someone has commented. Among mammals we must consider muskrats and mink which swim in the water and also raccoons and bears that come to the shores to fish and feed.

Because of their sizes, the aquatic vertebrates are more conspicuous to the eye and generally of more interest to man than are the smaller animals without backbones. Man's concern with aquatic animals is based upon the direct utility of some—the edible fishes, ducks and geese, and the furbearing mammals—and upon the destructiveness of others, such as snakes, kingfishers, turtles, and some fishes of general ill favor.

As numbers go, and even when measured in total bulk, the vertebrates constitute a relatively small part of the life of the lake. They are at the apex of the "pyramid of numbers," except for the few aquatic vertebrates that are vegetarian. The lower and broader levels of the pyramid are occupied by the plants and the much more abundant smaller vegetarian animals. Obviously the animals of lower level in the pyramid must occur in such numbers as to support predators that consume each year many times their own weight of prey; and, if each kind is to maintain its own existence for its own good and for the continued support of the predators, there must also be always an excess of numbers in the species that are preyed upon. The base of the pyramid of numbers must be the plants, both those visible to the eye and those that can be seen only through the microscope. These have the double task of supporting all the animal life of the pond while maintaining each its own populations—not necessarily as a continuously adequate source of food for animals. Whatever contribution a particular species of plant makes to the total bill-of-fare for animals, it may make intermittently; yet, between the

PHOTO BY ALLEN RINEHART
Courtesy of National Park Service

Pl. 22. *Eastern brook trout over white sand bottom. The light-colored fish have been in the pond much longer than the others.*

Pl. 23. *Rainbow trout.*

PHOTO BY JACK DERMID
Courtesy of North Carolina Wildlife Resources Commission

From United States Bureau of Fisheries painting

Pl. 24. *Channel cat, or speckled cat.*

Pl. 25. *Yellow bullhead.*

Courtesy of North Carolina Wildlife Resources Commission

times of its abundance, it must maintain a reserve for its subsequent activity in propagation.

Although the principle of the pyramid of numbers is valid and generally indisputable—each kind on a lower level of the pyramid having to support the animals of higher levels while maintaining itself—yet the concept may readily be assumed to be much simpler than it is. Let us note a few significant qualifications. One is that recognition must be given, not merely to numbers in the populations existing at a given moment, or to volume or mass, but also to the fecundity of the species. It is not just the grass in the meadow on a particular day that measures the grazing capacity of the pasture; rates of growth and reproduction of the grasses have their parts in determining the number of cattle that may find continued sustenance in the area. Put in another way, it is not the food available on a given day that keeps the stock; it is the capacity of the land, or of the farmer, to keep on replenishing the granary and the pasture. Another qualification that must be kept in mind is that the apex of the pyramid is not reserved for large animals alone. The protozoan that feeds only upon other protozoa would be as close to the tip of the pyramid as is the largest and most voracious bass or pike, except for the fact that the little protozoan may regularly be the food of other and larger animals. So it is also for the dragonfly nymph, the back swimmer bug, and the water tiger or predatory diving beetle. Furthermore, even a fair-sized predator may, occasionally, step from the top to the base of the pyramid to take some plant food. A fourth and last qualification: as the apex of the pyramid is not the exclusive seat of larger predators, so also the predators of larger size are not *at all times* occupants of the topmost bench. "All oaks from acorns grow"; so all fish begin as eggs, to become minnow-sized "fry" and "fingerling," and all frogs were once tadpoles. Allusion has already been made to the fact that young fish serve as food for dragonfly nymphs, beetles, and bugs (which may be eaten by larger fish) and even, on occasion, for the tiny hydra. As fish come in all sizes and behave in diverse ways, so they play diverse and variable roles in the general ecology of the pond, in the "turnover" of materials through the cycle of food.[4]

It has been remarked that the fry of all fish feed chiefly upon Entomostraca (the small Crustacea) and the less numerous animals of corresponding sizes. As they become older, midge larvae, mayfly larvae, the smaller beetles and bugs are sought and then the larger insects, crayfishes, frogs, and young fish are preyed upon. Tadpoles and omnivorous catfishes play a great and useful part as scavengers, consuming the dead animals and fragments of animals that might otherwise cause excessive bacterial decomposition. Larger fish, feeding upon bugs and beetles, aid in controlling the numbers of insects, as the bugs and beetles, feeding upon young fish, contribute to a proper control of the fish population. Suckers, passing the bottom mud through their intestines, feed to a considerable extent upon numerous bodies of small animals and probably on plants and detritus as well. Surface-feeding top-minnows capture mosquito larvae as they rise to the surface for oxygen. Bass, pike, bowfin, and gar pikes, of extremely predacious habit, fatten their own bodies while rendering a necessary service in controlling the numbers of other fishes—and even of their own kinds, for bass eats bass. A pond stocked with sunfishes but lacking bass, pike, or other strong predators, may produce excessive numbers of sunfish which, in the rigorous competition for a limited food supply, are individually poorly nourished and dwarfed in size. (See following chapters on the fish pond.) Predators have their uses, even to the prey.

It is noteworthy that very few fishes are vegetarian; nearly all depend upon other animals to convert plant substance into food suitable to their use. Muskrats, on the other hand, are to be ranked partly as converters of the first order, feeding directly upon plants, although they may also capture and devour mussels and other aquatic animals.

We cannot now discuss the vertebrates at length; yet mention should be made of the fact that, through certain vertebrates, the pond contributes in a material way to the life on land. The toads,

4. The Eltonian concept of the "pyramid of numbers" was treated briefly on page 96, above. It is well analyzed by Odum (1953).

leaving the pond in which they have been reared as toadpoles, carry away from the pond a substantial amount of organic matter in their own tissues; and so it is with herons and shore birds, with raccoons and bears, which feed from the shore; all of these draw on the life of the pond for life on land, making a predominantly one-way outward flow of organic matter. The outflow may, of course, be balanced by income to the pond from other sources.

THE COMMUNITY AS A WHOLE IN SUMMARY

As we have surveyed the animal life of the pond, we have gotten, perhaps, some suggestion of the complexity of the interrelations between the several members of the community. The diversity of members, both plant and animal, is immense. The web of life they form together is not capable of being completely unravelled. Provisionally we may think of the community of life within the pond as a unit, as a single organism,[5] and of the various kinds of animals and plants as parts or tissues of that organism. Our studies would then have to do with what we might call the *metabolism* of the pond as a whole, or what the Germans call "Stoffwechsel" (the materials-change). In the last analysis, the foundations of life in the pond are the inorganic substances dissolved in water, the light and heat from the sun, and, to a less extent, the gases of the atmosphere. The plants are the producers, utilizing those raw materials and the wastes of animals, as well as their own, to make protoplasm and protoplasmic products, and to liberate oxygen; the animals are the converters, transforming the products of plant metabolism into animal tissue; the bacteria of decomposition are the reducers, returning the otherwise unutilized parts and products of animals and plants to the original form of inorganic salts and water. The reducers never make return of the energy drawn from the sun, and this must, therefore, be a regular although intermittent contribution from without.

5. Analogy between a community and an organism has merit only for certain special purposes. An organism, plant or animal, is mortal; it is an individual that begins life, matures, becomes senescent, dies, and is no more. A community has no term of life; it changes, it evolves, it becomes something other than what it was; but, barring a cataclysm, there is no end to the community.

It is an easy matter to conceive of the operation of this cycle in the littoral and illuminated regions in summer when plants are continually growing and often reproducing themselves and animals find unceasing replenishment of their basic food supply. Even here, though, we may notice a certain appearance of waste: the larger pondweeds seem scarcely to be utilized as food, although they may be serving a secondary and immediately useful purpose in affording bases of attachment for small algae and protozoa and offering lodging—or protection ("shelter")—for insect larvae and even for fish. Further reference to these plants is made in the next paragraph. In the limnetic region, too, we readily envision a considerable part of the organic cycle: the microscopic plants of the plankton make use of sunlight, dissolved chemicals and gases, to produce proteins, carbohydrates, and the precursors of vitamins, which are to be utilized by their animal associates. What becomes of the dead or weakened bodies that fall below the zone of sunlight?

The dark profundal region presents another aspect of the whole picture. Without original production in the darkness, the animals of this region are dependent for food in part upon bodies of dead or weakened limnetic organisms that rain down as manna from above and of the small organisms that drift outward from the zones of vegetation. There is yet another source of nutriment for them. Throughout the pond, on the bottom, there are vast numbers of small animals whose food is generally described as "detritus." So numerous are the detritus feeders that we naturally look for a prolific source of this finely divided organic matter. The seemingly unutilized plants of the littoral zone come particularly into consideration. Most of the rooted plants around the margins of the pond are little consumed by animals during the growing season; sooner or later they die; eventually, in consequence of wave action and in course of processes of decomposition, the dead plants suffer fragmentation and become divided into the small particles that we know as plant detritus.

Equally basic, with inorganic salts and sunlight, is the gaseous oxygen, required in respiration of plants and animal and aerobic bacteria of decomposition; it must be found in solution in the water. Since water, at the best, will hold in solution but a very small proportion of the atmospheric gases, oxygen is not available *ad libitum* to animals of the water, as it is to those of the land. Indeed, the oxygen problem in water may at times be a critical one; the movements and the distribution of animals are often governed primarily by the distribution of dissolved oxygen. The sources of this free oxygen in the pond are, of course, the atmosphere at the surface, the larger plants, the filamentous algae and the microscopic algae of the plankton and those of the bottom. Its distribution throughout the pond, as has been previously mentioned, is accomplished at times by vertical convection currents, at times by the wind-driven circulation of water.

The greater the amount of decomposition going on in the pond, the greater is the demand upon the oxygen supply by bacteria. It follows, then, that the richer the pond may be in plankton and in life of the littoral (and the greater the bulk of consequent organic waste that goes to the bottom), the scantier is the residual oxygen supply in the profundal region. That region of deep lakes may, indeed, become by midsummer quite uninhabitable for ordinary benthonic animals.

Our picture is a mere sketch without the details that are essential to a thorough understanding of the actual interrelations of the various units of life in the pond. We glimpse the activities of the plants and of the animals that feed everywhere upon them, upon detritus, or upon one another; we sense the unceasing bionomic battle, the preying and the being preyed upon, the competition for food and oxygen between those that are not actually mutual enemies, the deaths and the decay which are really so essential a part of the cycle of life. We conceive of a great organic cycle, the links being inorganic salts (in water and soils), the water itself, the light from the sun, the plants and the animals, one offering support or competition to another, and each in some measure affecting the abundance of all the others.

The interrelations are too complex for arbitrary judgments of what is useful and what is harmful in the lake. In a lake without predators, the vegetarian animal might reproduce to such an extreme as to exhaust the available food supply and bring themselves to the verge of starvation. A reasonable control of numbers promotes the best welfare of any particular group. The farmer promotes the welfare of his stock or his crops when he limits the number of animals in the pasture or the number of plants per acre. In a natural body of water, nature practices a similar control by pitting one kind against another, until a proper balance is obtained. If the animal breeder is a friend to his cattle when he reduces the number to fit the pasture, so, the pike may not be doing disfavor to the perch when it regulates its abundance. The usefulness of enemies is a reality in nature.

On the whole a sort of equilibrium prevails. To some extent the condition of balance in a particular pond or lake and the whole picture of life in it change from season to season and from year to year; yet ordinarily the state of equilibrium never shifts far from that normal to the pond. The strength of the community is in the condition of equilibrium—the maintenance of a balance between all kinds of conflicting agents and forces. We can appreciate this fundamental principle, and, by patient and persistent research, we can learn more and more about the various kinds of animals and plants involved and about their interrelations.

CHAPTER 14

The Fish Pond and Its Residents

Each Pond a Special Problem

Perhaps the first thing to recognize in building a fish pond is that, no matter how faithfully one follows all the rules of construction, stocking, fertilization, and management, the pond will not always produce in accordance with reasonable expectations. There are several reasons for this. In the first place, all the conditions of productivity in ponds are not yet fully known. In the second place, each pond is a special case; it is well known to experimental fish-culturists that two ponds, made as nearly alike as possible and supplied with equal quantities of water from the same source, will often differ notably in the composition and density of the populations of food organisms that develop in them; and the several ponds in a region are never exactly alike in size or in form; nor are they supplied with just the same water, when the surface flow from surrounding land is considered. In different regions there are even greater differences in the soils and the waters that supply the basic inorganic food substances.

Another reason for obscurity as to what goes on in ponds is the obvious one, that the pond manager has only indirect evidence of the results of any particular procedure of management. The farmer who seeds and fertilizes a pasture can watch the grass grow. He puts cattle to graze on different clovers and can weigh them when he pleases; he does not have to plow up the pastures to count his sheep. With a pond, he can only count and weigh his fish after draining out the water—and the "pasturage" with it! Of course, if he is a serious fish farmer, he can learn a lot by sampling techniques, when he knows how to interpret the results of sampling. Ordinary methods of capture of fish by angling or seining are only particular methods of sampling and are apt to be selective and misleading.

The basic difficulties and obscurities that have been mentioned do not militate at all against the interest or profit of fish-farming. They should only add zest to the pursuit and stimulate the spirit of experimentation with analysis of results. It is not the purpose in this chapter to offer specifications for pond contruction or management. Helpful circulars on these subjects can readily be obtained from federal and state agencies or from county advisers. Good books on fish-culture are available, such as those of Edmister (1942) and Davis (1953). Edmister gives detailed instructions for construction, stocking, fertilization, and management of fish ponds. Of a more technical nature and more comprehensive is that of Rounsefell and Everhart (1953). It may be of use here, however, to consider some of the principles of fish-culture in ponds.

The primary considerations in pond construction and management are: area, depth, form, water supply, and amount of flow through; temperature, light, turbidity, and condition of shore line and of drainage area; vegetation for oxygenation, food, and shelter; association of species of fish, control of numbers, enemies, and exploitation; conditions for reproduction; bottom conditions, food, and fertility. At first glance, consideration of all of these items seems a large order; but one cannot have much understanding of a pond without recognition of the fact that it is an elaborate complex of interacting factors within and without. Let us consider the several items as they have been grouped.

Pond and Water Supply

In respect to area, depth, and form, only a few general remarks need be made. A pond may be of any size, but one less than a quarter of an acre in size cannot be expected to provide food or protection for significant numbers of legal-size fish of any species. For such predator fishes as the black basses, an acre or more is desirable for maintenance of adequate food supply for even a few large fish. As to depth, there needs to be a substantial area of shallow water to afford spawning grounds and nurseries for food organisms. Such waters are likely to become very warm in summer and perhaps to freeze solid in winter. If it is a wintering pond, a third of the pond, at least, should have a depth of six feet or more—in northern states and Canada perhaps ten feet or more. So much depends upon climatic conditions that advice should always be sought from competent local sources. Form is important but no rule can be stated. A pond may be bowl-shaped, or it may have two or more substantial arms; the terrain available will largely determine form. The desired relations of areas of shallow and deeper water must, however, be kept in mind. The more irregular the form with given slopes of land, the greater is the amount of shallow water.

The greater the flow of water through the pond, the less is the pond self-contained, the greater is the loss of food material and of the fertilizer applied. Since the pond owner is usually not interested in fertilizing the stream below the dam, he may want no discharge at all from the pond. Water must come in to compensate for loss by evaporation and seepage, but an approximately exact balance is properly sought. This means that there should be, on one or both sides, channels of diversion for excess flow in the stream supplying the pond. These are particularly needed in times of flood, and even more so when the flood water of surface drainage is likely to be muddy. Silt brought into the pond with flood water not only makes an unwanted condition of turbidity, but also, as it settles, tends to smother food organisms on the bottom and to fill the basin. Even with an entirely spring-fed pond, diversion channels may be needed against surface drainage in times of heavy rains. More about diversion channels will be said in the next section. There are, of course, a great and growing number of ponds that depend entirely upon surface drainage —"sky ponds," they are often called; the extremes of level and depth in times of drought and heavy rainfall make these less suitable for game fishes; but they can be productive of fishes of more sluggish habit that are tolerant of the fluctuations in area and depth—and sometimes even of trout.

Temperature, Light, and Turbidity

Temperature and light are both critical factors in organic production. Temperature has already been mentioned as affected by the amount of shallow water. Much of the heat absorbed directly by the water is used for evaporation. The earth under shallow water is easily warmed by the sun's rays that reach it, and the warm bottom heats the water above it by conduction. Everyone knows that water in a shallow pool may become really hot on a bright summer day. The shade of trees protects water and bottom, but trees also drop leaves and this is sometimes harmful.

Temperature determines to a great extent the kinds of fish that can be reared with success in ponds of a particular region. At high altitudes or in cold regions trout thrive in ponds. Smallmouth bass will tolerate somewhat warmer water. In most lowland regions dependence must be on warm-water fish, such as largemouth bass, crappie, bream, sunfishes, and many others.

The farmer can do little about light except as he tries to prevent turbidity and to keep the pond free from floating-leaved plants and algae blankets. Pond lilies and some other aquatics in dense populations keep too much light from the submerged oxygenating plants, drifting or rooted. The floating "blankets" of filamentous algae may have pernicious effects in more than one way; these are usually removable with little difficulty by the appropriate use of copper sulphate. The prevention of turbidity by the use of diversion channels has been mentioned in a preceding paragraph. A frequent cause of turbidity in farm ponds is the trampling of cattle or the rooting of pigs along the margins and in the shallows. Decision has to be made between the respective values of the pond for stock watering or for fish production. In any case, attention should be given to all practicable grooming of the banks with covering grasses, as a protection against erosion and turbidity caused by wave action. The more the whole drainage area can be kept in lush permanent pasture, the less is the erosion of the soil and the beclouding of water in the pond. Fertility lost from the pasture may be recovered in fish from the pond. In some regions it is found that, even with good cover crops, the surface drainage picks up clay or silt and carries it to the pond. Diversion channels on both sides of a pond will, of course, prevent the salvage by the pond of the fertilizer lost from the pasture. It is the conditions of a particular situation which must guide the manager of the pond. The effects of turbidity and some methods of dealing with it are discussed earlier.

Rooted Vegetation

The question of vegetation in ponds has long been a moot one. I believe that the trend of thought in some quarters is now against the use of rooted aquatics at all. To an extent, the answer to the question may depend upon how meticulously one wants to manage his pond with fertilization, periodic control of numbers of each species of fish, and so on. At the risk of offending some competent specialists in fish production, I will deal briefly with the chief functions of the larger aquatic plants in natural ponds. (See also, Eddy, 1940.) These are oxygenation, forage (green or dead), and shelter. It is, of course, the photosynthesis of green plants that, in supplement to surface absorption from the atmosphere, provides the oxygen necessary to the growth and activities of animals and plants, including the more desirable bacteria of decomposition. Oxygenation is affected both by rooted aquatics and the microscopic algae of the plankton. With proper fertilization the minute drifting algae may adequately do the job. In most natural ponds it seems likely that the submerged rooted plants are the chief oxygenators. Plants with floating leaves are of less value in this respect, since part of the oxygen is given off into the atmophere rather than into the water.

Plants with vegetative structures completely submerged, although flowering or fruiting stems may break through the surface, or those with narrow leaves or with finely divided and often needle-like foliage, have a maximum of surface exposure and are good oxygenators while offering a minimum of shade. Some of these will be mentioned shortly. It can be said now, however, that we ought to have more precise knowledge of the relative efficiencies of the different kinds of aquatic plants in supplying oxygen.

As food the green aquatics are not directly consumed to as great an extent as might be expected. Carp and goldfish feed heavily on aquatics; but the fish we want are largely carnivorous; the insects, crustacea, worms, and mollusks that the small fish feed upon are grazers chiefly on the microscopic and filamentous algae, on small animals, adrift or on the bottom, or on detritus, the dead and comminuted organic material at the bottom. Some insect larvae forage lightly on the leaves of higher plants. It is in contribution to the great supply of nutritive detritus that aquatics play their greatest role as forage. It has been suggested, indeed, that it is a special and peculiarly favorable adaptation of nature that the plants in water should not, while they are growing, be consumed to any great extent, so that there might be a large crop in the fall[1] to die, to be broken up by wave action and partial decomposition, and thus to produce a fairly enduring deposit of organic detritus. Certainly this organic detritus is a principal food of many of the small insect larvae and worms and thus constitutes a large link in the food chain that leads up to the larger fish. It is also feed for some fishes.

Another important function of plants is in providing support and shelter. Microscopic examination of the leaves and stems of plants in water will reveal immense numbers of microscopic organisms that require some base of attachment, even if clinging only temporarily: diatoms, protozoa, rotifers, and crustacea. Fish-culturists have this in mind when they speak of plants as "food producers," in distinction from plants as food.[2] The leaves are good browsing ground for snails, insect larvae, and crustaceans. The stems and leaves also provide another requirement in natural ponds—"shelter," or a place of concealment. In the clear open water a small organism survives, or is consumed, according to whether a hungry predator comes along; there is, literally, "no place to hide." We want the vegetarians and other small food

1. The suggestion could well have been based on the observation that a farmer keeps his livestock out of his grain or hay fields—at least until the season's crop is made.

2. The food-producing values of rooted aquatics are not to be accepted as axiomatic and invariable. Dense growth of plants in a pond was found to have an adverse effect on the minute algae and rotifers of the drifting community, without unfavorably affecting the crustacea (Hasler, A. D., 1949).

organisms to be eaten by larger animals; but it is clearly undesirable that *all* should be consumed, that there should not be at
least a continuing brood stock. This is where the aquatics in
shallow water serve a useful function. Even though these underwater "jungles" are invaded by predators, it is not easy for them
to reduce the population of the prey below a level that insures
reproduction and thus an enduring food supply. It may be easier
to shoot quail over an open field; but would inland game birds
and animals survive so well without trees, shrubbery and other
"shelter"? It may be mentioned here that brush piles put into
the pond are favored shelter for crappies and many other fishes.

Two personal experiences may be illustrative. Some years ago,
before the era of pond fertilization and modern pond management, a friend of the writer sought counsel as to stocking a fish
pond he was planning. He was advised to use certain submerged
aquatics but to avoid pond lilies if he wanted the best results in
fish production. But, he said, he *wanted* lilies. In the end, he had
a really good lily pond, with some fish. After two or three years,
another friend sought advice and received the same suggestions.
He elected, however, to follow the advice of the first friend,
which was to shun *all rooted aquatics,* because hooks became
entangled in them! A couple of years later the second pond
owner was sure that the advice of the first was sound; he was then
catching easily large numbers of sizable bream. After another
year or two he was complaining that, while he had large numbers
of small fish, there were none of desirable size. Examination of
the pond revealed the fact that there was no shelter whatever in
the pond, except where, close along the shores, a little grass had
escaped control. In the light of present knowledge the conditions
might have been improved by fertilization and drastic reduction
of stock. That was realized at the time, but such practices were
not then commonly acceptable. The only point to be made is
that, in ponds left to natural development after stocking, some
sort of shelter, such as is provided by proper rooted aquatics, is
favorable to maintenance of food organisms and a desirable balance of populations.

An excellent illustration of the value of shelter to aquatic insects, even when the insects and the shelter is *not* wanted, was afforded by the observations of the late Dr. S. F. Hildebrand in brickyard pits near Augusta, Georgia, during the First World War. Dr. Hildebrand (1922) of the United States Bureau of Fisheries, working with the United States Public Health Service, had seen to it that the pools were clear of ordinary aquatic vegetation that might afford shelter to mosquito wigglers and that they were stocked with top-minnows to consume what larvae might start upon life in the pits. Nevertheless, Anopheles mosquitoes continued to appear. By particularly close examination he found that there was along the margins a low-growing semiaquatic grass, *Hydrochloa carolinensis,* which sent out runners a foot or so into the water and that these gave effective protection to the larvae: with his guidance I personally observed the mosquito larvae swimming freely in the water near the shore, while fish were not in view. Whenever the top-minnows came near, the wigglers quickly swam to the grass and aligned their bodies along the stems, where they seemed to be unobserved by the minnows. Even the slight shelter afforded by this quite inconspicuous grass insured the local perpetuation of that unwanted species of mosquito.

As to whether or not aquatics should be introduced into a particular pond, the manager should consult local or state authorities. He or his adviser should consider how carefully and continuously he proposes to operate the pond with due attention to control of numbers, fertilization, and feeding. It is the intention here to deal with principles rather than with details of pond management. When a pond, after original stocking, is to be left substantially to nature, the submerged aquatics with narrow or finely divided leaves can be depended upon to provide oxygen, support for the useful epiphytes, protection for a diversity of desirable periphytes, shelter for larger organisms and, in time, an abundant supply of organic detritus, an important basic food supply. The interested pond owner will obtain valuable information from such comprehensive treatises on aquatic plants as those of Fassett and Muenscher, as well as from other sources. Dr. Emmeline Moore (1915 and 1920) did pioneering work on the forage value of some pond weeds and algae. An old but still useful pamphlet by Titcomb (1923) gives the experiences and impressions of many fish-culturists in respect to aquatics in hatching and rearing ponds. Fassett (1940) lists plants used by fish and also those used by birds and mammals.

The plant life of lakes was considered in a previous chapter. Merely as illustrations, there may be mentioned here a few common and apparently generally satisfactory aquatic plants for the fish pond.

There are numerous species of "pondweeds," as plants of the genus Potamogeton are called. Many kinds are good duck food, for their foliage or their nutlets in season. A number of common aquatic plants are shown in Figs. 13 and 14. Some, such as the floating-leaf pond weed, *P. natans,* are less desirable for fish ponds because of their fairly broad floating leaves. More to be favored are the eelgrass-leaved, or flat-stemmed pond weed, *P. zosteriformis,* the curly crisp-leaved pond weed, *P. crispus,* and the flat-growing Robbins' pond weed, *P. robbinsii,* which lies on the bottom. The water weed, Anacharis (also called Philotria and, by aquarists, who use a giant variety, Elodea) and the tape grass, or wild celery, Vallisneria, have satisfactory growing habits, forming dense gardens on the bottom. Some of the arrowheads or duck potato (Sagittaria), the bur reeds (Sparganium), and the pickerel weeds (Pontederia) have submerged ribbon-leaves resembling the wild celery, but these are likely to have also leaves at or above the surface. The quillwort, Isoetes (a "club moss," akin to the ferns), with generally rigid, awl-shaped leaves, is favored by some; it grows in shallow water and along shores. A spike rush, Eleocharis, is also a good shallow-water plant. The pipewort, Eriocaulon, with its rosettes of slender pointed leaves, should be mentioned for its adaptability to the "sandy shores of soft-water lakes," where it may extend out into water of two meters depth. Another good shallow-water plant is the false loosestrife, Ludwigia, with richly colored green and purplish leaves; there are species that live on the moist exposed shores and extend out into shallow water and some that grow in deeper water.

There are species of the buttercup or crowfoot family, Ranunculus, that are fully aquatic and have finely divided leaves, the divisions of which are needle-like or sometimes like a broad fan of elaborately branching narrow ribbon. A water plant that seems to have every feature of satisfactoriness is the hornwort or coontail, *Ceratophyllum demersum,* a flowering plant that does not root, but merely lies loose in the water. It is easily recognized from its whorls of repeatedly forked leaves, the branches of which are toothed along one side. It is, naturally, a favorite with aquarists. A plant I have found most satisfactory in aquaria and have seen making a fine green carpet along shore and in the shallows of an old warm-water pond is the water purslane, *Didiplis diandra* (Coker, 1935). It was showy and prolific and it appeared in no way objectionable. Unfortunately, its occurrence seems to be sporadic and a stock for seeding is hard to find.

A plant often favored for aquaria is the parrot's feather, one of the water milfoils (Myriophyllum), with copius foliage of finely divided submerged leaves and somewhat broader emergent leaves. In my limited experience with some milfoils in ponds, they have proved objectionable because of great density of growth, the tendency for emergent leaves to blanket the surface, and the messiness of the tangle of long and decaying stems under water.

P. crispus, Anacharis, Ceratophyllum, and *Vallisneria* (its younger leaves, at least) are good for remaining green in winter and for continuing oxygenation.

Unquestionably aquatic plants sometimes overrun ponds and thus become nuisances. There are conditions, too, under which their service as protective shelters for insect larvae applies undesirably to mosquito wigglers. This is particularly the case with plants whose leaves break through the surface of the water. There are methods of control by mowing, by poisoning, or by fertilization, for which directions should be sought from federal or regional authorities. (See, particularly: Surber, 1943; Hogan, 1946; and Martin, 1953.) It is found that fertilization of the pond, by stimulating the growth and multiplication of "clouds" of drifting algae causes a shading that tends to smother out the rooted aquatics. Whatever action with reference to aquatics seems desirable in a particular case, it is never to be overlooked that the *periphytic* communities, that is to say, the algae and animals associated in one way or another with the higher aquatic plants, are major elements in the life of a pond. Virtually all the aquatic plants mentioned are forage for ducks and other forms of wildlife.

In more than one place reference has been made to mosquitoes breeding. The possibilities of this nuisance cannot, of course, be ignored; but it is not at all necessary that a pond for any good purpose should become a breeding place for mosquitoes or other vectors of disease. The advice of local health authorities or of specialists in pond management may be sought. The difficulty is most likely to arise with *new* ponds, especially if one tolerates flotage in the forms of bark, twigs or leaves, vegetation-bogged shallows, or isolated pools along the margins of the pond. (See Rector, 1950.)

Finally, some reference should be made to vegetation around the pond. Proper "grooming" of banks was suggested on an earlier page as preventative of soil erosion and turbidity, but this does not mean close mowing of all vegetation. As Wilson (1920) pointedly remarked:

A total absence of trees, shrubs, bushes, and weeds, with close-cut turf extending to the water's edge, may add to the sightliness of the pond, but it will operate against the odonate [dragonfly] fauna. The larger vegetation is not necessary; an area covered with tall weeds and grass somewhere around the margin of the pond will prove amply sufficient. (p. 233-234)

It is to be remembered that dragonflies and damselflies are the prime destroyers of mosquitoes and flies in the air and that their nymphs in the water feed heavily upon mosquito larvae when they are available. The nymphs are also food for fish.

The Fish Populations

Whatever the choice in association of species of fish for the pond, it is properly based on the principle of the *food chain,* which starts with the microscopic plants and protozoa, the organic detritus, and, to a limited extent, with the living green higher plants. The pond manager in this country is generally interested not in carp or other economically produced fish, but in the biologically inefficiently produced predators, the last link of the chain within the pond. If one were interested only in pounds of fish meat, the carp has, long since, been found to be an ideal fish-farm animal. It is said that "more animal protein can be produced on a hectare of land as carp flesh than in any other form" (Neess, 1946). The problem is to get the basic food converted into table-sized fish with as little waste of efficiency in conversion as is practicable; every link of the chain represents loss of basic food, material, and energy in the activities and wastes of the organisms constituting the successive links of the chain. The object is to shorten the chain. A popular combination of species includes bream (also called bluegill) and black bass. The bream consume more of the smaller animals and the bass devour the bream. The bream are both food for bass and, the larger ones, fish for the table. Red-ear sunfish or hybrid sunfish may be substituted for the bream.

The ideal arrangement is to have with the game fish others that are near the lowermost link of the chain—fish that may be called "vegetarian," although they are not strictly so, since they consume with the algae and plant remains all sorts of small animals, protozoans, worms, insect larvae, and others. Among such fishes are the golden shiner, *Notemigonus,* various forage minnows, and the gizzard shad, *Dorosoma cepedianum,* especially for southern waters. The mullet (Mugil) of the sea lives well in fresh water and, with fine filtering apparatus, is near the bottom of the food chain. The rearing of mullet in ponds is not new, but is not yet established in the United States. At North Carolina State College in Raleigh, the mullet is now being experimented with as to its possibilities as either food or forage fish in ponds of the interior.[3] It is at most questionable if the mullet

3. Information from Dr. F. S. Barkelow. In the United Nations volume, previously cited, the pond culture of mullet, *Mugil cephalus,* is discussed by S. Y. Lin (for *China*) and Mohamed Kamel El Saby (for *Egypt*). The latter assumes that the mullet must spawn in the sea. The rearing of mullet in ponds in certain countries of Europe, although well known, is not mentioned in that volume.

can be gotten to reproduce successfully in freshwater ponds. If it does not, that could be an advantage in cases where annual restocking was practicable: there would be no risk of overpopulating the pond with forage fish. The gizzard shad is not usually taken with hook and line, is not a desirable food fish, and serves only as prey for the game fish. Unless there are sufficient predators, the gizzard shad may become excessively abundant. Gold fish, as partly vegetarian, have sometimes been used as forage fish. In the writer's experience they may lose their color in ponds and become quite large.[4]

If we start with the principle of the food chain, we end with the equally critical and related principle of *balance*. We want the several components of the chain to be present in proper proportions. It is quite possible, indeed it is quite common, to have too many forage fish. Where numbers are excessive the competition for the available stock of small feed is too severe. The members of the group merely starve each other. The pond passes through a stage when there are far too many ill-fed feeders. The forage fish are driven to prey too much upon the young of the desired predators; so that roles may well be reversed. On the other hand, it is possible to have too many of the large predators, with the result that the surviving forage fish become too few to afford good feeding for the game fish, or even to maintain the integrity of their own populations. Inevitably, then, the preferred game fish, for lack of abundant prey, grow too slowly. It is not easy always to fix the condition of balance. Sometimes an unbalanced pond is notably improved by introducing a more effective predator, such as the northern pike. If predators are too numerous for their own good, the remedy may be found in more intensive fishing. Probably "underfishing" is a more common fault in the management of the pond than is "overfishing." Krumholz (1952), referring particularly to Indiana ponds, said:

Ordinarily, at least half of the total weight of any fish population can be harvested annually without having any detrimental effect on the ability of the population to maintain itself. In fact, the experi-

4. Goldfish became acclimated in the Potomac River. I have bought them in a food market in Washington under another name. They had the color and appearance of small carp.

mental evidence at hand indicates that such a harvest is highly desirable. Thus, most ponds in Indiana are capable of giving sustained annual yields of upwards of 150 pounds per acre. Even though such yields are possible, they are rarely, if ever, achieved because of inadequate fishing.

The land farmer has little difficulty in recognizing a lack of balance between the numbers of his cattle and the growth of the pasturage upon which they graze. The lack of balance in the pond is less directly obvious. It is clearly indicated, however, when there seems to be plenty of fishes, but unsatisfactory catches with respect to size of fish. Balance is realized when year after year the pond yields catches of fish of a reasonably good size and in satisfactory numbers relative to the conditions of fertility in the pond (Swingle, 1952; Meehean, 1952).

This will not ordinarily be the case, unless there is effective fishing. Under-fishing is probably the more common cause of improper balance. Misguided legislation and regulations have been accustomed to impose so many restrictions governing sizes, seasons and bag-limits that, as one investigator pointedly remarked, "All too often in the past, ridiculous as it appears, the law violator has actually been the true conservationist" (Stroud, 1952). It is always well to keep in mind that the total *weight of fish* in the pond need not be essentially different, whether you have a thousand small ones or a hundred big ones (Macan and Worthington, 1951, pp. 200, 202).

A bulletin of The Sport Fishing Institute mentioned among desirable forage fishes the "kokanee" for cold lakes of the Northwest. The kokanee is an interesting salmon of small size which, through generations it appears, has become habituated and adapted to live permanently in lakes of some northeastern states and Canada. It is identified as a sockeye salmon, *Oncorhynchus nerka,* being given the subspecific name of *kennerlyi* Suckley. Presumed to be of fairly recent origin, it differs from the parent species in size and color, in having a notable degree of immunity to the freshwater copepod parasite, Salmincola, and in not running down to the sea to complete its development. (See Ricker, 1940.)

Although the black bass-bream combination is now most popular for warm water regions, there are various other combinations that offer interest. Crappie are widely used, and rock bass in cooler waters—both as predators, smaller than the black basses, and as good panfish. White crappie are said to do better than bass and bream in turbid water (Meehean, 1952). It is the largemouth bass that is generally favored in warm-water ponds. It is said that the smallmouth bass does well in warm mud-bottomed ponds in Illinois if it does not have to compete with largemouth, crappies, sunfish, or bullheads (Bennett, 1952). The spotted bass is also used without the others. The carp-tench-pike and other carp associations, popular in European countries, and the most productive in fish meat, may be ignored because of the unpopularity of the carp on this side of the Atlantic.

Bullheads, small members of the catfish family, seem to respond well to the conditions of farm ponds, even turbid ones, and, although small, make good table fish. The speckled cat, or channel cat, *Ictalurus punctatus*, whose nesting habit is mentioned in a following section, is not only an excellent table fish, but quite gamey and often popular with sportsmen. A native of the Mississippi Basin and gulf drainage, it was introduced long ago into the Potomac River. As an indication of its popularity, the Washington papers used to give, and presumably still do, free publicity to the early runs of "Potomac cat." As will be seen below, it can readily be reared in ponds. According to a note by Roy Schoonover of Kansas Fish and Game, in *The Fisherman* for May, 1952, the channel catfish has such popularity in Kansas that the demand for stocking this species in farm ponds equals that for bass. The white bass (*Morone*) is advocated by some to serve both as forage fish and as panfish.

Cool water regions offer other possiblities in the trouts and, particularly, the rainbow trout. One of the finest home ponds I know of is in the mountains of southwestern North Carolina, where table-size rainbow are available at any time. In this particular case, the trout are regularly fed with commercial feeds and have made extraordinarily rapid growth. In farm ponds in New York State brook trout often do well. If the temperature of the water is not high, they do better than bass and bluegill, which grow too slowly in cold water. Productivity in trout responds well to applications of inorganic fertilizer. Natural reproduction in the pond may not be successful; so that annual restocking may be required (Saila, 1952).

In the matter of selection of species for stocking the pond and determination of numbers of each kind, as with other aspects of pond management, the best advice that can be given from this source is to "see your doctor," who in this case will be a regional agent or agency concerned with fish culture.

Control of populations is essential in a pond, as in a pasture, but it is easier to do in a pasture. A direct method which, however, is only occasionally applicable, is to drain the pond on occasion, perhaps once a year or two, salvage the fish, refill the pond, restock it with the desired number of individuals of each species, and discard or utilize the remainder. The disadvantages of this method are the labor involved, the time required to refill where water supply is limited, the difficulty in retaining the fish meanwhile, and, inevitably, the great loss of food carried away with the water drained out. Some of these difficulties are lessened when there are series of ponds. The conditions of over-population may sometimes be alleviated by seining out substantial number of the superabundant small fish. Generally the most practicable control is through proper predator-prey relations—nature's original method. Long ago European fish-growers sensed the importance of such control and, in ponds producing carp for the market, prescribed pike in the ratio of one pike to ten brood carp (Coker, 1918). One does not introduce a "wolf in the sheepfold" simply because there are better ways of controlling the populations of sheep on the range—ways that are not as readily available to the fish farmer. The common combination of bass and bream is, of course, a combination of predator and prey, with the predator most valued.

Control of populations is also effected in some degree by various kinds of enemies, which may not be viewed with complacency by the pond-owner. Among such are destructive fishes: carp, bowfin (grindle, mudfish), and gar pikes, which are not likely to occur in farm ponds. Other active enemies are: king-fishers, snapping turtles, water snakes (often called "moccasin," although not poisonous or closely related to the cottonmouth moccasin of southern swamps), mink, otters, and raccoons. The manager of the pond will use his own best judgment about dealing with these by shooting or trapping. It is an odd vagary of human psychology that, with natural lakes, sportsmen often object strongly to the use of traps or seines for the removal of the most vicious piscine enemies of game fish!

Definitely related to control of populations is the matter of exploitation—how much fishing should be done and at what seasons? It is only a few years since it seemed to be generally believed that it interfered more with the productivity of a pond to remove a fish on April 15 (or some other specified date) than on April 14; that production was less impaired by removing a fish having a length of x inches than one of length x-1 inches. The trend of thought now seems toward abandonment of the idea of "closed" seasons. It is not the intent here to propose rules or to discredit such as are in use. "Circumstances alter cases"; the intelligence of the manager, local experience and advice from those following the currents of experimentation and research will be better guides than any that could be prescribed in a general work. The writer would only express his strong conviction that most established ponds soon become over-stocked and that it is rarely possible to over-fish a pond or lake. It is obvious that every fish removed leaves for other fish the food it would have consumed. It should hardly be necessary to tell an experienced angler that lack of success in catching fish does not mean necessarily that fish are not present—and perhaps in over-abundance. Whether fish take the hook depends in some measure upon the skill of the angler, but also upon conditions of food supply, upon temperature and other physical conditions, and, doubtless also, upon the little understood idiosyncrasies of the fish themselves.

In justice to an apparently opposing view, the following quotation is made from a paper by Samuel Eddy (1940), which includes other interesting data:

Preliminary studies on sunfish and crappies have shown that only a very small number of fry, varying from 1% to 3%, survive to become fingerlings. From 10% to 75% of the fingerlings or 1 year-old fish survive to become 2 year-olds and from 10 to 40 per cent of the 2-year-olds survive at the end of the third year, when most of these fish reach what might be called adult size. Tagging studies of wall-eyed pike carried on in several Minnesota lakes by the U.S. Forest Service and the University, show that about 12% of the three and four year old fish die a natural death each year and that from 6% to 25% of these age classes are caught annually by fishermen.

These studies are but the beginning in determining the fate of the fish populations and have shown that the survival rate is not constant but varies in different lakes and also varies from year to year in the same lake. The results clearly indicate that a large number of fry must be produced annually, as only a small fraction will survive to become adults and that only a relatively small number of the adults can be taken without upsetting the sustained yield. (p. 11)

Taking the means of the several percentages of survival given above for fry, one-year fingerling, and two-year fish, and computing the cumulative percentage of survival, it would appear that three-year fish represent something on the order of .2 per cent of the original number of fry. The last clause of the quotation seems to imply that sport fishing can be pursued to the extent that an insufficient number of spawners remain. Consideration should be given to the possibility that, with a smaller number of spawners (and of consumers), the percentage of survival might be higher. It may be suggested also that, where fish in a pond of any size take the hook to the point of extreme depletion, a shortage of natural food is indicated. The spawners would then be more avid predators. It need always be remembered that if, year after year, more than one pair of young survived to breeding condition for each pair of original spawners, the population of the species would increase in geometric ratio until a catastrophic condition of starvation should bring an end to the uncontrolled increase.

There is, of course, the theoretical possibility that a particular pond or lake can be depleted of its brood stock by angling. The conditions under which this can occur must be rare. Special cases do not afford justification for indiscriminate imposition of restrictive regulations in the absence of evidence derived through sound scientific studies.

As Meehean (1951) has well said:

It is very difficult to convince the fisherman that ponds must be fished heavily to obtain maximum production. For over more than half-a-century he has been educated to the idea of protection by closing areas to fishing and by regulation of size and bag limits. Consequently, public thinking cannot be changed in a short period of time. (p. 139)

Finally, it may be stated as a basic principle that maximum production in a pond or lake depends upon a proper relation between the sizes of populations of the desired fishes and the food supply; populations of feed-organisms depend, in the first instance, upon fertility of the water and the bottom, and, in the second, upon the ravages of the predators. There is no gain in adding more fish (the desirable predators) if the balance is already weighted on that side. The need here is to reduce the number of fishes in any practicable way or to increase the basic food supply by fertilization. There is no gain, either, in enforcing restrictions that prevent the removal of coarse fishes (the undesirable predators).

Propagation Within the Pond

Whether or not a pond eventually becomes overstocked, there must be suitable conditions for the spawning of all kinds of fish it is desired to rear in the ponds. As pointed out elsewhere, one may sometimes prefer to restrict reproduction in the pond or to restock annually with fish that will not reproduce in the pond and possibly overcrowd it. The largemouth black bass and some sunfishes make their nests in relatively shallow and warm waters, with which a selfcontained pond should be well-supplied. It may be desirable to introduce quantities of sand or gravel on the spawning shoals. Smallmouth black bass are fish of cooler waters. Crappie are said to prefer running water for nesting. Where fish culture is practiced intensively as a business, as in Poland, it is common to have spawning ponds 15 to 30 inches in depth, fry-rearing ponds somewhat deeper, raising and stock ponds of successively greater depths up to 5 feet and wintering ponds of yet greater depth (Snieszko, 1941). Certain kinds of fish have special requirements. The buffalo-fish, important in rivers and sloughs of the Mississippi Basin, long baffled attempts to induce it to spawn in artificial ponds. Since it was known to spawn in overflow waters in the spring, it occurred to a scientist (Mr. A. F. Shira), at the former Fisheries Biological Station at Fairport, Iowa, to keep the water of a buffalo pond low in early spring and then, when the fish were ripe for spawning, to raise the level and let the water flow out over marginal land. The fish readily moved out over newly submerged ground and made their nests!

Another fish that had repeatedly failed to breed successfully in ponds was the channel catfish, speckled cat, or fiddler, *Ictalurus punctatus,* a particularly gamey and tasty fish. After a couple of years of further failure, the writer recalled hooking from the bottom of a lake in Michigan a broken pitcher which contained a catfish over a nest of eggs. The catfish of the pitcher was not a channel cat, but this suggested the provision of similar nooks, such as in natural waters would be afforded by old logs or nooks under projecting roots. Following this lead, Superintendent H. L. Canfield inserted a lot of hollow tile pipe lengths horizontally into the banks of the pond well below the surface of the water. Many of these were pre-empted by the fish which deposited eggs and reared young successfully. The problem of propagation of the channel catfish in ponds was solved by so simple a procedure. Obviously, there are possibilities in prevention of overpopulation by limiting the number of nesting sites provided.

With many pond fish the nest is guarded by the male parent, the female having completed her stint in deposition of eggs at behest of the male, who has formed the nest and extrudes sperm over the eggs. The eggs in the nest may be attacked by aquatic fungi, particularly in over-flowed ground or in dirty lakes, against which the guardian is relatively helpless. They may be devoured by catfishes, carp, and snakes, against which the male protector would seem to have a better chance in *clear* water.

The deposition of eggs in the nest is only the start of the new crop. The young fry hatched from the eggs live for a time on the nutriment of the yolk sacs carried with them from the egg. For some period they are well guarded. Soon, however, they must seek small food organisms in the water. After they go out "on their own," they must, if they are to survive, find protection from enemies, among which the parents may soon be counted. In clear open water their only protection is in their numbers, which may be so great that, although a vast majority is consumed by predators, a fair proportion survive. If not too small a fraction of 1 per cent come to maturity, the multiplication is good.

Another protection of great potency is an adequate food supply of other sorts for the larger fish. I was interested in observing a large marine aquarium in which there were hundreds, perhaps thousands, of fish of dozens of species, including large rapacious sharks and porpoises and fishes of all smaller sizes down to very little ones. When the custodian was asked what kept the larger fish from devouring all the small ones, he replied that the secret of keeping together in close confinement fishes of all sizes and feeding habits was in not letting the larger fish get hungry. The same principle applies in ponds. In natural waters small fish also find protection in hiding places, as in the shelter of submerged vegetation.

At least some reference should be made to the fact that we have as yet hardly worked at the possibility of developing improved breeds of fish by selection and cross-breeding within the species. Undoubtedly there are, among present populations of game fishes, genetic differences in rate of growth, quality of meat, and other characteristics of interest. That some fish lend themselves to diversification of types through controlled breeding is fully attested by the success of the Chinese with their innumerable forms of gold fish or that of Europeans with special varieties of carp. It does not seem credible that the possibilities in elaboration of varieties are restricted to the carp family.

The use of infertile crosses between species, as with the hybrid sunfishes that are sometimes employed, has real merit (Ricker, 1948). That does not, however, meet the need for definitely improved strains, such as are the mainstays in all branches of animal husbandry on land.

A Common History for an Unmanaged Pond

It is a common experience that a new pond, after two or three years, yields a gratifying number of fish of particularly large sizes; this is the "burst of youth." The pond owner is sure that he has a bonanza. In the next following years there may come serious disappointment; fish are numerous but small in size. The explanation seems obvious. At the beginning there was in the submerged land a rich stock of mineral nutritives for the algae and bacteria that were introduced by natural means. They and their quick-growing small predators could multiply almost without check. The larger predators, introduced fish, were relatively few in number and they had, for a time, a virtually unlimited food supply. Much more than is the case with warm-blooded farm animals, cold-blooded fish respond readily, in rate of growth and in maturing, to the amount of food available. Hence came the early harvest of large fish. But new generations appear, adding a heavy population of young predators. Soon the growing number of predators quite outruns, relatively, the number of prey, to usher in the years of large numbers of ill-fed and small game fish. Under natural conditions it may be several years before a state of relatively stable equilibrium is attained—or longer if "shelter" is wanting.

Some years ago the remarkably fine fishing afforded by a new reservoir in North Carolina was widely acclaimed. This had endured a year or two when I went to see what could be the nature of this exceptionally productive body of water. But, just then, the show was over. Hardly anyone was fishing and those that were reported a number of undersized bass but rarely one of legal size. Inquiry revealed that the whole bed of the very large reservoir had been closely stripped of all brush. The slopes of the banks were generally steep; rooted aquatic plants had not gotten in—at least none were visible—except near the mouths of tributary creeks; minnows of any kind were nowhere seen or caught by hauls of fine-meshed seines—except where the vegetation was becoming established. Throughout the body of the reservoir, if there were a place for a minnow to hide and to propagate, I could not find it. Generally one had only to throw out the bait to get a strike from an undersized bass. It is pleasant to record that, some years later, when this reservoir, Lake James, North Carolina, had established its own enduring equilibrium, it became again, and continues to be, an excellent water for angling.

CHAPTER 15

The Fish Pond and Production

The Food

THE FOOD OF A FISH CHANGES AS IT GROWS. ALL VERY YOUNG fish are plankton-eaters, meaning that they devour the small organisms that live adrift in the water. A daphnia or a copepod, a millimeter or less in length, may be sizable prey for a tiny fish. Some kinds of fish, when very young, have in their mouths special equipment for seizing and manipulating small plankters.[1] Some, such as the very large paddlefish and members of the herring and related families, including the previously mentioned gizzard shad (not a herring) go through a brief period of early youth when they snap up small drifting organisms. Then they develop in connection with their gills a fine filtering mechanism that enables them to retain through life the capacity to feed on plankton. Most fishes, as they grow, soon graduate from this exclusively micro-feeding class to go successively through the higher grades of "feed-school," using larger and larger prey until, in the cases of black bass and pike, they become major predators upon the larger fish of other species and even upon their own kind.

A conspicuous example of change of feeding habits with size is afforded by the sheephead, *Aplodinotus grunniens.* Accord-

[1]. An interesting and most informative paper with a non-intriguing title is that by the late Professor S. A. Forbes, entitled "On the Food Relations of Fresh-water Fishes. A Summary and Discussion," 1888. Another old but invaluable paper by the same author is "Fresh Water Fishes and Their Ecology," 1914.

ing to Dr. Forbes, it, like other fishes, begins as a *plankton feeder*; when it is a few inches long it becomes *insectivorous,* "living almost wholly on the insect larvae of the bottom"; "as it reaches adult size its habits change again"—it becomes "a *mollusk-eater*" (italics mine). In adaptation to its last feeding habit "it develops in its throat a powerful crushing apparatus, with pharyngeal jaws capable of smashing the thickest shells of our water snails, and even those of clams or mussels of considerable size" (Forbes, 1888, p. 6).

It would be a misapprehension to assume that the larger fish of most kinds ever disregard the smaller items of food. It does not take a big fly to get a rise from a bass that might also devour a fair-sized game fish. The grown fish may also, to some extent, avail themselves of plankton organisms.

Although the chief sources of food are within the pond, mention should be made of the terrestrial insects that leap or fall into the pond to be devoured by fish. On this, a good many years ago (1918), I wrote the following:

The sloping banks, the green sward, the meadows beyond, do not these contribute to the food supply of the pond? No one can be doubtful of this after walking around a pond and noting the small frogs that leap from the banks to be snapped in by a hungry bass, or observing the grasshoppers and crickets resting on the lotus leaves or in the stems of *Persicaria* or of cattails, or watching the dragonflies and mosquitoes and dozens of other insects that pass from bush or grass to pond and back again (if luck is with them). Read the reports of stomach examinations by Forbes and others, and note the extent to which non-aquatic insects and other animals enter into the food of fishes. Mr. H. W. Clark, of the Bureau of Fisheries, tells of trout feeding upon masses of woolly plant lice as fast as they fell from overhanging alders. Professor C. B. Wilson, while working at the Fairport Laboratory, finds a certain dragonfly that, like others, through its larvae supplies food to fish, but that almost invariably completed its metamorphosis on a hillside slightly removed from the pond, although in order to arrive at this chosen environment after emerging from the pond, it was obliged to cross a dusty road. Professor J. M. Bates writes in *Science* of serious losses of fish in Pine Creek, Nebraska, caused apparently by feeding upon rose chafers dropping from overhanging willows. These are merely typical illustrations showing some of the various ways in which the land environment affects the fish life within the pond.

Doubtless, in due time fish farmers can be given definite and helpful advice, not only about the maintenance of a suitable environment in the pond, but also regarding the provision of a proper environment about the pond. (pp. 126-27)

As everyone knows, a great many flying insects spend the greater part of their lives as eggs or larvae in the water. Fish feed, not only upon the larvae, but also, at times of emergence, upon the winged insects, either as they emerge or as they return to the surface of the water for deposition of eggs.

The use of artificial feeds is not within the scope of this discussion. For those who wish to feed their fish, there are commercial preparations; directions for making up feeds and for their use can be obtained from regional advisers.

Fertility and Fertilization

Both for the sustenance of young fish and for their protection against predators, there should be abundant food. This means, obviously, that the water should be fertile. A varying degree of fertility in the pond is derived from the fertility of surrounding lands. Mention has already been made of the value of a well-kept pasture from which drainage runs into the pond.

It is quite practicable now to apply commercial fertilizer directly to the pond and there are more or less generally accepted rules of procedure for the application of fertilizer. The practice is not new. It is sometimes mentioned that a certain Roman (Vedius Pollion, a friend of the emperor Augustus) fertilized his moray ponds with the bodies of slaves that were held to merit execution (Daremberg and Saglio, 1913-18). Probably, however, the idea was not one of adding fertility to the water so much as one of artificial feeding of a rapacious and scavenger fish, just as the Archduke Albrecht of Austria is reported to have established a horse-meat rendering plant in connection with his extensive fish ponds. It is of record that the fresh-water fish of the Archduke's ponds tired of horseflesh and the plan was abandoned (Gasch, 1885). It is not of record that the marine fish of Pollion's pond tired of slave meat; if they were the rapacious muraenas, as we assume, it is probable that they would not. At least, European fish culturists have long practiced fertilization with manure and compost, and in Germany, as at Hamburg and Munich, in recent decades, with municipal sewage.

In this country, with its seemingly unlimited capacity for producing food through agriculture, we were slow to develop fish farming except in rather tentative ways, and fertilization of ponds was late in development. Many years ago it was thought of, it was proposed, but little was done.[2] Unquestionably, the experimental work of Swingle and Smith of Auburn, Alabama, has played a leading part in putting pond fertilization on an acceptable and practicable basis for the operator of the farm pond. It has also stimulated a lot of experimentation and critical analysis, of which much more is needed. The Auburn investigators seem to have had best results with the use of mixed commercial fertilizer containing nitrogen, phosphorus, and potassium in the ratio, 6-8-4, and added at regular intervals. The "Alabama rules" have been widely applied—and, apparently, not always with full consideration of the fact that what is needed in one place may not be just right in another.

For nearly six centuries carp farming of a sort has been practiced in the land that is now Czechoslovakia, and, for a lesser period, in other parts of Europe. It was a common practice to have a series of ponds, drain most of the ponds and allow the bottom to remain dry for the winter or for a year, during which the area was cultivated and planted to crops that could be plowed under or harvested as suited the convenience of the farmer.[3] Two centuries ago, the heavy manuring of poor ponds was recommended, as well as crop-rotation in the pond bottom when left dry.

Agriculture, along with hunting and trapping and the mak-

2. Fertilization experiments started by the writer and associates at the United States Fisheries Biological Station at Fairport, Iowa, many years ago, are mentioned incidentally in Coker, 1918 (p. 126) and Wilson, 1923 (p. 31), both previously cited. Unfortunately the fish-cultural experiment work at that place was largely discontinued by the government before it could become well-established.

3. With acknowledgment to Snieszko (1941), Gasch (1883, 1885) and to Neess (1946).

ing of weapons, is among the oldest of human occupations. *Aqui-culture,* principally concerned with the rearing of fish in ponds, came very much later; but, if we think of China, it has an anti-quity of more than 2,000 years. In both fields of endeavor sub-stantial advance was made through the centuries by the trial-and-error methods of experiment, observation, and as careful analyses of the results as was possible in the existing state of knowledge of all the factors involved. Agricultural science, in the modern sense, so far as it had to await the development of the biological and chemical sciences, is scarcely a century old. Aquicultural science, or, more familiarly, fish-cultural science (although the latter term is not broad enough), has not, in Europe, lagged far behind. There has long been much competent research and there are several comprehensive handbooks. The short paper of Neess, previously cited, gives an interesting review of the situation as regards pond fertilization. In this country, aquicultural science is really just beginning to take form.

Certain basic considerations mentioned on an earlier page need to be brought back to mind in connection with fertilization. No two ponds are ever just alike in their conditions and needs. This is natural since any pond or lake is an almost undecipher-able complex. The elements of the complex, disregarding for the moment latitude, altitude, and climatic conditions, are the water, the land environment, the bottom, and the inhabitants. Even though the primary water sources for each of two ponds may be nearly identical, the environments are not so much alike. Water entering at the surface reflects the environment. The in-habitants of a pond, apart from what is intentionally introduced, are there by chance (so far as the farmer is concerned). One or another of competing species may get the start and predominate over the others. The bottom is the product of the original sub-merged soil, the environment, and the inhabitants. Between the bottom and the waters above there is constant interaction, as substances leave the soil by solution into the water or leave the water by precipitation onto the bottom or by absorption into it.

Not only is the bottom the home of a great part of the food organisms, but also the chemical interchanges between water and bottom are critical and tax the capacities of biochemists, bacteriologists, and soil chemists. The mere analysis of the pond water does not tell the full story of the condition of fertility. It may be the bottom soil that should be tested. Without going deeply into the subject, we may find indications of its complexity in the following quotations from Neess:

In any event, most of a pond's potassium is not free in solution and may be overlooked by routine water analysis. As might be expected, ponds with sandy, non-absorptive soils are usually potassium-poor and respond most markedly to fertilization. Other than very general observations of this kind, however, there is little consistency in the results of most investigators.

The phenomenon of phosphorus retention has been demonstrated in several indirect ways. Walter found that the addition of an entire year's allotment of phosphate in a single dose did not succeed in raising the phosphorus content of the water more than momentarily although effects of the fertilization were apparent in the growth of fish at the end of the season. (p. 345, 347)

The basically productive green plants use nitrogen, not in the elemental state, but in compounds, such as nitrates and to a lesser extent nitrites and ammonia. As was discussed previously, elemental nitrogen can be "fixed" or put into available compounds by nitrogen-fixing bacteria and other organisms; *nitrifying* bacteria build up, while *denitrifiers* break down the more generally useful compounds, ultimately releasing free nitrogen. The amount of available nitrogen depends, then, upon the relative activities of nitrogen-fixers, nitrifiers, and denitrifiers. Neess reports evidence that adding nitrogen fertilizers may, instead of increasing the available supply of nitrate, merely stimulate the denitrifiers to such an extent that the gain in protein meat is slight, or, at least, not in proportion to the amount of fertilizer added. (But see reference to Ruttner, p. 66, above.)

What the discussion in the immediately preceding paragraphs points to is not the discredit of pond fertilization, but the need for much more research and experimentation under carefully controlled conditions and with quantitative appraisal of results. Besides basic scientific research on the underlying phenomena of fertilization, there is immediate need for more practical experimentation in the use of fertilizers (as well as in association of species and other phases of pond fish culture) in regions having different conditions of soil, temperature, and length of growing season.

The Objective

When comparisons are made with fish-cultural practices in other countries, it is well to keep in mind that, in fish culture, as in any business, the objective governs in great measure the procedures to be followed. Carp for food have been reared in China for, apparently, 2,000 years, or more, and goldfish for ornamental use nearly as long (MacGowan, 1885). The Greeks, according to Daremberg's Dictionnaire, had fish culture in the time of Plato. They got their fish-cultural practices from the Egyptians, who had ponds on a grand scale along the Nile, and the Greeks carried them over into Sicily. The Romans took this and many other customs from the Greeks, but the wealthy Romans were interested chiefly in ponds along the sea coast for marine fish, which they are said to have maintained chiefly for gourmanderie, show, and extravagance; the rearing of fresh-water fish was left to the common folks.

In Europe of modern times the objective in so many cases has been the production of protein meat and its sale for profit. In an early publication of the United States Fish Commission, Adolf Gasch, who was then the farmer of the Archduke Albrecht's Kaniow Estate, gave an instructive and vivid account of his farming methods (Gasch, 1883). The seriousness of his fish-growing business may be judged from the fact that 45 per cent of the whole farm was in fish ponds. This was 450 acres, to which he added by rental 22 acres of ponds on an adjoining farm. Fish culture and cattle raising were closely interlocked. He liked for his ponds the marginal reeds and other aquatic vegetation the cattle could feed upon. If the cows, like "boys just out of school," rushed eagerly out into the ponds "exploring in every direction," in search of aquatic or semi-aquatic forage, apparently the incident turbidity did not disturb him—but he was growing carp;

if the cattle trampled out the "worms" in the bottom, it was easier for the fish to get them. When ponds were drained he used the rich mud for fertilizing fields, and he cultivated the drained bottoms to produce fodder for cattle as well as to improve the condition of the bottom for the pond when re-flooded. He found it desirable, when draining, to leave a substantial pocket of water to carry over the "seed" of food organisms—a good point.

Interestingly enough, Gasch practised meticulous selection of brood stock for form and rate of growth, with segregation from the first year fish and successive segregations with each year of growth. (This was about 75 years ago!) He managed the whole outfit with one assistant on the main estate and another on the rented acreage. He seemed enthusiastic as to the interest of the occupation, the opportunities for experimentation, and the profit —but he had a market for his fish! Among other things, Gasch said that, without draining the pond periodically, "there can be no systematic and profitable pond cultivation, but only irregular lake fishing." Possibly the basic question for us is: To what extent do we wish to shift from "irregular lake fishing" to profitable pond cultivation"?

In this country we seem not yet to have come to the point of giving serious consideration to the objective of producing fish for profit. It is done, with trout for example, but not widely. Perhaps administrators of fish-cultural programs should give more thought to this aspect of the matter—at least to the encouragement of the private production of "seed" fish in a commercial way and, perhaps, *improved* "seed." It could be that farmers would be helped by being able to market their excess production of fingerling fish. The fact that tax money now supplies the fish for stocking new ponds does not improve their quality.

Fertilization of Lakes

The question has naturally arisen: If fertilization of ponds is profitable, why may not fertilization of small natural lakes be equally so? Brief mention of some experimentation with lakes may be of interest. Considering the great importance of the bottom, previously stressed, it is to be remembered that an old lake and a new pond present quite different situations. The lake cannot be drained periodically, as can most ponds. The lake's bottom has matured through the centuries; it is not like the pond's bottom, which is former dry land recently submerged and now covered by only a thin organic deposit. The expense of fertilizing a large lake renders that impracticable at the present time. Some small northern lakes have been fertilized to apparent advantage. In certain cases there have also been results that were not desired.

Following fertilization there seems generally to have been a conspicuous increase in plankton algae and the small drifting animals that feed upon them and in algae and other organisms attached to the leaves and stems of rooted aquatic plants. There have been found notably greater numbers (and sometimes larger sizes) of insect larvae and other invertebrates of the bottom. That the rate of growth of fishes is enhanced was evidenced by the greater width of growth bands on the scales. In some cases it is reported that the dense growth of microorganisms and filamentous algae on the rooted aquatics has so shaded them from sunlight as to cause death of the plants.

Unfavorable effects were noted in a number of instances. The lively growth and multiplication of filamentous algae in some waters, following fertilization, made conditions that were unsightly, sometimes odoriferous, and less attractive for swimming or boating. Mats of algae in shoal areas were unfavorable for the spawning of sunfishes and the black bass. Changes in vertical distribution of oxygen and heat, attributed to organic turbidity following fertilization, could, seemingly, alter a trout lake to make it more suitable for warm-water fish. Where there is a long winter season under a thick covering of ice, the increase of organic matter for decomposition during the winter may lead to excessive stagnation and serious "winter-kill" of fish. Substantially increased fertility and heavier deposition of organic matter tends to fill the lakes, to shorten its life as a lake, to speed up the "aging" process.

After a careful study of fertilization for natural lakes, Hasler and Einsele (1948) concluded (for Wisconsin) that only experimental fertilization should be undertaken at this stage of knowledge of the subject. The following quotations from their summary are of special interest:

In considering the fertilization of shallow lakes and ponds, if fertilization can be justified thoroughly, experience of the past suggests that addition of phosphorus at 12 kilogram per hectare is most effective, provided previous chemical tests have shown adequate amounts of other nutrients. Nitrogen fertilizers have been of negligible value in this type of basin. (p. 550)

Dry fallow of drainable basins and flowages to permit oxidation of the bottom sediments is recommended as an effective and cheap fertilizing measure. (p. 551)

Ball and collaborators have made a number of studies of fertilization of small lakes in Michigan. In the latest paper (Ball and Tanner, 1951) they arrive at this conclusion: "We have shown fertilizer to be useful in increasing the growth of desirable sport fish, but have also shown certain limitation resulting from usage under conditions of this experiment." He attributes "winter kill" to excessive fertilization and believes that "by adjusting the amount of nutrients added, winter kill can be avoided and the desirable effects of fertilization can still be obtained" (p. 30).

In the farther northern waters of Canada, the long period of ice cover, the short period of exposure to productive sunlight, and the generally colored water, absorbing sunlight quickly, make a special situation. It has been said that "the addition of fertilizer to the highly colored lakes would not increase their productivity significantly, since the radiant energy available to the algae is so small (Biological Bureau of Quebec, November, 1949, p. 11).

In New Brunswick and in Nova Scotia, however, there are many small lakes in drainage areas with igneous rock formations. Consequently, the waters are deficient in minerals and in nutrient salts. Results of the experiments being conducted there are not yet assured, although an increased growth rate of trout is reported. Because undesirable fish also respond to the improved fertility, it is suggested that fertilization should be preceded by some measures of control of the coarse fish, as by poisoning (Smith, 1951).

As regards fertilization, it seems clear that it has its place, not only in new ponds, but also in small natural lakes, particularly those adapted for warm-water fish that seem to lack an adequate supply of mineral nutriment of some kind and that, in consequence, are relatively unproductive. It seems equally certain that it may be wasteful to go at pond fertilization with blindfolds. The rules-of-thumb worked out for ponds in a particular region may be the best we now have to use; nevertheless, they ought not to be accepted as precisely applicable everywhere. We need more fundamental research and more practical experimentation until we can determine with understanding what combinations of fertilizing materials and what modes of application give best results, and yield them most economically, in ponds with diverse waters and bottom soils.

Finally, there is real meat in a paragraph that may be quoted from Dr. O. Lloyd Meehean's paper in the United Nations Scientific Conference:

Fishery management technicians and soil conservationists have a large educational job to perform. The whole fabric of thinking by the fisherman must be changed. He must be taught to utilize the available supply; he must be taught that the management of the farm pond involves principles of good fish-husbandry; and he must be made to realize that fish cannot be produced in quantity simply because water is available. This is the major problem in promoting a successful farm fish-pond programme. Additional research is also required to adapt management practices to the ecological characteristics of the land and fishing preferences of fishermen. (p. 140)

Productivity of the Pond

The question is often asked: Which is more productive, an acre of land or an acre of water? The question is not answerable until there is agreement on what is meant by productivity—and that is not easily obtained.

It seems generally accepted that areas of water usually give off to the atmosphere more carbon dioxide than they take from it. Since carbon dioxide is a by-product of respiration as well as a raw material of organic production, this would seem to argue for the greater productivity of water. The movement of carbon dioxide is from deeper waters to surface waters to atmosphere. It must be remembered, however, that some of the carbon dioxide passing from the water is waste of decomposition of organic material that was produced on land and carried into the water with surface drainage. It has been mentioned above that more animal protein can be produced per acre in the form of carp flesh than in any other way. This too might seem to give an uncontested vote to the water, except that the carp subsists in some part on wastes from the land.

What is meant by productivity? On land, roots, stems, leaves, flowers, fruit, seed, trunks, and bark are the products of organic syntheses. As produced by one plant or another (turnip, sprouts, cabbage, grain, etc.), we eat some of all of the first six products mentioned; we make other uses of trunks and bark. Considering, however, any particular acre of land, we use only one or two of the materials mentioned and throw away the balance. Theoretically, we may count for productivity whatever is produced, regardless of its immediate usefulness. Emphasis is on "immediate," because things that are not directly utilized may have the highest indirect value. Neither the farmer nor the cows eat the roots of clover, but the land-owner never questions the value of the roots, with their nitrogen-fixing nodules and their humus value, as well as for their part in producing the desired crop of clover.

Water produces aquatic plants in profusion; but we make no direct use of them except in a few special cases, as ornamental aquatics, water cress, some kinds of rice, water-chestnuts, and the products of hydroponics. Water yields enormous populations of minute algae, bacteria, and fungi, on the bottom, on fixed objects, and adrift or afloat. We make little use of these yet, but the time may come when we will get more from microbiological water cultures than yeast, acetic acid, alcohol, antibiotics and such. Now we expect the minute vegetation to be converted into small animal bodies, the small animals into little fish, and these into larger fish, with great waste all along the conversion chain. There simply is not available today any satisfactory appraisal of the several conversion factors involved. Probably the best way of arriving at an estimate of basic productivity in water is to use sampling procedures and measure the amount of photosynthesis that takes place per unit of area and time, and, then, from these data to compute the production. Numerous such efforts have been made, but there are not yet generally satisfactory approximations for ponds and lakes.[4] In time more dependable results are to be expected. They will have scientific interest and should also be helpful toward better water-management.

Suppose, however, that we wish to compare water with land in yield of edible meat. The answer depends in part upon what is considered edible. If it is carp, it seems to be accepted that the water produces more effectively than land. Snieszko (1941) mentions (p. 233) a yield per acre in Poland of 200 pounds of carp and 77 pounds of other fish, a total yield of 277 pounds. He adds: "The yield of carp in Polish ponds can be increased to 400 pounds per acre and even more, if the fish are fed artificially, or the ponds are fertilized" (p. 233).

Macan and Worthington (1951, p. 211) say that European carp farmers count on a gain in weight per fish of rather less than a pound a year, but that in the warm climate of Palestine and India production at the rate of one pound per month is claimed. It is said that in Israel 40 grams of artificial food a day resulted in growth of young carp at the rate of 10 grams a day, or about a pound in 50 days. Undoubtedly, however, the carp found also some natural food. "Ground oil nuts," Arab beans, and waste cotton seed are mentioned as feed. As the carp become older, growth is slower and feeding becomes uneconomic. The carp are marketed at a weight of a little more than one pound (0.5-0.6 kg.) with a yield of two tons from a three or four acre pond; two to three crops are harvested a year! (Hardy, 1952.) Incidentally Hardy mentions that in Hungary the muddy flavor of carp is removed by starving the carp for two weeks before marketing.

Swingle and Smith (1941) speak of yields from fertilized ponds of 750 to 1100 pounds per acre of gold fish and golden

4. Reference may be made to Chapter 14 of Welch's *Limnology* (1952), to Riley, 1940, and to Odum, 1953.

shiners, fish that, feeding on algae, etc., are, like carp, at the bottom of the food chain. Bluegill and bull heads, which feed largely on insects, gave 500 to 600 pounds per acre; largemouth black bass and crappie, which feed largely on other fish, "gave the lowest production, from 150 to 200 pounds per acre in well-fertilized ponds" (pp. 220-221). It is understood that there was no artificial feeding. A number of writers seem to regard a yearly production of 175-200 pounds of game fish flesh per acre as a reasonable expectation.[5]

Ford and Ball (1951) harvested from four ponds at a hatchery in Michigan, a little more than two years after stocking, 195 pounds of game fish of usable size per surface acre. This, however, was starting from scratch, which makes some difference. A steer, they say, will gain about 250 pounds on grass each season, but requires from two to six acres for grazing.

How can one arrive at a satisfactory figure for production of meat per acre of land, when there are so many variables as to climate, soil, kinds of grass, management, and fertilization, and as to kinds of stock that are feeding? There are reliable estimates of 50 pounds of beef per acre produced per year on average range land of Southern Plains, as in Oklahoma, but more on improved ranges; and there are reports of 700 to 1000 pounds of beef per acre with the most favorable conditions of humidity and with generous use of fertilizer. I am indebted to Dr. N. R. Ellis, in charge of Animal Nutrition Investigations, United States Bureau of Animal Industry, for the figures just used and for the following summary statement in a personal communication:

Perhaps probable yields of beef can be summarized about as follows: Western Plains—35 to 70 pounds per acre; Midwestern and Eastern natural pastures—100 to 150 pounds; managed pastures in the same areas—200 to 250 pounds; fertilized pastures, likewise; in areas of reasonably high rainfall—400 to 600 pounds per acre.

5. Dr. C. F. Hickling (1948) gives interesting figures for production of fish per acre per annum in various countries, for natural waters and for fish farms, unfertilized or fertilized. The greatest yields reported are for Malaya, 3500 pounds, and South China, 4000 pounds. Undoubtedly these high yields are for carp in ponds heavily manured. See also several papers in the *United Nations Scientific Conference on the Conservation and Utilization of Resources* (259 pp.), Section on "Management and Cultivation of Fresh Water Fish," pp. 119-164. (United Nations Department of Economic Affairs, New York, 1951.) Several of these papers are quoted herein.

Actually we are very deficient in precise knowledge of the loss with each successive link of food chain—or with what may be called conversion factors. One investigator concludes that it takes 18 pounds of food to make a pound of a certain fish; another says, for a different fish, about 3.5 pounds; still another gives the figure of 16.4 pounds. So it is with other links in the chain. Probably because the figure 10 is a nice round figure and is certainly somewhere in the general range, it is not uncommon to find that taken as an average. Thus, speaking roughly, Mac-Ginitie (1935) says that "in most food chains each link is about one tenth the weight of the link preceding it. This means that about nine tenths of the food consumed is expended for the energy of work and heat or wasted as feces." He adds: "10,000 pounds of algae make 1,000 pounds of tiny crustacea, 1,000 pounds of tiny crustacea make 100 pounds of small fish, 100 pounds of small fish make 10 pounds of large fish, and 10 pounds of large fish make one pound of man" (p. 649). Figures such as these are, of course, not to be taken as literally authentic. They are useful only as giving the order of difference between measures of productivity in basic organic substance (algae) and of productivity in fish of market size. The difference is of the order of 1,000 to one—maybe higher, maybe lower—and, of course dependent upon the fish.[6]

As the late Dr. Lindeman has well said, there are so many complicating interrelationships among both prey and predators that efficiency ratios based on natural populations should not be taken too seriously. Nevertheless, even if the estimate of 1,000 pounds of wet algae to one pound of edible fish should be fairly wide of the mark, it would still contrast sensibly with the estimate of six to eight pounds of mixed dry plant foods (corn and hay) to make one pound of beef, three and one-half pounds of feed to make a pound of pork, or three pounds of food to make a pound of broiler chicken.[7] Such differences prevail in spite of the fact that steers, pigs, and chickens have to use foods to main-

6. See also, among other publications: Pearse, 1926; Bajkov, 1932; Lindeman, 1941; Clarke, George L., 1946; Ricker, 1946; Riley and Gorgy, 1948; Odum; 1953.
7. Ratios taken from a letter from Dr. N. R. Ellis, In Charge Animal Nutrition Investigations, U.S. Bureau of Animal Husbandry.

tain body temperature, an expense from which the fish by nature is spared. The length of the food chain, as well as the differentials in metabolic efficiency, make a difference.

Comparison of efficiences between fish in the wild and domestic animals are deceptive, because, in one way or another, the energies of man and machinery go into the preparation of domestic feeds.

It needs to be emphasized that the food chain, food web, or the food cycle that we speak of patly is not a tangible or fixed series of steps. As Meehean (1933) has well pointed out, there may be two distinct food cycles, a longer and a shorter one, operating in the pond at the same time. In the longer cycle nitrogenous fertilizing materials (1) are converted by bacteria into ammonias (2), the ammonia by other bacteria into nitrites (3), the nitrites by still other bacteria into nitrates (4), which are utilized by algae and other plants to make plant proteins (5), consumed by minute animals (6), which are food for small fish (7); quite a time element is involved. In the shorter cycle, starting again from the fertilizing matter (1), these support the bacterial populations (2), —of 2, 3 and 4, above—which are food for the minute animals (3) that are eaten by the small fish (4); the time between fertilizer and fish is very much shorter. Any particular rotifer or crustacean of the plankton may figure in either cycle at different moments.

It is obviously true also that a predator that, on one occasion, figures at the end of a long chain may, at another time cut in at a lower link. Thus a large bass that devours a small bass that ate a bream that had fed on a minnow which had eaten an insect larva, and so on, might shortly thereafter itself seize an insect larva. The food chain represented by the second short meal would lack most of the links involved in the first meal. So many interconnections are possible that the term *food web* may be preferable to food chain.

Because of all these conditions and many others, the comparisons of production from land and water become quite involved. Let us note just a few other complicating factors. Only a part of the fish (barely over 50 per cent) or of the steer (probably slightly better) is meat for the table. There are more valuable by-products from the steer. Both the pasture and the pond may be fertilized, at some expense for materials and labor. Almost always there is supplemental feeding for cattle and sometimes for fish. More labor is usually involved in handling of range cattle.

It would be of real interest to have more fully satisfactory quantitative comparisons of the yields (in edible meat) of equivalent land and water areas having similar soils, coupled with precise analyses of food values, and with itemization of all expenses for fertilizer, feed, other materials, and labor. The present writer cheerfully leaves that task to others. Without dogmatic expression, a seemingly well-founded impression may be voiced: A fish pond, well managed, may compare favorably with an equal area of land in production of meat for the table. It also adds variety to the family diet, offers opportunities for recreation of several kinds, and provides water for diverse farm uses, such as stock-watering, irrigation, and fire protection. It contributes to water conservation and it can have esthetic values. To put in other words the same thought that was expressed in the section on "Objectives," the value of the pond depends upon what is wanted from it.

Selected Bibliography

PUBLICATIONS CITED

(Not to be taken as a complete or adequately representative bibliography)

Allee, W. C. 1934. Recent Studies in Mass Physiology. Biol. Rev., 9: 1-48.

Allee, W. C. and Karl P. Schmidt. 1951. Ecological Animal Geography. 2nd Edition. xiii + 715, illustrated. Wiley, New York.

Allen, Winford Emory. 1920. A Quantitative and Statistical Study of the Plankton of the San Joaquin River and Its Tributaries in and Near Stockton, California, in 1913. Univ. of Cal. Publ. in Zool., 22: 1-292.

American Public Health Association. 1946. Standard Methods for the Examination of Water and Sewage. (9th Edition). A.P.H.A., New York.

Bajkov, A. D. 1932. Fish Population and Productivity of Lakes. Trans. Amer. Fish. Soc., 62: 307-316.

Ball, Robert C. 1952. Farm Pond Management in Michigan. Jnl. Wildlife Management, 16 (3): 266-269.

Ball, Robert C. and Howard A. Tanner. 1951. The Biological Effects of Fertilizer on a Warm-water Lake. Mich. State Col. Agric. Exp. Sta., Technical Bull. 223.

Banner, Albert H. 1953. On a New Genus and Species of Mysid from Southern Louisiana. Tulane Studies in Zoology, 1 (1): 1-8.

Banta, A. M. 1939. Studies on the Physiology, Genetics, and Evolution of Some Cladocera. Carnegie Inst. Wash., Department of Genetics, Paper No. 39: x + 285, illustrated.

Bell, Hugh Stevens. 1942. Stratified Flow in Reservoirs and Its Use in Prevention of Silting. Misc. Publ. No. 491, U. S. Dept. of Agric. (Soil Conservation Service), 46 pp., illustrated.

Bennett, George W. 1952. Pond Management in Illinois. Jnl. Wildlife Management, *16* (3): 249-253.

Berg, Clifford O. 1950. Biology of Certain Aquatic Caterpillars (Pyralididae: Nymphula Spp.) Which Feed on Potamogeton. Trans. Amer. Micr. Soc., *69* (3): 254-266.

Berg, Kaj. 1931. Studies on the Genus Daphnia O. F. Müller with Especial Reference to the Mode of Reproduction. 222 pp., illustrated. Bianco Luno A/S, Copenhagen.

Berner, Lester M. 1951. Limnology of the Lower Missouri River. Ecology, *32* (1): 1-12.

Betten, Cornelius. 1934. The Caddis Flies or Trichoptera of New York State. 576 pp., illustrated. N. Y. St. Mus. Bull. 292, Albany.

Biological Bureau of the Quebec Fish and Game Department. 1949. Notes Biologiques, Nov. 1949.

Birge, E. A. 1904. The Thermocline and Its Biological Significance (Annual Address of the President, delivered in 1903). Trans. Amer. Micr. Soc., 25: 5-33.

———. 1906. Gases Dissolved in the Waters of Wisconsin Lakes. Trans. Amer. Fish. Soc. for 1906, 143-163.

———. 1907. The Respiration of an Inland Lake. Trans. Amer. Fish. Soc., *36*: 223-245.

———. 1922. The Plankton of the Lakes. Trans. Amer. Fish. Soc., 52: 118-130.

Birge, Edward A. and Chancey Juday. 1926. Organic Content of Lake Waters. Bull. U. S. Bur. Fish., *42*: 185-205.

———. 1930. A Second Report on Solar Radiation and Inland Lakes. Trans. Wis. Acad. Sc., Arts & Letters, 25: 285-335.

Boycott, A. E. 1936. The Habitats of Fresh-water Mollusca in Britain. Jnl. An. Ecol., 5: 116-186, Cambridge.

Bridgman, P. W. 1952. Physical Effects of High Pressure. Progress of Science, No. 3, The Times, London.

Briggs, John Carmon. 1949. The Quantitative Effects of a Dam Upon the Bottom Fauna of a Small California Stream. Trans. Amer. Fish. Soc., *78*: 70-81.

Brinley, Floyd J. 1942. Biological Studies, Ohio River Pollution Survey. I. Biological Zones in a Polluted Stream. Sewage Works Journal, *14*: 147-152.

Brooks, John Langdon. 1946. Cyclomorphosis in Daphnia. Ecol. Monog., *16*: 409-447.

Bryson, R. A. and V. E. Suomi. 1951. Midsummer Renewal of Oxygen within the Hypolimnion. Jnl. of Marine Research, *10* (3): 263-269.

———. 1952. Circulation of Lake Mendota. Trans. Amer. Geophys. Union, *33* (5): 707-712.

Bryson, R. A. and P. N. Kuhn. 1952. On Certain Oscillatory Motions of Lakes. Report No. 5 to the University of Wisconsin Lake Investigations Committee, 10 pp., 5 figs. Dept. of Meteorology, Univ. of Wis.

Butcher, R. W. 1932. Studies in the Ecology of Rivers. II. The Microflora of Rivers with Special Reference to the Algae of the River Bed. Ann. of Bot., *46*: 813-861.

———. 1933. Studies on the Biology of Rivers. I. On the Distribution of Macrophytic Vegetation in the Rivers of Britain. Jnl. Ecol., *21* (1): 58-91.

———. 1946. Studies in the Ecology of Rivers. VI. The Algal Growth in Certain Highly Calcareous Streams. Jnl. Ecol., *33*: 268-283.

Cadieux, Charles. 1953. Death under the Ice. The Fisherman, *4* (2): 18-20.

Campbell, M. S. H. 1939. Biological Indicators of Intensity of Stream Pollution. Sewage Works Journal, *11*: 123-127.

Cannon, Herbert Graham. 1928. On the Feeding Mechanism of the Copepods, *Calanus finmarchicus* and *Diaptomus gracilis*. Brit. Jnl. Exper. Biol., *6* (2): 131-144, London.

Chandler, David C. 1937. Fate of Typical Lake Plankton in Streams. Ecol. Monog., *7*: 445-479.

Claassen, P. W. 1927. Biological Studies of Polluted Areas in the Genessee River System. N. Y. State Dept. of Conservation Suppl. to 16th Annual Report, 1926: 38-46. (*In* A Biological Survey of the Genessee River System.)

Clark, Minor. 1952. Kentucky's Farm Fish Pond Program. Jnl. Wildlife Management, *16* (3): 262-266.

Clark, O. H. 1948. Stream Improvements in Michigan. Trans. Amer. Fish. Soc., *75*: 270-280.

Clarke, Frank Wigglesworth. 1924. The Composition of the River and Lake Waters of the United States. U. S. Geol. Surv. Professional Paper 135, iv + 199, Washington.

Clarke, George L. 1939. The Utilization of Solar Energy by Aquatic Organisms. Pp. 27-38 *in* Problems of Lake Biology. Publication of the Amer. Assn. for Adv. Sci. No. 10. (The Science Press.)

———. 1946. Dynamics of Production in a Marine Area. Ecol. Monog., *16*: 321-335.

Coker, Robert E. 1915. Water Conservation, Fisheries and Food Supply. Pop. Sci. Monthly (now the Scientific Monthly), July, 1915: 90-99.

———. 1917. The Question of Fishways. U. S. Bur. Fish. Economic Circular No. 24. 6 pp.

———. 1918. Principles and Problems of Fish Culture in Ponds. Sci. Monthly, Aug., 1918: 120-129.

———. 1919. Fresh-water Mussels and Mussel Industries of the United States. Bull. U. S. Bur. Fish., *36*: 11-89, illustrated.

———. 1927. Aquiculture and the Future of the Waters. Sci. Monthly, *52*: 256-260.

———. 1929. Keokuk Dam and the Fisheries of the Upper Mississippi River. Bull. U. S. Bur. Fish., *45*: 85-139.

———. 1933. Influence of Temperature on Size of Freshwater Copepods (Cyclops). Intern. Rev. Ges. Hydrob. u. Hydrog., *29* (5/6): 406-427.

———. 1934. Contribution to Knowledge of North American Freshwater Harpacticoid Copepod Crustacea. Jnl. Elisha Mitchell Sc. Soc., *50*: 75-141.

———. 1934a. Influence of Temperature on Form of the Freshwater Copepod, *Cyclops vernalis* Fischer. Intern. Rev. Ges. Hydrob. u. Hydrog., *30*: 411-427.

———. 1935. A Practical Aquarium Plant. The Aquarium, *4* (3): 49, 50, Philadelphia.

———. 1939. The Problem of Cyclomorphosis in Daphnia. Quart. Rev. Biol., *14* (2): 137-148.

———. 1949. This Great and Wide Sea. xvii + 325, illustrated (Rev. Ed.), Univ of N. C. Press, Chapel Hill.

Coker, R. E., A. F. Shira, H. W. Clark and A. D. Howard. 1921. Natural History and Propagation of Fresh-water Mussels. Bull. U. S. Bur. Fish., *37*: 75-181, illustrated, Washington.

Coker, R. E., Vera Millsaps, and Ruby Rice. 1936. Swimming Plume and Claws of the Broad-shouldered Water-strider *Rhagovelia flavicinta* Bueno (Hemiptera). Bull. Brooklyn Entomological Society, *31* (3): 81-85.

Collins, W. B. 1937. Water for Industrial Purposes. Part I., pp. 1-3. The American City, July, August, September, 1937.

Compton, Lawrence V. 1952. Farm and Ranch Ponds. Jnl. Wildlife Management, *16* (3): 238-242.

Comstock, John Henry. 1948. The Spider Book. Revised and Edited by W. J. Gertsch, ii + 789, illustrated. Comstock Publ. Co., Ithaca.

Conger, Paul S. 1941. Fixation of Silica by Diatoms. A Symposium on Hydrobiology. Univ. of Wis. Press, Madison, pp. 395-396.

————. 1941. Aspects of the Hydrobiological Importance of Diatoms. *Ibid.*: 396-397.

Corrsin, Stanley. 1950. Patterns of Chaos. The Johns Hopkins Magazine, *3* (4):

Daremberg, Charles Victor et M. Edmond Saglio. 1913-1918. Dictionnaire des Antiquités Grecques et Romaines, V, 1082 pp., Hatchette, Paris.

Daly, Reginald Adworth. 1942. The Floor of the Ocean, x + 177, illustrated. Univ. of N. C. Press, Chapel Hill.

Davis, H. S. 1953. Culture and Diseases of Game Fishes. 10 + 332. Illustrated. Univ. of Cal. Press.

De, P. K. 1939. The Role of Blue-green Algae in Nitrogen Fixation in Rice-fields. Proc. Royal Soc. London, B, *127*: 121-139.

Deevey, Edward S. 1941. Limnological Studies in Connecticut. VI. The Quantity and Composition of the Bottom Fauna of Thirty-six Connecticut and New York Lakes. Ecol. Monog., *11* (4): 413-455.

Doan, Kenneth H. 1940. Relation of Sauger Catch to Turbidity in Lake Erie. Ohio Jnl. Sci., *41* (6): 449-452.

Duggar, B. M. and A. R. Davis. 1916. Studies in the Physiology of the Fungi. I. Nitrogen Fixation. Ann. Mo. Bot. Garden, *3*: 413.

Eddy, Samuel. 1940. Minnesota Lake Surveys and Fish Management. Proc. Minn. Acad. Sc., *8*: 9-14.

Edmister, F. C. 1947. Fish Ponds for the Farm. 12 + 114 pp., illustrated. Scribners, New York.

Eldridge, E. F. 1942. Industrial Waste Treatment Practice. 11 + 401 pp. McGraw-Hill, New York.

Eller, James Gerald. Unpublished Manuscript on Biology of Mayflies.

Ellis, M. M. 1944. Water Purity Standards for Fresh-water Fishes. U. S. Bur. of Fisheries, Special Report, 14 pp. (mimeographed).

————. 1937. Detection and Measurement of Stream Pollution. U. S. Bur. Fisheries, Bulletin *48*, No. 22: 363-437.

Ellis, M. M., B. A. Westfall and Marion D. Ellis. 1948. Determination of Water Quality. U. S. Fish & Wildlife Service Research Report 9: 2 + 122 pp.

Embody, George C. 1915. The Farm Fishpond. Cornell Reading Courses, *4* (94): 213-252, illustrated. New York State College of Agriculture at Cornell University, Ithaca.

Fassett, Norman C. 1940. A Manual of Aquatic Plants. 7 + 382 pp. (well illustrated). McGraw-Hill, New York.

The Fisherman. Published monthly by Fisherman Press, Inc. Oxford, Ohio. George S. Fichter, Editor.

Fogg, G. E. 1942. Studies on Nitrogen Fixation by Blue-green Algae. Brit. Jnl. Exper. Biol., *19*: 78-87.

Forbes, S. A. 1888. On the Food Relations of Fresh-Water Fishes: A Summary and Discussion. Bull. Ill. State Lab'y of Nat'l Hist'y, 2 (8): 475-538.

———. 1914. Fresh Water Fishes and Their Ecology. 19 pp., 21 Pls. Ill. State Lab'y of Nat'l Hist'y.

———. 1919. Some Recent Changes in Illinois River Biology. Ill. State Nat'l Hist'y Surv. Bull., *13* (6): 137-156.

Ford, John R. and Robert C. Ball. 1951. Weight Loss on Dressing and Processing Game Fish. Mich. Agric. Exper. Sta. Quarterly Bull., *34* (1): 65-74. East Lansing.

Gainey, P. L. and Thomas H. Lord. 1952. Microbiology of Water and Sewage. xi + 430, illustrated. New York, Prentice-Hall.

Galtsoff, P. S. 1924. Limnological Observations in the Upper Mississippi, 1921. Bull. U. S. Bur. Fish., *39*: 347-438.

Gasch, Adolf. 1883. Pond Cultivation on the Kaniow Estate (District of Biala Galica), the Property of His Imperial Highness Archduke Albrecht of Austria. Rept. U. S. Fish Com. for 1880: 533-543. Washington.

———. 1885. Pond Culture. The Food and Spawning of Carp. Rept. U. S. Fish Com. for 1883: 1142-1150.

Gerking, Shelby D. 1953. Evidence for the Concepts of Home Range and Territory in Stream Fishes. Ecology, *34* (2): 347-365.

Gilbert, Grove Karl. 1914. Transportation of Debris by Running Water. U. S. Geol. Surv. Professional Paper 86. 263 pp., 3 Pls. Washington.

Greenbank, John. 1945. Limnological Conditions in Ice-covered Lakes, Especially as Related to Winter-kill of Fish. Ecol. Monog., *15* (4): 343-392.

Gutsell, J. S. 1921. Danger to Fisheries from Oil and Tar Pollution of Waters. 10 pp., Document 910, Report of the U. S. Com'r Fish. for the Fiscal Year 1921, with Appendices.

Hardy, Eric. 1952. Pond and Lake Breeding of Fish—A World Survey. World Fishing, *1* (8): 300-303.

Harvey, H. W. 1945. Recent Advances in the Chemistry and Biology of Sea Water. vii + 164. Cambridge Univ. Press.

Hasler, Arthur D. 1938. Fish Biology and Limnology of Crater Lake, Ore. Jnl. Wildlife Management, 2 (3): 94-103.

Hasler, Arthur D. and Wilhelm G. Einsele. 1948. Fertilization for Increasing Productivity of Natural Inland Waters. Trans. 13th N. Amer. Wildlife Conference: 527-555. (Wildlife Management Institute.)

Hasler, A. D. and E. Jones. 1949. Demonstration of the Antagonistic Action of Large Aquatic Plants on Algae and Rotifers. Ecology, *30* (3): 359-364.

Henrici, Arthur T. 1939. The Distribution of Bacteria in Lakes. *In* Problems of Lake Biology. Amer. Assn. Adv. Sci. Publ., No. 10: 39-64 (Science Press).

Hickling, C. F. 1948. Fish Farming in the Middle and Far East. Nature, *161* (4098): 748-751.

Hildebrand, Samuel P. 1922. Fishes in Relation to Mosquito Control. Jnl. Elisha Mitchell Sc. Soc., *37*: 161-166. Chapel Hill.

Hodgman, Charles D. (Editor). 1941. Handbook of Chemistry and Physics, 25th Ed. Chemical Rubber Publishing Co., Cleveland.

Hoff, C. Clayton. 1942. The Ostracods of Illinois, Their Biology and Taxonomy. 196 pp., illustrated. Univ. of Ill. Press, Urbana.

Hogan, Joe. 1946. The Control of Aquatic Plants with Fertilizers in Rearing Ponds at the Lonoke Hatchery, Arkansas. Trans. Amer. Fish. Soc., *76*: 183-189.

Hubbs, Carl L. 1930. Fishery Research in Michigan. Trans. Amer. Fish. Soc., *60*: 182-186.

Hungerford, H. R. 1919. The Biology and Ecology of Aquatic and Semi-aquatic Hemiptera. Kansas Univ. Sc. Bull. 11. Lawrence.

Hutchinson, G. Evelyn. 1941. Ecological Aspects of Succession in Natural Populations. Amer. Nat., 75: 406-418.

———. 1941a. Limnological Studies in Connecticut. IV. The Mechanism of Intermediary Metabolism in Stratified Lakes. Ecol. Monog., *11*: 21-60.

308   *Selected Bibliography*

Hutchinson, G. E. and Jane K. Setlow. 1946. Limnological Studies in Connecticut. VIII. The Niacin Cycle in a Small Inland Lake. Ecology, *27* (1): 13-22.

Irwin, W. H. and James B. Stevenson. 1951. Physicochemical Nature of Clay Turbidity with Special Reference to Clarification and Productivity of Impounded Waters. Bull. Okla. Agric. and Mech. Col., Stillwater, Okla., *48* (4), Biol. Ser. No. 4: 1-54.

Jahoda, Wm. J. 1947. Survival of Brook Trout in Water of Low Oxygen Content. Jnl. Wildlife Management *11* (1): 96, 97.

Ketchum, Bostwick H., Alfred C. Redfield and John C. Ayres. 1951. The Oceanography of the New York Bight. Papers in Physical Oceanography and Meteorology, *12* (1): 1-46. Mass. Inst. Techn. and Woods Hole Oceanog. Inst., Cambridge and Woods Hole.

Kofoid, C. A. 1903, 1908. The Plankton of the Illinois River, 1894-1899. Bull. Ill. State Lab'y Nat'l Hist'y, *6* (2): *8* (1), illustrated.

Kolkwitz, R. and M. Marsson. 1909. Ökologie der tierischen Saprobien. Intern. Rev. Ges. Hydrob. u. Hydrog., *2*: 126-152. Leipzig.

Krumholz, Louis A. 1952. Management of Indiana Ponds for Fishing. Jnl. Wildlife Management, *16* (3): 254-257.

Kunz, George Frederick. 1898. The Fresh-water Pearls and Pearl Fisheries of the United States. Bull. U. S. Fish. Com., *17*: 375-426, illustrated.

Lackey, James B. 1944. Stream Microbiology. Chapter 7 *in* Phelps, Stream Sanitation, q.v.

Liebmann, Hans. 1951. Handbuch der Frischwasser und Abwasserbiologie Biologie des Trinkwassers, Badewassers, Fischwassers, Vorfluters und Abwassers, Band I, 436 Text-abbildungen, 5 Farb- und 13 Schwarzweisztafeln. R. Oldenbourg. München.

Lin, S. Y. 1951. Pond Culture of Warm-Water Fishes, pp. 131-135 *in* Proc. Un. Nat. Sc. Conference on the Conservation and Utilization of Resources, Wildlife and Fish Resources. United Nations Dept. of Econ. Affairs. New York.

Lindeman, Raymond L. 1941. Seasonal Food-Cycle in a Senescent Lake. Amer. Mid. Nat., *26*: 636-673.

Lowndes, A. G. 1935. The Swimming and Feeding of Certain Colanoid Copepods. Proc. Zool. Soc. London, Part 3, 1935: 687-715, 2 Pls.

Lucas, C. E. 1947. The Ecological Effects of External Metabolites. Biol. Rev., *22*: 270-295.

Lundbeck, Johannes. 1936. Untersuchungen Über die Bodenbesiedlung der Alpenrandseen. Archiv für Hydrobiologie, Supplementband X, Heft 2. Stuttgart.

Macan, T. T. and E. B. Worthington. 1951. Life in Lakes and Rivers. xvi + 272. Collins, London.

MacGinitie, G. E. 1935. Ecological Aspects of a California Marine Estuary. Amer. Mid. Nat., *16* (5): 629-765.

MacGowan, D. J. 1885. Carp Culture in China. Bull. U. S. Fish. Comm., 5: 235-240.

Martin, Alexander C. 1953. Improving Duck Marshes by Weed Control. U. S. Fish and Wildlife Service, Circular 19, 49 pp.

Matthews, Velma Dare. 1932. The Aquatic Vegetation of Quaker Run. Jnl. Elisha Mitchell Sc. Soc., *47* (1): 74-84.

Meehean, O. Lloyd. 1933. The Role of Fertilizers in Pondfish. [Sic] Trans. Amer. Fish. Soc., *63*: 103-109.

———. 1951. Pond Culture of Warm-Water Fishes as Related to Soil Conservation, pp. 138-142. *In* Proc. Un. Nat. Sc. Conference on the Conservation and Utilization of Resources, Wildlife and Fish Resources. United Nations Dept. of Econ. Affairs. New York.

———. 1952. Problems of Farm Fish Pond Management. Jnl. Wildlife Management, *16* (3): 233-238.

Meyer, Adolph F. 1928. The Elements of Hydrology. 2nd Edition. Wiley, New York.

Miall, L. C. 1934. The Natural History of Aquatic Insects. Fifth Impression. 11 + 395, illustrated. Macmillan, London.

Miller, E. C. 1938. Plant Physiology. 2nd Edition. 31 + 1201. McGraw-Hill, New York.

Moore, Emmeline. 1915. The Potamogetons in Relation to Pond Culture. Bull. U. S. Bur. Fish., *33*: 249-291, illustrated. Washington.

———. 1920. Some Plants of Importance in Pondfish Culture. Appendix IV to Report of the U. S. Comm'r of Fish. for 1919 (Document 881).

Moore, J. Percy. 1918. The Leeches (Hirudinea). *In* Ward and Whipple, Freshwater Biology, 1918 (Chapter 20: 646-660). Wiley, New York.

Morgan, Anne Haven. 1930. Field Book of Ponds and Streams. 16 + 448, illustrated. Putnams, New York.

Muenscher, Walter Conrad. 1944. Aquatic Plants of the United States. 10 + 374, illustrated. Comstock, Ithaca.

Muttkowski, Richard A. 1927. The Ecology of Trout Streams *and* The Food of Trout Stream Insects. Bull. N. Y. State Col. of Forestry at Syracuse Univ. Roosevelt Wild Life Annals, 2 (2).

Needham, James G. 1921. Burrowing Mayflies of our Larger Lakes and Streams. Bull. U. S. Bur. Fish., *36* (for 1917-18):265-292. Washington.

Needham, James G. and Paul R. Needham. 1941. Guide to the Study of Freshwater Biology. 88 pp., illustrated. Comstock, Ithaca.

Needham, James G. and Hortense Butler Heywood. 1929. A Handbook of the Dragonflies of North America. 8 + 378 pp. Charles C. Thomas, Springfield and Baltimore.

Needham, James G., Jay R. Traver and Yin-Chi Hsu. 1935. The Biology of Mayflies. 16 + 759, illustrated. Comstock Publ. Co., Ithaca.

Neess, John C. 1946. Development and Status of Pond Fertilization in Central Europe. Trans. Amer. Fish. Soc., *76*: 335-358.

Nitta, T., K. Arakawa, H. Sugimoto, and M. Fujiya. 1953. Study in Pollution by Industrial Sewage. Bull. of Kaikai Regional Fisheries Research Laboratory, Fisheries Agency, *3,* Contribution No. 10: 85 pages in Japanese, abstract in English.

Odum, Eugene P. 1953. Fundamentals of Ecology. xii + 384, illustrated. Saunders, Philadelphia.

Olson, R. A., H. P. Brust, and Willis L. Tressler. 1941. Studies on the Effects of Industrial Pollution on the Lower Patapseo River Areas, Curtis Bay Region. Chesapeake Biol. Lab'y Publ. No. 43.

Patrick, Ruth. 1948. Factors Effecting the Distribution of Diatoms. Bot. Rev., *14* (8): 473-524.

———. 1949. A Proposed Biological Measure of Stream Conditions, Based on a Survey of the Conestoga Basin, Lancaster County, Pennsylvania. Proc. Acad. Nat. Sci. of Philadelphia, *101*: 277-341.

———. 1953. Biological Phases of Stream Pollution. Proc. Penn. Acad. of Science, *27*: 33-36.

Pearse, A. S. 1926. Animal Ecology. 9 + 417. McGraw-Hill, New York.

Pearse, A. S. and Henrietta Achtenberg. 1921. Habits of the Yellow Perch in Wisconsin Lakes. Bull. U. S. Bur. Fish., *36*: 293-366. Washington.

Pennak, Robert W. 1943. Limnological Variables in a Colorado Mountain Stream. Amer. Mid. Nat., *29*: 186-199.

———. 1953. Fresh-water Invertebrates of the United States. 9 + 769, illustrated. Ronald Press Co., New York.

Phelps, Earle B. 1944. Stream Sanitation, with a chapter on Stream Microbiology by James B. Lackey. xi + 276. John Wiley & Sons, New York.

Powers, Edwin B., A. Randolph Shields and Mary E. Hickman, 1939. The Mortality of Fishes in Norris Lake. Jnl. Tenn. Acad. Sci., *14* (2): 239-260.

Pratt, Robertson (and Collaborators). 1944. Chlorellin, an Antibacterial Substance from Chlorella. Science, *99* (2574): 351, 352.

Prescott, G. W. 1939. Some Relationships of Phytoplankton to Limnology and Aquatic Biology. Pp. 65-78 *in* Problems of Lake Biology. Amer. Assn. Adv. Sci., Publ. No. 10.

Prosser, C. Ladd (Editor). 1950. Comparative Animal Physiology. ix + 888, illustrated. Saunders, Philadelphia.

Purdy, W. C. 1923. A Study of the Pollution and Natural Purification of the Ohio River. I. The Plankton and Related Organisms. U. S. Pub. Health Bull. No. 131. Washington.

Raney, Edward C., Ernest F. Tresselt, Edgar H. Hollis, V. D. Vladykov and D. H. Wallace. 1952. The Striped Bass, *Roccus saxatilis*. Bull. Bingham Oceanog. Collection, *14* (1): 1-177.

Rawson, D. S. 1939. Physical and Chemical Factors in the Metabolism of Lakes. *In* Problems of Lake Biology. Amer. Assn. Adv. Sc., Publication No. 10: 9-26.

———. 1942. A Comparison of Some Large Alpine Lakes in Western Canada. Ecology, *25* (2): 143-161.

———. 1950. The Physical Limnology of Great Slave Lake. Jnl. of Fish. Res. Board of Canada, *8* (1): 1-66.

———. 1953. The Standing Crop of Net Plankton in Lakes. Jnl. Fish. Res. Board of Canada, *10* (5): 224-237.

Rector, Nelson H. 1950. Public Health as Related to Water Use. Minutes of Water Panel Meeting at Rainbow Lake, Spartanburg, S. C., Aug. 19, 1950.

Reinhard, Edward George. 1931. The Plankton Ecology of the Upper Mississippi, Minneapolis to Winona. Ecol. Monog., *1* (4): 385-464.

Richardson, Robert E. 1921. Changes in the Bottom and Shore Fauna of the Middle Illinois River and the Connecting Lakes since 1913-1915 as a Result of the Increase, Southward, of Sewage Pollution. Ill. Nat'l Hist'y Survey, Bull. *14* (4): 31-75.

———. 1928. The Bottom Fauna of the Middle Illinois River, 1913-1925. Its Distribution, Abundance, Valuation, and Index Value in the Study of Stream Pollution. Bull. Ill. State Nat'l Hist'y Survey, *17* (12): 385-472. Urbana.

Ricker, William E. 1937. Physical and Chemical Characteristics of Cultus Lake, British Columbia. Jnl. Biol. Bd. of Canada, *3*: 363-402.

———. 1940. On the Origins of Kokanee, a Fresh-water Type of Sockeye Salmon. Trans. Royal Soc. Canada, Sect V: 121-135.

———. 1946. Production and Utilization of Fish Populations. Ecol. Monog., *16*: 373-391.

———. 1948. Hybrid Sunfish for Stocking Small Ponds. Trans. Am. Fish. Soc., *75*: 84-96.

Riley, G. A. 1940. Limnological Studies in Connecticut. III. The Plankton of Linsley Pond. Ecol. Monog., *10*: 279-306.

———. 1941. Plankton Studies. III. Long Island Sound. Bull. Bingham Oceanographic Collections, 7 (3): 1-93.

Riley, Gordon A. and Samy Gorgy. 1948. Quantitative Studies of Summer Plankton Populations of the Western North Atlantic. Jnl. Marine Research, *7*: 100-121.

Ross, Herbert H. 1944. The Caddis Flies, or Trichoptera, of Illinois. Ill. State Nat'l Hist'y Survey Bull. *23*: 6 + 326 pp. Urbana.

Rounsefell, George A. and W. Harry Everhart. 1953. Fishery Science. Its Methods and Applications. 12 + 444, Ilustr. New York, Wiley.

Ruttner, Franz. 1953. Fundamentals of Limnology. xi + 242. Translated by D. G. Frey and F. E. J. Fry. Univ. of Toronto Press, Toronto.

El Saby, Mohamed Kamel. 1951. The Lake Fisheries of Egypt. Pp. 126-130 *in* Proc. Un. Nat. Sc. Conference on the Conservation and Utilization of Resources, Wildlife and Fish Resources. United Nations Dept. of Econ. Affairs. New York.

Saila, Saul B. 1952. Some Results of Farm Pond Management Studies in New York. Jnl. Wildlife Management, *16* (3): 279-282.

Savory, Theodore H. 1928. The Biology of Spiders. 20 + 376. Sidgwick and Jackson, London.

Schmassmann, Hansjörg. 1951. Untersuchungen über den Stuffhaushalt flussenden Gewässer. Schweizerische Zeitschrift für Hydrologie, *13* (2): 300-335, illustrated.

Seckinger, Daniel L. 1950. Soil Erosion and Pollution of Streams. Minutes of Water Panel Meeting at Rainbow Lake, Spartanburg, S. C., Aug. 15, 1950.

Second Southern Municipal and Industrial Waste Conference, Proceedings. 1953: 9 + 252. Department of Sanitary Engineering,

School of Public Health, University of North Carolina, Chapel Hill.

Sharpe, R. W. 1918. The Ostracoda. Chapter 24 *in* Ward and Whipple, pp. 790-827.

Shelford, Victor E. 1917. An Experimental Study of the Effects of Gas Waste upon Fishes, with Especial Reference to Stream Pollution. Ill. State Lab'y Nat'l Hist'y, Bull. 11 (6): 380-416; 1 fig., 4 charts.

Shetter, David S. 1950. Results from Plantings of Marked Fingerling Brook Trout (*Salvelinus f. fontinalis* Mitchill) in Hunt Creek, Montmorency County, Michigan. Trans. Amer. Fish. Soc., *79*: 77-93.

Simms, R. B. 1950. Municipal Water Supply and Use. Minutes of Water Panel Meeting at Rainbow Lake, Spartanburg, S. C., Aug. 15, 1950, pp. 12-14, mimeographed. U. S. Dept. Agric. Soil Conservation Service.

Smith, Gilbert M. 1950. The Fresh-water Algae of the United States. 2nd Edition. 7 + 719 pp. McGraw-Hill, New York.

Smith, M. W. 1952. Limnology and Trout Angling in Charlotte County Lakes, New Brunswick. Jnl. Fish. Res. Board of Canada, *8* (6): 381-452.

Snieszko, Stanislas. 1941. Pond Fish Farming in Poland. Pp. 227-240 *in* Symposium on Hydrobiology. Univ of Wis. Press, Madison.

State Water Pollution Control Board. 1952. Water Quality Criteria. State Water Pollution Control Board, Publication No. 3, Sacramento, Cal. 512 pp., map, bibliography of 1369 numbers. (Not ecological).

Storch, Otto. 1924. Morphologie und Physiologie des Fangapparates der Daphniden. Ergeb. d. Zool., *6*: 125-234. Jena.

———. 1925. Des Phyllopoden-Fangapparat. Intern. Rev. Ges. Hydrob., u. Hydrog. *12*: 369-391; *13*: 78-93. Leipzig.

———. 1929. Die Schwimmbewegung der Copepoden auf Grund am Mikro-Zeitlupenaufnamen analysiert. Verh. Deuts. Zool. Ges., *33*: 118-129, 3 figs.

Storch, Otto und Otto Pfisterer. 1925. Der Fangapparat von Diaptomus Zeitschr. für Vergleichende Physiologie, *3* (3): 330-376.

Stroud, Richard H. 1952. Management of Warm-water Fish Populations in Massachusetts' Lakes, Ponds and Reservoirs. Trans. 17th N. Amer. Wildlife Conference, March 17, 18, and 19, 1952. Wildlife Management Institute, Washington.

————. 1953. Spot-poisoning Applied to the Massachusetts Lake and Pond Survey. Progressive Fish Culturists, *15* (1): 3-10.

Sumner, F. B. (Chairman). 1940. Dams and the Problem of Migratory Fishes. Stanford Ichthiological Bulletin (Special Symposium Issue), *1* (6): 173-216.

Surber, Eugene W. 1943. The Effects of Various Fertilizers on Plant Growths and Their Probable Influence on the Production of Smallmouth Black Bass in Hard-water Ponds. Trans. Amer. Fish. Soc., *73*: 377-393.

Suter, Russell and Emmeline Moore. 1922. Stream Pollution Studies. N. Y. State Conservation Studies, Albany. 27 pp.

Svensen, Harold A. 1951. Forestry and Applied Ecology. Sci. Monthly, *73*: 345-347.

Sverdrup, H. U., Martin W. Johnson and Richard H. Fleming. 1942. The Oceans. x + 1087, illustrated. Prentice-Hall, New York.

Swingle, Homer S., and E. V. Smith. 1941. The Management of Ponds for the Production of Game and Pan Fish. Pp. 218-226, A Symposium on Hydrobiology. Univ. of Wis. Press, Madison.

Swingle, H. S. 1952. Farm Pond Investigations in Alabama. Jnl. Wildlife Management, *16* (3): 243-249.

Thienemann, August. 1926. Das Leben im Süsswasser. 108 pp. illustrated. Ferdinand Hirt, Breslau.

————. 1925 ff. Die Binnengewässer Mitteleuropas. Eine Limnologische Einführung.

Thomas, Harold E. 1951. The Conservation of Ground Water. A Survey of the Present Ground-water Situation in the United States. Sponsored by the Conservation Foundation. First Edition. xv + 327. McGraw-Hill Book Company, Inc., New York, Toronto, London.

Thompson, David H. 1941. The Fish Production of Inland Streams and Lakes. *In* A Symposium on Hydrobiology, pp. 206-217. Univ. of Wis. Press, Madison.

Titcomb, John W. 1923. Aquatic Plants in Pond Culture. 24 pp., illustrated. Rept. U. S. Com'r Fish. for 1923, Washington.

United States Atomic Energy Commission. 1952. Some Applications of Atomic Energy in Plant Science. 6 + 211. U. S. Atomic Energy Commission, Washington.

United States Forest Service and Soil Conservation Service. 1940. Influences of Vegetation and Watershed Treatments on Run-off, Silting, and Stream Flow. A Progress Report of Research. U. S. Dept. of Agric. Publ. No. 397, Washington.

Utterback, Clinton L., Lyman D. Phifer and Rex J. Robinson. 1942. Some Chemical, Planktonic and Optical Characteristics of Crater Lake. Ecology, *23* (1): 97-103.

Walker, Theodore J. and Arthur D. Hasler. 1949. Detection and Discrimination of Odors of Aquatic Plants by the Bluntnose Minnow, *Hyborhynchus notatus.* Physiol. Zool., *22* (1): 45-63.

Wall, Judson G. 1914. Flood Prevention and its Relation to the Nation's Food Supply. Science, N. S., *40*: 44-47.

Wallen, I. Eugene. 1951. The Direct Effect of Turbidity on Fishes. Bull. Okla. Agric. Mech. Col. *48*, Biol. Ser. No. 2: 27 pp. (With review of the literature.)

Ward, Henry Baldwin and George Chandler Whipple. 1918. Freshwater Biology. 9 + IIII pp., illustrated. Wiley, New York.

Welch, Paul S. 1952. Limnology. 2nd Edition. xi + 538, illustrated. McGraw-Hill, New York.

———. 1948. Limnological Methods. 18 + 381, illustrated. Philadelphia, Blakiston.

Wells, Morris M. 1918. The Reactions and Resistance of Fishes to Carbon Dioxide and Carbon Monoxide. Bull. Ill. State Lab'y of Nat'l Hist'y, *11* (8): 557-571.

Westfall, B. A. and M. M. Ellis. 1944. Pulp-mill Pollution of the Rainy River Near International Falls, Minnesota. U. S. Fish and Wildlife Service, Special Scientific Report, No. 7, Chicago.

Whipple, George Chandler. 1933. The Microscopy of Drinking Water. 4th Edition (Rev'd by Gordon Maskew Fair and Melville Conley Whipple, 1927). Last printing 1947. xix + 586 pp., 19 pls. John Wiley & Sons, New York.

Wiebe, A. H. 1928. Biological Survey of the Upper Mississippi River with Special Reference to Pollution. Bull. U. S. Bur. Fish., *43*, Part II: 137-167.

Wilson, C. B. 1920. Dragonflies and Damselflies in Relation to Pondfish Culture. Bull. U. S. Bur. Fish., *36*: 181-266.

———. 1923. Life History of the Scavenger Water Beetle *Hydrous* (*Hydrophilus*) *triangularis,* and Its Economic Relation to Fish Breeding. Bull. U. S. Bur. Fish., *39*: 7-38, illustrated. (Document No. 942.)

———. 1923a. Water Beetles in Relation to Pondfish Culture, with Life Histories of Those Found in Fishponds at Fairport, Iowa. Bull. U. S. Bur. Fish., *39*: 229-345. Washington. (Document No. 953.)

Wilson, L. R. 1939. Rooted Aquatics Plants and Their Relation to the Limnology of Fresh-water Lakes. Amer. Assn. Adv. Sci. Publ. No. 10: 107-122.

Wolcott, Robert H. 1918. The Water-Mites (Hydracarina). *In* Ward and Whipple, 1918, Chapter 26: 851-875. Wiley, New York.

Woodward, F. L. 1951. Applied Ecology in Public Health. Scientific Monthly, *73*: 343-345.

Yeatman, Harry Clay. 1952. Some Effects of Temperature and Turbulence on the External Morphology of *Cyclops carolinianus* Yeatman. (Manuscript in Library, University of N. C.)

ZoBell, C. E. 1935. The Assimilation of Ammonium Nitrogen by *Nitzschia closterium* and other Marine Phytoplankton. Proc. Nat. Acad. Sc., 21: 517-522.

———. 1946. Marine Microbiology, A Monograph on Hydrobacteriology. xv + 240 pp., illustrated. Chronica Botanica Company, Waltham, Mass. (Sulfur bacteria of fresh water, as well as those of the sea, are discussed.)

Index